Solid Mechanics

D1586497

Ray Hulse
Associate Dean
School of Science and the Environment
Coventry University

Keith Sherwin
Formerly Course Tutor
Mechanical Engineering
The University of Huddersfield

Jack Cain
Formerly Senior Course Tutor
Civil Engineering
Coventry University

palgrave
macmillan

First published 2003 by
PALGRAVE MACMILLAN
Houndmills, Basingstoke, Hampshire RG21 6XS and
175 Fifth Avenue, New York, N.Y. 10010
Companies and representatives throughout the world

PALGRAVE MACMILLAN is the global academic imprint of the Palgrave Macmillan division of St. Martin's Press, LLC and of Palgrave Macmillan Ltd. Macmillan® is a registered trademark in the United States, United Kingdom and other countries. Palgrave is a registered trademark in the European Union and other countries.

ISBN 0–333–97116–7

A catalogue record for this book is available from the British Library.

This book is printed on paper suitable for recycling and made from fully managed and sustained forest sources.

10   9   8   7   6   5   4   3   2   1
12   11   10   09   08   07   06   05   04   03

Printed and bound in Great Britain by
J. W. Arrowsmith Ltd, Bristol

CONTENTS

PREFACE

This book contains fourteen programmes incorporating material which will be found in most undergraduate and HND syllabuses in Strength of Materials and Solid Mechanics at first- and second-year level. The book is intended for use by students of Mechanical Engineering and related disciplines as a main text in Solid Mechanics, as taught in most College and University departments of Engineering.

The aim of the text is to provide a sound understanding of fundamental principles of Solid Mechanics, by presenting the principles and concepts involved in a distinctive programmed learning format whereby the student can work and learn at his/her own pace and test his/her understanding by answering a series of carefully constructed questions and graded practical problems.

Although it is assumed that students using the book will have some grasp of elementary mechanics, the first chapter provides useful revision of the basic principles of statics, which provides a foundation for the rest of the book. Subsequent chapters deal with concepts of components and types of loading. Techniques for analysing statically determinate, simply supported and cantilevered beams are introduced. The drawing of shear force and bending moment diagrams for beams subjected to different types of loading is given comprehensive coverage.

A number of programmes cover stress analysis, including the analysis of components subjected to direct, bending, shear or torsional stress. Problems involving pressure loading of cylinders are also considered. The analysis of complex stress situations using Mohr's Circle of Stress forms the basis of one complete programme, as does the analysis of complex strain situations, including the use and interpretation of strain gauge rosettes.

Later programmes show how the deflection of statically determinate beams may be calculated using integration techniques, and Strain Energy methods are introduced as a foundation for further, more advanced study. Subsequently, the theory of elastic buckling of slender members, loaded in axial compression, is considered and the final programme examines failure theories whereby the results from simple tensile tests can be related to complex stress situations.

The book is suitable for general class use and for individual study supported by seminar and/or tutorial work. It is appreciated that the coverage of the text may be a little greater than that required for some first-year courses, and that the last few programmes will, in many courses, form part of second-year work. This is intentional, as the earlier programmes are suitable for use by HND students or those undergraduates on technology courses where the depth of study of Solid Mechanics may not be so great. Engineering undergraduates will find that most of the text will be required in both their first-year and second-year studies.

Throughout the book the emphasis is on student-centred learning, with the intention of providing the student with a sound grasp of the fundamental principles of Solid Mechanics.

This text has been developed from the book *Structural Mechanics* (R. Hulse and J. A. Cain, 2nd edition, Palgrave, 2000). which has been widely used and adopted as a standard text for students of Civil Engineering and Construction for over twelve years. The acknowledged success of that text has led to this new publication, which includes major sections of both new material and examples that are of direct relevance to students of Mechanical Engineering and related disciplines. It is hoped that this new text will meet the needs of another group and generation of engineering students.

RAY HULSE
KEITH SHERWIN
JACK CAIN

HOW TO USE THIS BOOK

This book contains fourteen 'programmes'. Each programme is a self-contained unit of study which deals with one specific topic. However, as the later programmes build on material studied in earlier parts of the book, you are advised to work systematically through the text, studying the programmes in the given sequence.

You *must* start at the beginning of, and work sequentially through, each programme. Every programme is subdivided into a number of short 'frames', each of which contains a limited quantity of information. The frames are designed to enable you to learn at your own pace, and most of them end with a short question or problems for you to tackle. These enable you to test your understanding of the material you have just studied. The correct answer to each problem is given at the top of the next frame.

To use the book most effectively you should use a piece of paper or card to conceal the next frame until you have answered the given question. Use the paper for rough working if necessary. Only when you have made a response should you look at the answer. If you have given an incorrect answer you should not proceed until you have found out why you made a mistake. Usually a worked solution or some further explanation will be given immediately below each answer, so you should be able to find out where and why you went wrong. If you still cannot understand how to get the correct answer, you should make a note to discuss it with another student or with your tutor.

At the end of each programme, and at intermediate stages throughout, you will find sets of problems to tackle. Attempt as many of these problems as possible. They are graded in difficulty and will give practice in applying the techniques you have learnt.

The most important thing to remember is that you should work systematically sequentially and carefully through the book at whatever pace of learning you find comfortable. Do not miss out any part of any programme, don't 'cheat' by looking at the answers to questions before offering your own solution, and don't proceed at any stage until you are satisfied that you have grasped the information in the frame you have just studied.

Programme 1

REVISION OF THE FUNDAMENTALS OF STATICS

On completion of this programme you will be able to:

- Recognise and explain the nature of force systems
- State and apply the conditions for equilibrium
- Combine force systems into force resultants and equilibrants using graphical methods
- Resolve forces into components
- Determine the resultant of force systems using analytical methods
- Calculate unknown forces in systems of forces in equilibrium
- Recognise and explain the nature of the moment of a force
- Calculate the moment of a force system about a point
- Determine the centroid of regular and irregular geometrical shapes

1

In this programme we shall review the basic principles of Statics which will be needed in following programmes. You may have learnt these principles in your previous studies, in which case this will be useful revision. If you have not studied Statics before, do not worry; by working conscientiously through the following frames and exercises you will be able to master the subsequent programmes. You will need a scale rule and a protractor.

2

Statics is the study of bodies at rest. A body is a general word used to describe, for example, a vehicle, a bridge or a component of a machine such as a beam, shaft or support. All bodies are subject to the action of forces which are expressed in units of Newtons (N). Most forces found in engineering applications have magnitudes considerably greater than a Newton and are usually expressed in kiloNewton (kN). It may be helpful to think of a small car as weighing approximately 10 kN.

If a wind force of 10 kN is acting on a body is it sufficient to say 'the wind force is 10 kN'?

3

> No – force is a *vector* quantity and must be specified
> both in magnitude and direction

We need to say, for example, that the wind force is 10 kN in a horizontal direction. We can indicate forces in various ways, such as:

(a) by the use of arrows on 'free body' diagrams (diagrams showing the geometrical arrangement of the structure and load system) such as shown in figure (a) below; or

(b) by the use of *vectors* (see figure (b) below).

Vectors will be used in *vector diagrams* later in this programme.

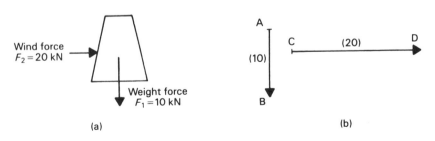

(a)   (b)

In figure (b) the vector **AB**, drawn parallel to the force denoted F_1 and to some convenient scale measuring 10 kN in length, represents the force F_1. Similarly vector **CD** drawn parallel to the force F_2 and to the same scale measuring 20 kN, represents the force F_2. Note that the direction in which the force acts is shown by the arrow head and by the way the vector is lettered. Thus **AB** implies the force acts in the direction A to B. If the force acted in the opposite direction, we would refer to the vector as vector **BA**.

It should be apparent to you that the combined effect of the two forces acting on the body shown in figure (a) will be to move the body downwards and to the right (if no other forces are acting on the body).

If there are only two forces acting on a body and the body does not move, can you suggest what conditions must be satisfied by those forces?

4

> (1) They must be equal in magnitude.
> (2) They must act in opposite directions.
> (3) They must be collinear (that is, act along the same straight line).

The forces F_1 and F_2 in figure (a) below satisfy these conditions. The body does not move and is said to be in *equilibrium* under the action of forces F_1 and F_2.

If these same forces were not collinear but acted as in figure (b), then the body on which they act would tend to rotate (in this case in a clockwise direction) and the body would not be in equilibrium.

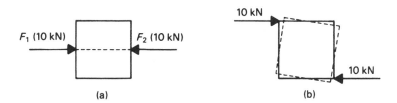

(a)   (b)

Now look at the diagram below showing a body acted upon by two forces.

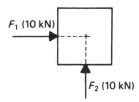

Is the body in equilibrium?

5

NO

In fact, the body would move in the direction indicated in figure (a) below. It is as if the body was acted upon by a single force R as shown in figure (b). The force R, which has the same effect upon the body as the original forces, is described as the *resultant* of the original two forces. If we wished to prevent the body moving under the action of the forces F_1 and F_2, we would have to apply to the body a force equal in magnitude but opposite in direction to the resultant R, as shown in figure (c). The force E, which when acting on the body in conjunction with F_1 and F_2, maintains the body in a state of equilibrium, is described as the *equilibrant* of the original two forces (F_1 and F_2). Note that in figures (a) and (c), all the forces pass through a single point.

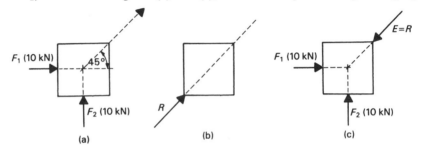

RESULTANTS OF FORCES

In our future work it will be necessary for us to determine the resultant (or equilibrant) of any number of forces acting at a single point. Such a point might be the centre of gravity of a solid body, or a joint in a car body. We shall now consider *graphical methods* of determining resultants, and in later frames study *analytical methods*.

The following diagrams illustrate how two, three and four forces may be combined graphically to give their respective resultants.

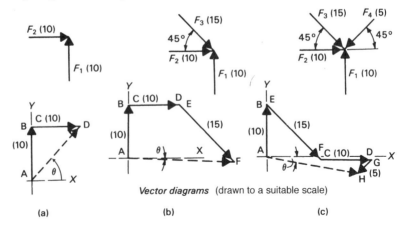

Vector diagrams (drawn to a suitable scale)

In each case, and preferably drawn on graph paper, line AB is drawn parallel to F_1 and to a convenient scale to represent the magnitude of force F_1. Line CD similarly represents F_2 and so on. *The vectors must be drawn such that the arrows showing the direction of force progress sequentially* (that is, they follow one another round the diagram). Thus if you put a pencil at A in vector diagram (b) and trace along the lines ABCDEF, your pencil moves in the direction of each force as it traces along the line representing that force. It is not, however, necessary to draw the vectors in any particular order. Thus in figure (b) the sequence is F_1, F_2, F_3, but in figure (c) it is F_1, F_3, F_2, then F_4.

In each case we have drawn an open-sided polygon. The length and direction of the open side gives us the magnitude and direction of the resultant of the force system. *The direction of action of the resultant is always from the start point to the end point of the polygon.* Thus, measuring from the scaled diagrams:

For figure (a), Resultant $= AD = 14.1$ kN acting from A to D, $\theta = +45°$

For figure (b), Resultant $= AF = 20.6$ kN acting from A to F, $\theta = -1.7°$

For figure (c), Resultant $= AH = 17.5$ kN acting from A to H, $\theta = -13.6°$

Note that the angles θ have been measured from the X-axis assuming that they are positive if drawn in an anticlockwise sense.

Now try drawing the polygon of forces for figure (c) taking the forces in the order F_1, F_4, F_2, F_3. (Hint: use a scale of 10 mm = 1 kN.)

6

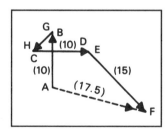

Now consider a number of forces acting at a point, P, as shown in figure (a) below. If we draw the force polygon in figure (b) we can determine the resultant by measuring line AF and, if on the free body diagram we draw a line through P parallel to AF, we have located the resultant in space. If the resultant, R, acted alone on the point P as in figure (c), it would have the same effect on P as the original forces.

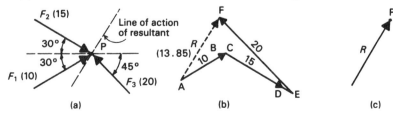

What is the effect of the three forces acting on the point P?

7

P would move in the direction of action of the resultant *R*.

EQUILIBRANTS OF FORCES

If we wished P to be in equilibrium, we would need to apply another force acting on P and equal in magnitude but opposite in direction to the resultant, *R*. Such a force would be the *equilibrant* of the original system of three forces. The equilibrant could be determined by measuring the length of line FA on the vector diagram. Figure (a) below shows the equilibrant plotted on the diagram. In this case, the equilibrant and the original three forces have no net effect on P and the system is in *equilibrium*. When a system of forces acting at a point is in equilibrium, as in figure (a), then the force polygon for those forces is a closed polygon. The vectors representing the forces follow each other in sequence from the start point, around the polygon and back to the start point, as in figure (b).

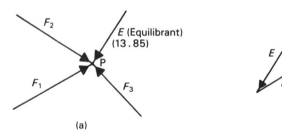

You should now be able to construct polygons of forces for any number of forces acting at a point and use the polygons to determine the resultant or equilibrant. Practise this by solving the following problems.

8

PROBLEMS

1. The following figures show four systems of forces. Determine the *resultant* of the systems in figures (a), (b) and (c), and determine the *equilibrant* for the system in figure (d). An A4 size sheet of paper is large enough, and a scale of 1 cm to 5 kN big enough to give acceptable answers. You may find it helpful to use squared paper. The direction of the forces should be specified by quoting the value of the angle θ measured from the X axis, anticlockwise being taken as positive. You will remember that this convention was used in Frame 5.

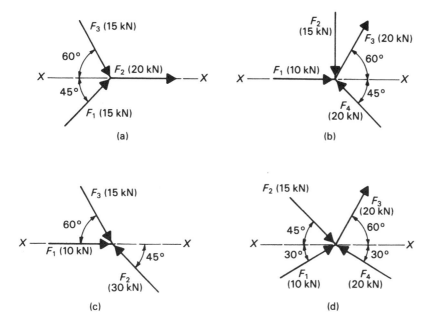

(a)

(b)

(c)

(d)

Ans. (a) 38.2 kN, +356.4° (b) 17.5 kN, +70.4° (c) 9.0 kN, +114.3° (d) 24.8 kN, +241.2°). The angles are given as the angle measured anticlockwise from the X axis.

9

Now that you are familiar with the technique for constructing force polygons, we shall simplify the lettering of the diagrams in the following way:

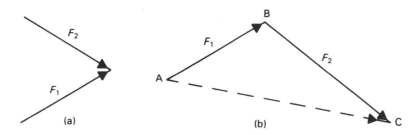

(a)

(b)

Figure (a) shows two forces acting at a point. Figure (b) is the force polygon (in this case a triangle) in which vector **AB** represents force F_1, vector **BC** represents force F_2 and the vector **AC** represents the resultant. You will see that we now have only one letter at each corner of the force polygon. This method of lettering is simpler and enables us to develop a very useful reference system when analysing the forces acting on components.

10

In Frame 7 you learnt that if a number of forces acting at a point are in equilibrium then they have no resultant, and the vector diagram of the force system will consequently be a closed polygon. In the case of three forces, this fact is traditionally quoted as the principle of the *triangle of forces* which can be stated as: 'three coplanar forces in equilibrium acting at a point may be represented in magnitude and direction by the three sides of a triangle'. The term *coplanar* reminds us that we are considering forces acting in a single plane.

An equally useful related fact is that if three non-parallel forces are in equilibrium they must be *concurrent*; that is, they must all pass through a common point.

Let us now see how these two facts may be used to solve a problem. Figure (a) shows a ladder of weight W standing on a rough floor and resting against a smooth wall. Since the wall is smooth, there is no friction, and the force (R_1) exerted by the wall on the ladder is at right angles to the wall. The weight force W is, of course, vertical, but we do not immediately know the direction of the force (R_2) exerted by the floor on the ladder.

The forces exerted by the wall and the floor are *reactions* and we shall be learning more about such forces in Programme 2.

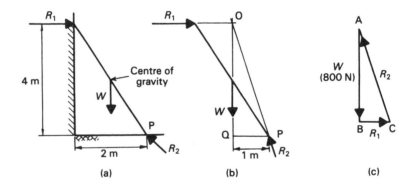

(a)   (b)   (c)

Figure (b) shows how we can use the fact that three forces in equilibrium must be concurrent to locate the line of action of the force at the foot of the ladder. We extend the lines of action of the forces R_1 and W to intersect at point O. The reaction at the foot of the ladder (P) must also pass through O and hence by joining P and O we obtain the line of action of R_2. It is then possible to construct the triangle of forces in figure (c).

Draw the triangle of forces and assuming that the weight of the ladder is 800 N determine:

(i) the magnitude of reaction R_1; and
(ii) the magnitude of reaction R_2.

Assume that the centre of gravity of the ladder is halfway along its length.

$$R_1 = 200 \text{ N}$$
$$R_2 = 825 \text{ N}$$

In the problem you have just done, the triangle of forces is a right-angled triangle and you may have noticed that it is similar to the triangle OPQ in figure (b). The ratio PQ/OQ = $\frac{1}{4}$. It follows that the ratio R_1/W in the triangle of forces is also $\frac{1}{4}$, thus:

$$R_1 = \frac{1}{4} \times W$$
$$= \frac{1}{4} \times 800$$
$$= 200 \text{ N}$$

and, making use of Pythagoras' theorem, $R_2 = \left(800^2 + 200^2\right)^{1/2}$
$$= 824.62 \simeq 825 \text{ N}$$

You should always look for such geometrical relationships to aid calculations.

NON-CONCURRENT FORCES

You can now cope with any number of forces acting at a point, but you may occasionally come across a system in which not all forces are concurrent. Such a system of forces would have to be dealt with as follows:

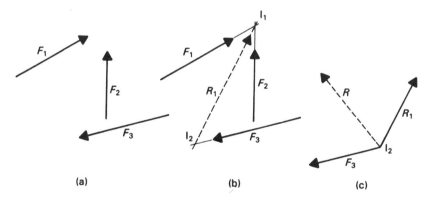

(a)　　　　　(b)　　　　　(c)

Figure (a) shows three non-concurrent forces. In figure (b) we have extended the line of action of forces F_1 and F_2 to locate their point of intersection at I_1. We can now combine F_1 and F_2 to give their resultant R_1 which will, of course, act through I_1.

In figure (c) we have replaced F_1 and F_2 by their resultant R_1. The problem is now reduced to a two-force problem, F_3 and R_1, whose lines of action intersect at I_2. It is now a straightforward matter to determine the resultant R of R_1 and F_3. R is then the resultant of all the original forces. Complex systems may be solved in this way.

12

COMPONENTS OF FORCES

Since any number of forces can be combined into a single force, it follows that a single force can be replaced by any number of forces whose resultant effect is the same as that of the original single force. We say that a single force may be *resolved* into *components*. In practice, it is sufficient for most analytical purposes to resolve a force into two components at right angles to each other. The directions taken for these components are normally, but not necessarily, vertical and horizontal.

Figure (a) shows a single force, F ($= 20$ kN), acting on a body. In figure (b) the vector AB represents F and lines BC and AC are drawn vertically downwards and horizontally to the right to complete a triangle of forces. If CB (length $= 17.3$ kN) is the vector for a force V, and AC (length $= 10.0$ kN) is the vector for a force H we see from figure (b) that F is the resultant of V and H, or, conversely, V and H are the vertical and horizontal components, respectively, of F. We can then replace force F by V and H as in figure (c). V and H acting together will have the same effect on the body as the original single force.

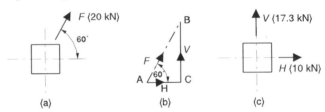

(a)	(b)	(c)

You will see from figure (b) above that by choosing to replace F by two components at right angles (V and H) we have drawn a right-angled vector diagram ABC from which $BC = AB\sin 60°$ ($V = F\sin 60°$) and $AC = AB\cos 60°$ ($H = F\cos 60°$). We can express this in more general terms as follows:

Given a force F acting at an anticlockwise angle θ to the X axis
Vertical component $\quad V = F\sin\theta$
Horizontal component $\quad H = F\cos\theta$

You should relate these equations to figure (d) below.

When resolving a force into components be careful to identify the direction of each component. The convention is to take horizontal forces acting to the right as positive and vertical forces acting upwards as positive. Thus in the above example of the 20 kN force, the components are $V = +17.3$ kN and $H = +10$ kN.

Now determine the horizontal and vertical components of the forces shown below in figures (e), (f) and (g).

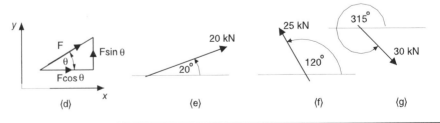

(d)	(e)	(f)	(g)

(e)	$V = +6.84$ kN;	$H = +18.79$ kN
(f)	$V = +21.65$ kN;	$H = -12.50$ kN
(g)	$V = -21.21$ kN;	$H = +21.21$ kN

ANALYTICAL DETERMINATION OF THE RESULTANT OF A FORCE SYSTEM

Since the effect of a resultant is the same as the total effect of the system of forces of which it is the resultant, it follows that the vertical component of the resultant must be equal to the sum of the vertical components of all the original forces in the system. Similarly for the horizontal component. This fact provides an *analytical method* for determining the resultant of any system of forces. The calculations are best done in tabular form, as in the following example.

Consider the system of forces shown in figure (a). If forces acting to the right are taken as positive and forces acting upwards as positive, then:

For F_1, $V = 10 \sin 30° = +5.00$ kN; $H = 10 \cos 30° = +8.66$ kN.

These components are tabulated below, together with the corresponding components of F_2, F_3 and F_4:

Force	Value	θ	Components	
			V	H
F_1	10	30	+5.00	+8.66
F_2	20	60	+17.32	+10.00
F_3	20	150	+10.00	−17.32
F_4	15	315	−10.61	+10.61
Totals			+21.71	+11.95

Thus, the vertical component of the resultant $= +21.71$ kN; and
the horizontal component of the resultant $= +11.95$ kN.

Then, as shown in figure (b), the components can be combined to give:

$$(R) = (21.71^2 + 11.95^2)^{1/2} = \underline{24.78 \text{ kN}}$$

and the direction of the resultant is given by θ where:

$\tan \theta = 21.71/11.95$ or $\underline{\theta = 61.2°}$ (see figure (b))

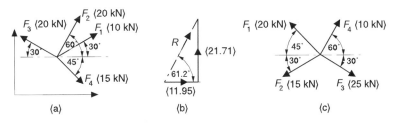

(a) (b) (c)

Now calculate the magnitude and direction of the resultant of the forces shown in figure (c). Present your calculations in tabular form as shown above.

14

> Resultant = 2.84 kN
>
> Direction $\theta = 99.4°$

As in previous examples, θ has been quoted as the angle measured from the X axis in a positive anticlockwise direction. Did you sketch a triangle of forces, as in figure (b) in Frame 13, to help you determine the correct direction of the resultant force?

CALCULATION OF UNKNOWN FORCES IN A SYSTEM OF FORCES IN EQUILIBRIUM

Now suppose that we had to analyse the problems shown in figures (a) and (c) to determine the unknown forces and angle (θ). The two systems of forces are shown acting on a point P, and both systems are in equilibrium. The solutions could be obtained graphically by constructing triangles of forces, and figure (b) shows how this is done for problem (a). Vector AB is drawn representing force F_3. A line AC_1 is then drawn from A parallel to F_1 and a line BC_2 from B parallel to F_2. The intersection of AC_1 and BC_2 determines the position of C and completes the triangle of forces. Vector CA then gives the magnitude and direction of force F_1 and vector BC gives the corresponding values of F_2. Note that the arrows follow in sequence around the diagram.

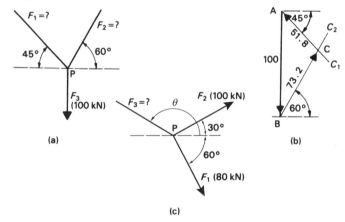

(a)   (c)   (b)

Construct the triangle of forces for the problem shown in figure (c).

15

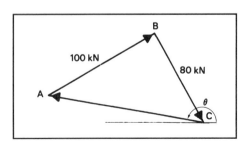

In figure (c) we are given the magnitudes and directions of two forces, so the construction of the triangle of forces is straightforward. You should have drawn vector **AB** representing 100 kN in the direction of, and parallel to, the line of action of force F_2. Then from point B you should have drawn **BC** representing 80 kN and parallel to F_1. Joining C to A completes the diagram and vector **CA** then gives the magnitude and direction of the third force.

*What is the difference between vector **CA** and vector **AC**?*

16

> The two vectors represent forces in different directions.
> Vector **AC** represents the resultant of F_1 and F_2.
> **CA** is the equilibrant.

This type of problem can also be solved analytically using the method of resolution into components since **the algebraic sum of all components in any direction must be zero if the original forces are in equilibrium**. Hence the algebraic sum of all the vertical components must be zero, otherwise the point P would move vertically. Similarly, the algebraic sum of the horizontal components must be zero.

Why must the horizontal components sum to zero?

17

> Otherwise P would move horizontally

Let us apply the method of resolution to figure (a) in Frame 14. Note that the signs used for the components of F_1 and F_2 are based on the assumption that these forces act in a direction away from point P. If we obtain a negative answer for either F_1 or F_2 we shall know that that force acts in the opposite direction towards P.

Force	Vertical component	Horizontal component
F_1	$F_1 \times \sin 135° = +0.707F_1$	$F_1 \times \cos 135° = -0.707F_1$
F_2	$F_2 \times \sin 60° = +0.866F_2$	$F_2 \times \cos 60° = +0.500F_2$
F_3	$= -100$	$= 0.0$

sum of vertical components $\qquad 0.707F_1 + 0.866F_2 - 100 = 0 \qquad (1.1)$

sum of horizontal components $\quad -0.707F_1 + 0.500F_2 \quad = 0 \qquad (1.2)$

Now solve these simultaneous equations for F_1 and F_2.

18

$$F_1 = 51.77 \text{ kN}$$
$$F_2 = 73.21 \text{ kN}$$

If you had difficulty solving the equations then proceed as follows:

Equation (1.1) was $\qquad 0.707F_1 + 0.866F_2 - 100 = 0$

(1.2) was $\qquad \dfrac{-0.707F_1 + 0.500F_2 \qquad\quad = 0}{1.366F_2 - 100 = 0}$

adding these equations we get

from which $\qquad\qquad\qquad\qquad F_2 = 100/1.366$
$$= \underline{73.21 \text{ kN}}$$

then substituting this value in equation (1.2):

$$-0.707F_1 + 0.5 \times 73.2 = 0$$
$$F_1 = 36.6/0.707$$
$$= \underline{51.77 \text{ kN}}$$

Use the method of resolution to determine the values of the unknown force and angle (θ) in the following problem. This is the same problem as given in figure (c) in Frame 14. Start by assuming that force F_3 acts away from P.

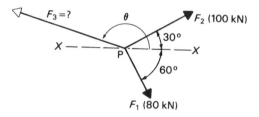

19

$$\boxed{F_3 = 128.53 \text{ kN}: \ \theta = 171.36°}$$

If you did not get this answer check your solution against the following:

Force	Vertical component	Horizontal component
F_1	$80 \sin 300° = -69.28$	$80 \cos 300° = +40.00$
F_2	$100 \sin 30° = +50.00$	$100 \cos 30° = +86.60$
F_3	$= F_3 \sin \theta$	$= F_3 \cos \theta$

Sum of vertical components $\qquad -69.28 + 50.00 + F_3 \sin \theta = 0$

$\qquad\qquad\qquad \therefore \qquad\qquad\qquad\qquad F_3 \sin \theta = +19.28$ (1.3)

Sum of horizontal components $\quad +40.00 + 86.60 + F_3 \cos \theta = 0$

$\qquad\qquad\qquad \therefore \qquad\qquad\qquad\qquad F_3 \cos \theta = -126.60$ (1.4)

Then, dividing equation (1.3) by (1.4) we get $\dfrac{F_3 \sin \theta}{F_3 \cos \theta} = \dfrac{19.28}{-126.60} = -0.152$

$$\tan \theta = -0.152$$

$$\therefore \quad \theta = \tan^{-1} -0.152 = 171.36°$$

Substituting this value of θ in equation (1.3): $F_3 \sin 171.36° = +19.28$

$$\therefore \quad F_3 \times 0.15 = +19.28$$

$$\therefore \qquad F_3 = \underline{128.53 \text{ kN}}$$

20

MOMENTS OF FORCES

In Frame 4 you saw how a force could rotate or tend to rotate a body. Consider the figure where a vertical force F is shown acting on one end of a bar with a hole at the other end loosely fitting over a shaft or hinge at O. The bar is thus free to rotate about O.

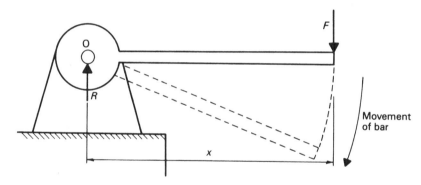

Force F would, if not resisted, push the whole bar including the hinge O downwards, but as O is fixed in space, being supported on a bracket sitting on the floor, then the support would provide an upward resisting reactive force (R). Thus O would thus not move vertically. You should appreciate, however, that while R is preventing O from moving vertically, there is nothing to prevent the bar rotating clockwise about the hinge. The arrangement shown is in fact a *mechanism*.

We see that this force, F, tends to turn the body on which it acts, and we measure the turning effect by saying that the force has a turning moment or *moment* equal to $F \times x$, where x is the horizontal distance from the hinge to the line of action of the force F.

This simple equation indicates that the turning effect is increased if the magnitude of the force increases and/or if the distance x increases.

Now to the next frame.

21

In the previous frame the concept of moment of force was explained. A more general definition would be:

The *moment* of a force about *any point* equals the value of the force multiplied by the *perpendicular* distance between that point and the *line of action* of the force

Calculate the moment of the force about O in each of the following figures. Qualify each answer by stating the direction in which the force is tending to rotate the body – that is, clockwise or anticlockwise.

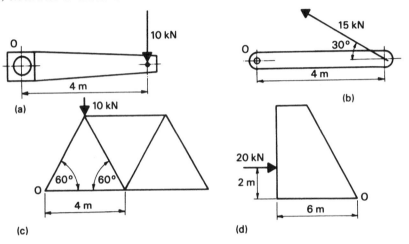

22

(a)	$10 \times 4 = 40$ kN m clockwise
(b)	$15 \times 2 = 30$ kN m anticlockwise
(c)	$10 \times 2 = 20$ kN m clockwise
(d)	$20 \times 2 = 40$ kN m clockwise

In (b) did you calculate the perpendicular distance from O to the line of action of the force?

RESULTANT OF A SERIES OF PARALLEL FORCES

The concept of a moment of force may be used to locate the line of action of the resultant of a number of parallel forces. The three forces F_1, F_2 and F_3 acting on the beam shown in the following figure could be replaced by a single force R of magnitude $F_1 + F_2 + F_3$, but we do not immediately know its line of action. We cannot use vector diagrams (as in previous problems) because the forces are not concurrent. What we do know is that the turning effect of the resultant must be the same as the total turning effect of the original forces. We can use this fact to calculate the line of action of the resultant by taking (calculating) moments about an appropriate point.

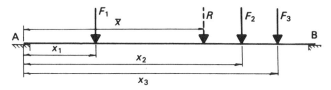

Let us take moments about A:

If the resultant R acts at distance $\bar{x}$ from A as shown, then:

The moment of R about A = sum of moments of original forces about A:

$$R \times \bar{x} = F_1 \times x_1 + F_2 \times x_2 + F_3 \times x_3$$

from which we can calculate $\bar{x}$.

Note that it is not essential to take moments about A. You can, in fact, choose any convenient point. You will discover in future work that we often choose to take moments about a point on the line of action of one of the forces in a force system, because by so doing the moment produced by that force is zero and it disappears from the calculation.

Calculate the resultant of the system of parallel forces shown in the figure below. Determine the line of action of the resultant by taking moments (a) about A and (b) about C (both methods should give the same answer).

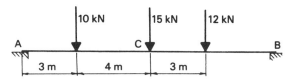

23

> Resultant $= 37$ kN
>
> Line of action is 6.89 m to the right of A

You should have calculated R equal to $10 + 15 + 12 = 37$ kN then:

(a) by moments about A: $37 \times \bar{x} = (10 \times 3) + (15 \times 7) + (12 \times 10)$ where $\bar{x}$ is measured from A

thus $\qquad\qquad \bar{x} = 6.89$ m

(b) by moments about C: $37 \times \bar{x}_1 = -(10 \times 4) + (15 \times 0) + (12 \times 3) = -4$ kNm where $\bar{x}_1$ is measured from C

thus $\qquad\qquad \bar{x}_1 = -0.11$ m (that is, 0.11m to the left of C).

Note the use of signs. Moments tending to rotate the system clockwise about A in case (a) and about C in case (b) are taken as positive. Anticlockwise moments are taken as negative. Thus in case (b), the moment of the 10 kN force is anticlockwise about C. The total moment about C is also negative thus the resultant must act to the left of C. Also note that, while the 15 kN force has zero moment about C, it still makes a contribution of 15 kN towards the total magnitude of the resultant force.

24

CENTROIDS OF SHAPES

A mechanical system usually consists of separate individual parts, each subject to its own weight force. These forces are vertical and parallel to each other and, as in the previous frames, may be replaced by a single vertical resultant of magnitude equal to the total weight of the body and acting at the *centre of gravity* of the body. The position of the centre of gravity of a body, such as the machine part shown below, may consequently be determined by taking moments.

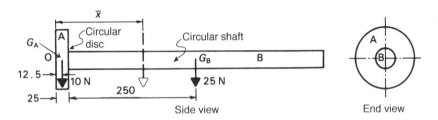

Disc A has a weight of 10 N acting through its own centre of gravity, G_A. Shaft B has a weight of 25 N acting at G_B. If we take moments about the end O of the shaft then the distance $\bar{x}$ to the centre of gravity of the whole body from O will be given by:

$$\text{Total weight} \times \bar{x} = \text{the sum of the moments of each part about O}$$
$$= (10 \times 12.5) + 25 \times (250 + 25)$$

thus
$$\bar{x} = (125 + 6875)/(10 + 25)$$
$$= \underline{200 \text{ mm}}$$

Suppose we now wish to locate the centre of gravity (G) of an irregular-shaped plate of material of uniform thickness and uniform weight w N/m^2 as shown in the figure below. Consider the plate is lying horizontally. The plan view is as shown, with the weight forces acting vertically downwards at right angles to the page.

X and Y are axes in the horizontal plane and intersect at a convenient origin O. The small element shown has an area δA and is located at a distance x from the Y-axis and distance y from the X-axis.

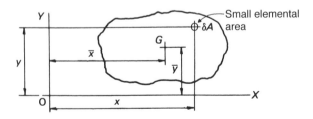

What is the moment of the weight force of the small element about the Y-axis?

$$\boxed{w\delta A \times x \ (\text{or} \ wx\delta A)}$$

The distance from the Y-axis to G will be given by:

Total weight $\times \bar{x} = \Sigma wx\delta A$

where Σ is the usual mathematical symbol to denote 'the sum of'

but total weight = sum of the weight of the small elements = $\Sigma w\delta A$

thus $\qquad \Sigma w\delta A \times \bar{x} = \Sigma wx\delta A$

or $\qquad \Sigma \delta A \times \bar{x} = \Sigma x\delta A$ (since w is uniform)

but $\Sigma \delta A = A$ (the total surface area)

thus $\qquad A\bar{x} = \Sigma x\delta A$

In the case of a plate of *uniform thickness*, then the position of G is independent of the weight per unit area and is purely a function of the shape of the plate. The expression $A\bar{x} = \Sigma x\delta A$ may be solved for any shape, and defines the position of the centre of area or *centroid* of that shape with respect to the Y-axis. Similarly, solving the expression $A\bar{y} = \Sigma y\delta A$ will locate the centroid with respect to the X-axis.

The concept of the centroid is important and will feature in future programmes, so let us consider a few common shapes. It should be obvious that for a square, rectangle and circle, the centroid will be central, as shown below.

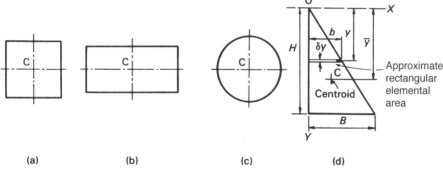

(a)   (b)   (c)   (d)

Now look at the triangle shown in figure (d) above. Taking moments of area of the approximately rectangular shaped elements about an X-axis passing through the apex, then

$$A \times \bar{y} = \Sigma y\delta A$$

that is $\qquad \tfrac{1}{2}BH \times \bar{y} = \Sigma by\delta y \qquad$ since $\quad \delta A = b\delta y$

$$= \Sigma(By/H)y\delta y \quad \text{since} \quad b/B = y/H$$

$$= \frac{B}{H}\int_0^H y^2 \mathrm{d}y = \frac{B}{H}\left[\frac{y^3}{3}\right]_0^H = \frac{BH^2}{3}$$

thus $\qquad \underline{\bar{y} = \tfrac{2}{3}H}$ from apex (or $\tfrac{1}{3}H$ above base)

What is the distance of the centroid, C, from the Y-axis?

$$\boxed{\tfrac{1}{3}B}$$

To locate the centroid for a complex shape, you will need to divide it into simple basic shapes for which you know the position of the centroid. You can then apply the principle that *the total area multiplied by the distance from the centroid to a convenient axis is equal to the algebraic sum of the moments of area of each part about the same axis.*

Thus, for the complex shape shown below, divide the area into two rectangles (A and C) and a triangle (B), as indicated. Then taking the corner (O) of the area as the origin and the X and Y axes as shown:

for part A $\qquad\qquad\qquad\qquad\qquad\qquad$ area $= 100 \times 50 \qquad = 5000$ mm^2

$\qquad$ distance y of centroid C_A of A from the X-axis $= 50 + 100/2 \quad = 100$ mm

$\qquad\qquad\qquad\qquad\qquad\quad \therefore \quad$ area $\times y = 500\,000$ mm^3

for part B $\qquad\qquad\qquad\qquad\qquad\qquad$ area $= \tfrac{1}{2} \times 100 \times 50 \; = 2500$ mm^2

$\qquad$ distance y of centroid C_B of B from the X-axis $\quad = 50 + 100/3 \quad = 83.33$ mm

$\qquad\qquad\qquad\qquad\qquad\quad \therefore \quad$ area $\times y = 208\,333$ mm^3

for part C $\qquad\qquad\qquad\qquad\qquad\qquad$ area $= 100 \times 50 \qquad = 5000$ mm^2

$\qquad$ distance y of centroid C_C of C from the X-axis $= \tfrac{1}{2} \times 50 \qquad\quad = 25$ mm

$\qquad\qquad\qquad\qquad\qquad\quad \therefore \quad$ area $\times y = 125\,000$ mm^3

Total moment of area of all parts about the X-axis:

$$= 500\,000 + 208\,333 + 125\,000$$

$$= 833\,333 \text{ mm}^3$$

$\qquad\qquad$ Total area $= 5000 + 2500 + 5000 = 12\,500$ mm^2

thus $\qquad\qquad\qquad\qquad \bar{y} = 833\,333/12\,500 = \underline{66.67 \text{ mm}}$

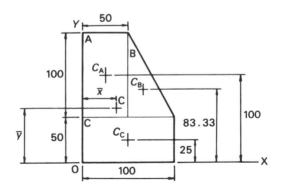

Now calculate $\bar{x}$ by taking moments about the Y-axis.

43.33 mm

The calculation of $\bar{x}$ together with the calculation for $\bar{y}$ is tabulated below. Tabular methods provide a concise way of setting out this form of calculation and you should adopt them wherever possible.

Part	Area (A)	x	Ax	y	Ay
A	5 000	25.00	125 000	100.00	500 000
B	2 500	66.67	166 675	83.33	208 333
C	5 000	50.00	250 000	25.00	125 000
total	12 500		541 675		833 333

$$\bar{x} = \frac{541\,675}{12\,500} \qquad \bar{y} = \frac{833\,333}{12\,500}$$

$$= \underline{43.33 \text{ mm}} \qquad = \underline{66.67 \text{ mm}}$$

In the previous two frames we had to calculate both $\bar{x}$ and $\bar{y}$ in order to locate the centroid, because the shape of the figure was not symmetrical. In many instances, however, when you are determining the positions of centroids of cross-sectional areas of structural members you will find that the area has at least one axis of symmetry. If there is an axis of symmetry, the centroid will lie on the axis of symmetry and it will only be necessary to locate the position of the centroid on that axis.

Let's do this for the T section shown. The centroid will lie somewhere along the Y-axis, since this is an axis of symmetry. Then, taking the X-axis through the base:

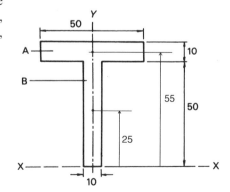

Part	Area (A)	y	Ay
A	500	55	27 500
B	500	25	12 500
total	1000		40 000

thus $\bar{y} = 40\,000/1000 = 40$ mm

Now to the next frame.

29

Force is a vector quantity: magnitude and direction must be quoted (units = N or kN).

The resultant and equilibrant of any system of coplanar concurrent forces may be determined by drawing a polygon of forces or by resolving the forces into components and combining the components algebraically.

If three coplanar concurrent forces are in equilibrium, they may be represented in magnitude and direction by the three sides of a triangle.

The moment of a force about any point equals the magnitude of that force multiplied by the perpendicular distance between the line of action of that force and the point (units = kNm).

It is important to distinguish between clockwise and anticlockwise moments.

The resultant and equilibrant of a system of parallel forces may be determined by taking moments about *any* convenient point.

Centroids of areas may be located using $A\bar{x} = \Sigma x\delta A$ and/or $A\bar{y} = \Sigma y\delta A$.

The centroid of a symmetrical shape lies on the axis (axes) of symmetry.

The centroid of a triangular shape is $\frac{1}{3}$ of the height above the base.

30

FURTHER PROBLEMS

1. Determine the magnitude and line of action of the resultants for the systems of forces shown in figures Q1(a), Q1(b) and Q1(c).

Ans. (a) 20.86 kN, $\theta = +269.7°$; (b) 148.36 kN, $\theta = +70.1°$; (c) 71.78 kN, $\theta = +164°$: positive values of θ are measured in an anticlockwise direction from the X axis)

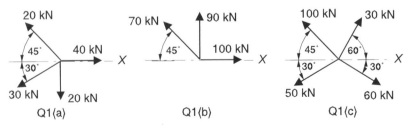

2. Figures Q2(a), Q2(b) and Q2(c) show force systems in equilibrium. Determine the magnitude and direction of the unknown forces.

Ans. (a) $F_1 = 77.65$ kN, $F_2 = 109.81$ kN; (b) 50.00 kN, $\theta = 240°$;
(c) -111.80 kN, $\theta = 333.4°$.

Problems Q1(a) to Q2(c) should be done both graphically and analytically.

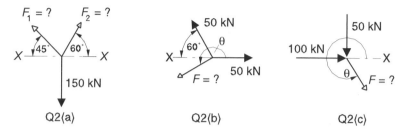

Q2(a)   Q2(b)   Q2(c)

3. Calculate the magnitude and locate the line of action of the resultants of the systems of forces shown in figures Q3(a) and Q3(b).

Ans. (a) 45 kN, 5.09 m to the right of A; (b) 85 kN, 7.29 m above O.

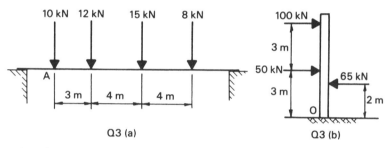

Q3 (a)   Q3 (b)

4. Determine the position of the centroids (C) of areas of the figures Q4(a) and Q4(b).

Ans. (a) C is on the Y-axis and 78.00 mm above the base; (b) $\bar{x} = 28.59$ mm, $\bar{y} = 75.41$ mm from the bottom left-hand corner.

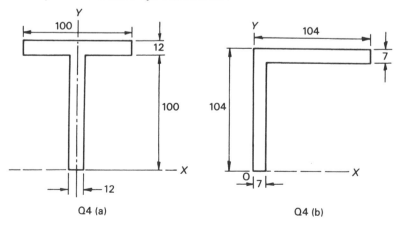

Q4 (a)   Q4 (b)

5. Determine the position of the centroids (*C*) of areas of the figures Q5(a) and Q5(b).

Ans. (a) C is on the Y-axis and 32.81 mm above the base; (b) C is on the Y-axis and 102.80 mm above the base.

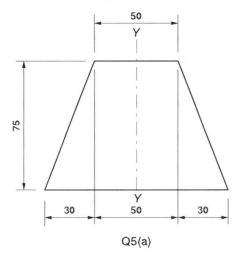

Q5(a)

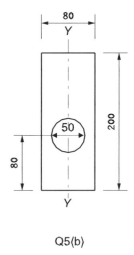

Q5(b)

Programme 2

LOADING OF COMPONENTS

On completion of this programme you will be able to:
- Recognise different forms of mechanical systems
- Identify different forms of loading acting on mechanical systems
- Identify different forms of support condition
- Draw free body diagrams for different forms of system subject to different loading and support conditions
- Recognise and apply the conditions of equilibrium to statically determinate problems
- Calculate the magnitude and direction of components of support reactions
- Calculate the magnitude and nature of member forces in pin-jointed plane frames

1

In this programme we shall look at the different types of loading on mechanical components. A mechanical component can be considered as one part of a mechanical system, as discussed in Frame 2. Under the action of a load, or a combination of loads, a component will distort or move. Such movement may be intentional, as in the rotation of gears and shafts in a gearbox. This form of movement can be analysed using a knowledge of kinematics (the study of bodies in motion).

The movement of components may simply take the form of a distortion of the component itself. Take an eraser between thumb and finger so as to squeeze (compress) it. Because of the applied load, the eraser will shorten. In other words, there is distortion as a result of the applied load. If the distortion of a component is excessive the component may fail because it breaks, or it can no longer function as intended. Therefore it is necessary to study the various loads that are applied in practice to different components so that we can, in subsequent programmes, predict the way in which components will react to loads.

2

MECHANICAL SYSTEMS

The following diagram shows a mechanical system in the form of a simplified reciprocating engine. Linear motion of the piston in the cylinder is translated into angular motion of the crankshaft by means of a connecting rod. The little end of the connecting rod is attached to the piston by the gudgeon (wrist) pin going through the skirt of the piston. All the moving parts – piston, connecting rod and crankshaft – are interconnected to make a mechanism. However, the engine could not function without the cylinder and cylinder head. The cylinder not only constrains the movement of the piston but also contains gas under pressure.

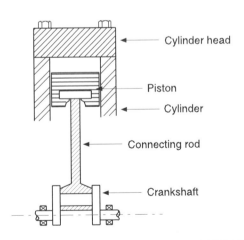

As the piston moves up the cylinder, the air/fuel mixture is compressed, the mixture volume is reduced and the pressure in the cylinder increases. Near the top of the stroke the mixture is ignited, creating a further increase in pressure. This high pressure forces the piston down the cylinder during the power stroke and the power is transmitted through the crankshaft. The cylinder head is an essential part of the system in order to seal the gas pressure within the cylinder. In practice, it would also house valves to allow the mixture into the cylinder and to exhaust the spent gas after the power stroke, again essential parts for the correct functioning of the engine. Therefore, the system as shown consists of interacting parts.

From this discussion can you think of a brief description of a mechanical system?

3

> A group of interacting parts

This is one possible definition, but there are several. However, the key words are 'parts' and 'interacting'. If we consider a motor car, it is a system that combines several subsystems for it to function: engine, transmission, braking system, to name a few.

Each of these systems contains several parts that interact. These are the component parts of each system, and for mechanical systems each part is referred to as a mechanical component, although it is usual to just use the term 'component' for brevity. A component must fulfil a specific function and for this it must be of the necessary shape, be manufactured to the required tolerances and have an inherent strength essential for that function.

A car body is part of a motor car, but is the body itself a system?

4

> Yes

The car body comprises several components such as the floor pan, roof, door pillars and bulkhead to form a structural system. It is different from the type of system considered in Frame 2, as it contains no moving parts.

The components of a car body are welded together so that they interact to carry all the loads to which the body is subjected, such as the weight of the engine, transmission and suspension. There are additional external loads caused by wind resistance or vibratory loading resulting from movement over rough surfaces; all of which must be considered when designing the car body.

Can you think of any other loads acting on a car body?

5

> The weight of the passengers

This is one of the more obvious loads that the car body has to support – you may have thought of others. A motor car is designed to provide motion.
Is there any load on a car body caused by motion?

6

> Yes

When a car is accelerating there is a force (F) caused by that acceleration. This can be calculated from Newton's 2nd law of motion which can be summarised as:

$$F = ma$$

where m is the mass of the car and a is its acceleration. The force must be created by the car to ensure acceleration and is considered to act through the centre of gravity of the whole car, as shown.

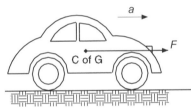

Determine the force acting on a car having a mass of 1000 kg if it starts from rest and accelerates uniformly to 72 km/hr in 10s.

7

> 2 kN

The final velocity (v) of the car can be converted to metres/second:

$$v = \frac{72 \times 10^3}{3600} = 20 \text{ m/s}$$

And the acceleration is given by:

$$a = \frac{v}{t} = \frac{20}{10} = 2 \text{ m/s}^2$$

Hence:

$$F = m \times a = 1000 \times 2 = 2000 \text{ N} \quad - \quad \text{i.e. 2 kN.}$$

Now move on to the next frame.

8

LOADING SYSTEMS

In design it is necessary to consider all significant loads acting on a system or component. Also it is necessary to consider the way in which loads are applied. Let's consider the most common types of loading systems:

Concentrated loads

Loads are applied over a finite area, but if that area is small it is generally accurate enough to consider the load as being concentrated at a point. Take the example of a washing machine in figure (a), where the weight of the machine is carried on small supports that can take the form of adjustable legs or rollers. The contact area of each support is small compared to the dimensions of the machine, so the load on each can be considered as a single force.

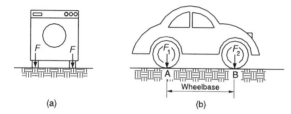

(a)   (b)

Similarly, the loads on the wheels of a motor car – see figure (b) – can be considered to be concentrated loads. Although there will be a finite contact area between each tyre and the road, this area is difficult to determine without specialist knowledge. It is sufficiently accurate to consider each contact area as small and the load on each wheel to be effectively a single force.

Determine the load on each front wheel if the car has a mass of 1000kg, the wheelbase is 2.5m and the centre of gravity of the car is situated 1m behind the front wheels

9

$$\boxed{F_2 = 2.94 \text{ kN}}$$

Weight of the car $= 1000 \times 9.81 = 9810$ N. This weight will be distributed between the front and back wheels as the forces F_1 and F_2. If we take moments of forces about any point it follows that the moment of total weight about that point must equal the moment of the two separate forces F_1 and F_2. For convenience moments can be taken about A which will eliminate F_1 from the calculation i.e.:

$$9810 \times 1.5 = F_2 \times 2.5 \quad \therefore \quad F_2 = \frac{9810 \times 1.5}{2.5} = 5886 \text{ N}$$

Since there are two wheels at the front, each has a load of 2943 N $= 2.94$ kN.
What will be the load on each of the rear wheels?

10

$$1.96 \text{ kN}$$

Since the total load on the wheels must equal the total weight of the car the load on each rear wheel is simply given by $(9810 - 5886)/2 = 1962 \text{ N} = 1.96 \text{ kN}$.

Distributed loads

Figure (a) shows a shelf in a book case carrying a row of books. Each book has weight, so each book applies a vertical force to the shelf. Since there is a row of books, the total load will be distributed along the length of the shelf.

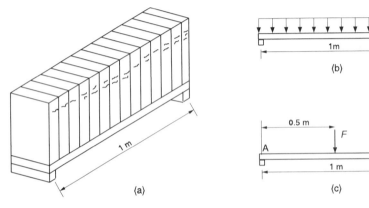

(b)

(a)

(c)

If there are 40 books each with a mass of 0.3kg what is the total load on the shelf?

11

$$117.72 \text{ N}$$

Total mass of books $= 40 \times 0.3 = 12 \text{ kg}$
Total weight of books $= 12 \times 9.81 = 117.72 \text{ N}$

Since it was assumed that each book is of the same mass, the load can be considered to be uniformly distributed along the length of the shelf. This is illustrated in figure (b) by a series of vertical arrows. Generally a uniformly distributed load is quoted in terms of the intensity, the load per unit length; in this case, 117.72 N/m.

For calculation purposes, the uniformly distributed load can be replaced by its resultant, the total load of 117.72 N, acting through the centroid of the load distribution diagram. In this case, the centroid is halfway along the shelf, and the moment about any point of the total load F, figure (c), acting at mid-span is exactly the same as the moment of the uniform load about that point.

What is the moment of the uniformly distributed loading about point A?

$$\boxed{58.86 \, \text{Nm}}$$

Moment $= 117.72 \times 0.5 = 58.86$ Nm

It is possible to have a distributed load that varies in intensity. For example, consider an aircraft propellor blade fixed in the hub at point A, with the loading varying from zero at A to 2 kN/m at the tip.

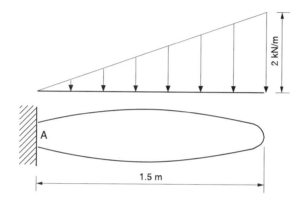

The triangular diagram above the blade represents the load distribution diagram.

Total force on the blade $=$ average intensity of load $\times$ blade length

$$= 1000 \times 1.5$$
$$= 1500 \, \text{N}$$

The value of the *resultant* force is also given by the area of the load distribution diagram. Thus for the whole blade $F = \frac{1}{2} \, 2000 \times 1.5 = 1500$ N.

The line of action of the resultant force F will be through the centroid of the load distribution diagram at a distance of $\frac{2}{3} \times 1.5$ m from A. The moment of the force about A is given by:

$$\text{Moment} = 1500 \times \left(\frac{2}{3} \times 1.5 \right) = 1500 \, \text{Nm}$$
$$= 1.5 \, \text{kN m}$$

Note that the book shelf in Frame 10 and the aircraft propeller above are two examples of an important category of component. They both act as beams, because the loading is normal to the longitudinal axis of the component and causes the component to bend.

Now move on to the next frame to see how to deal with another special category of loads.

13

Pressure loads

The distributed loading considered above was defined in terms of the loading per unit length of the component. However, pressure represents a distributed form of loading which is applied over each unit area of the component. Pressure has units of N/m^2.

A pressure of $1 \ N/m^2$ is very small, being equivalent to a film of water $\frac{1}{10}$ mm thick covering the surface. Most pressures found in practice have values several orders of magnitude greater than this, so that it is useful to quote pressure in bar where $1 \ bar = 10^5 \ N/m^2$. A bar is also approximately equal to the pressure of one atmosphere.

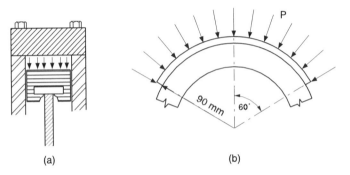

(a)   (b)

Pressure can be exerted on a component either through a fluid or mechanically. In an engine, the gas in the cylinder exerts a pressure on the piston as shown in figure (a). Alternatively, a brake shoe has a friction lining on which pressure is exerted between the shoe and the brake drum surrounding it, as shown in figure (b).

Determine the resultant force on the brake shoe if the applied pressure is 1 bar and the width of the shoe is 32 mm.

14

$$\boxed{499 \ N}$$

The shoe is symmetrical about the vertical axis shown in diagram (b). The pressure will cause a net resultant force in the vertical direction as the horizontal components of the forces acting to the left side of the vertical axis will be cancelled out by equal and opposite horizontal forces acting to the right of this axis. This vertical resultant force can be calculated by multiplying the pressure by the area of the shoe *projected on to a horizontal plane.*

The resultant force $= P \times$ projected area

Projected area $= 2 \times (90 \times \sin 60°) \times 32 = 4988 \ mm^2 = 4.99 \times 10^{-3} \ m^2$

$\therefore$ Resultant force $= (1 \times 10^5) \times 4.99 \times 10^{-3} = 499 \ N$

Not all pressures are uniform. Hydrostatic pressure caused by the weight of a liquid varies with depth. If we consider a column of liquid with height z the pressure (P) on the base is given by:

$$P = \frac{\text{weight of liquid}}{\text{area } (A)}$$

The mass of liquid = density × volume = $\rho(A \times z)$

and the weight of liquid = $\rho(A \times z)g$

$$\therefore \ P = \frac{\text{weight}}{\text{area}} = \frac{\rho(A \times z)g}{A} = \rho z g$$

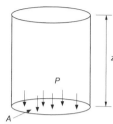

This pressure formula has been derived to give the pressure in the vertical direction acting on a horizontal surface. However, in a liquid the pressure at a point will be the same in all directions. Hence the formula is equally valid when calculating the pressure acting on any horizontal, vertical or inclined surface at a depth z below the surface of a liquid.

A glass window 500 mm diameter is built into the side of a swimming pool. Find the variation of pressure on the glass if the surface of the water is 1.5 m above the top edge of the window. Take the density of water as 1000 kg/m³.

15

> Top edge: 0.147 bar;   Bottom edge: 0.196 bar

The figure shows the variation of hydrostatic pressure with depth from zero bar at the surface and increasing linearly with depth.

Pressure at top of window $\quad = \rho z g = 1000 \times 1.5 \times 9.81$

$\qquad\qquad\qquad\qquad\qquad\quad = 14715 \text{ N/m}^2 = 0.147 \text{ bar}$

Pressure at bottom of window $= \rho z g = 1000 \times (1.5 + 0.5) \times 9.81$

$\qquad\qquad\qquad\qquad\qquad\quad = 19620 \text{ N/m}^2 = 0.196 \text{ bar}$

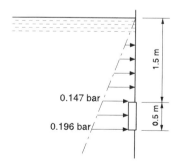

Now let's look at some additional types of loading.

16

COUPLES

If a force is applied at a distance from a point, then the force creates a moment about that point, as described in Programme 1. We shall now consider the special case of a force applied in such a way that a moment is induced at the point of application of the load.

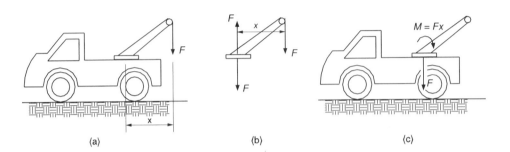

(a)   (b)   (c)

Consider the tow truck in figure (a), with a vertical force F applied to the end of the crane. To understand the effect of the force, we can imagine equal but opposite forces F applied at the point where the crane is fixed to the floor of the truck (figure (b)).

The two forces acting through the fixed point cancel each other out, so effectively the loading is not changed from figure (a). However, the three forces can now be viewed as a vertical force acting through the fixed point and a pair of equal and opposite forces acting at a distance of x apart. This pair of forces cause a moment about the anchor point of magnitude Fx, as illustrated in figure (c). Since this moment is created by two forces acting in equal but opposite directions, it is called a *couple*.

A couple not only creates a moment about a point within the line of action of the forces but also about other external points. Consider the pair of forces which give rise to a clockwise couple system shown below and A, which is an arbitrary fixed point at a distance L from the left-hand force:

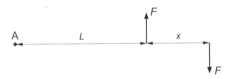

If moments are taken about A:

$$\text{Moment of right-hand force} = F(L + x) \qquad \text{(clockwise)}$$
$$\text{Moment of left-hand force} \; = FL \qquad\qquad \text{(anticlockwise)}$$

What is the resultant moment of the two forces about A?

17

$$\boxed{Fx}$$

Summing the two moments gives the actual moment acting about A:

$$M_A = F(L + x) - FL = Fx$$

Thus, as x is the fixed distance between the two forces, the moment of the couple about A is independent of the distance of the couple from A. It follows that *the moment of a couple about any point is the same irrespective of the position in space of that point.*

Now let's look at our final example of a loading system.

18

TORQUE

When a moment or couple is applied to a body or a component, the body is considered to remain static and can be analysed using the laws of statics. If a moment causes rotation during the whole period over which the moment acts, this form of moment is called a torque. The figure below shows the cross-section of a circular drive-shaft of radius r and with a force F applied tangentially to the shaft:

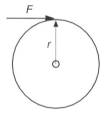

The force exerts a *torque* or *torsional moment* about the centre of the shaft given by:

$$\text{Torque} = \text{force} \times \text{radius} = F \times r$$

Force applied to the periphery of a circular shaft through, for example, a drive belt, will generate a torque and cause it to rotate. As the shaft rotates it will cause *work* to be done by the torque and *power* can be transmitted through the drive shaft. In Programme 7 we shall look at examples of drive shafts and see how to calculate power outputs.

What is the unit of torque?

19

$$\boxed{Nm}$$

Torque is a special type of moment and has the same units as moment. Now try some problems.

20

PROBLEMS

1. The wing of an aircraft can be considered as a beam firmly attached at one end to the fuselage. If the length of one wing is 15 m and has a uniform lift of 4 kN/m, find the moment acting on the fuselage.

Ans. 450 kN m.

2. The cylinder head of an engine is held by four bolts. If the maximum pressure in the engine is 40 bar and the cylinder diameter is 60 mm find the load on each bolt.

Ans. 2.83 kN.

3. A rectangular lock gate spans a canal that is 4 m wide. If the water level on one side of the gate is 3 m and on the other side is 1 m, calculate the resultant force on the gate. Take the density of water as 1000 kg/m^3.

Ans. 157kN.

21

FORCES AND REACTIONS

According to Newton's 3rd law of motion, *for every action on a body there is an equal and opposite reaction*. It follows that, for every force that is applied there must be an equal and opposite reactive force in order to keep a component or system in equilibrium.

In figure (a), the weight W is tending to pull the rope down. The ceiling has to provide an upward acting reaction R to prevent the rope from being pulled down. For equilibrium, it is clear that R must equal W. The rope itself is being stretched; it is in *tension*. A member in tension has internal reactive forces developed within it.

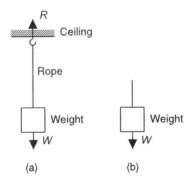

By taking a section through the rope and considering the free body diagram of the weight (figure (b)), can you identify the direction of the force exerted by the rope on the weight?

22

> Upwards

You can see this by considering the *free-body diagram* of the weight as shown in figure (a) below. The weight is acted upon by an upward force T and the load W. These must obviously be of equal magnitude if the weight is not going to move up or down. Similarly, at the top of the rope $T = R = W$. The tensile force remains constant at value T throughout the length of the rope, because no external loads act on the rope other than at the ends. In figure (b) below, we see a component acted upon by a vertical downward load W. In this case the load is tending to compress the component. By considering the free body diagram we can see that the ground must exert an upward acting reaction $R = W$ for equilibrium and a compressive force $C = W$ will develop internally in the component.

Note that in the diagrams showing the internal forces, two arrowheads are used, one at each end, and facing in different directions, since the internal forces act in opposite directions.

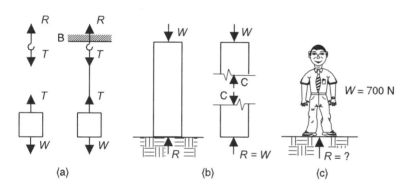

(a)   (b)   (c)

An engineer has a mass of 71.4 kg and stands on the ground. What is the reaction of the ground upon the engineer?

23

> 700N

The reaction = weight of engineer
$$R = 71.4 \times 9.81 = 700.4 \text{ N} \approx 700 \text{ N}$$

Remember that any reaction is only there as long as the external force is applied. Remove the force and the reaction disappears. The reaction is not tending to move the component or body but is there to resist the tendency of a force to cause movement. On to the next frame.

24

Now we shall consider some simple problems to illustrate the techniques of calculating forces and reactions.

In figure (a) below, the student weighs 700 N. This force of 700 N acts downwards through her centre of gravity. She is holding a balloon exerting an upward pull of 150 N. What is the effect on the ground? If you look first at the balloon you can see that a tensile force equal to 150 N must develop in the string in order to prevent the balloon rising. Putting the two arrows on the string to indicate the internal forces, you can then see that, at the bottom of the string, an upward force of 150 N acts on the student. She is now subject to two forces, 700 N down and 150 N up. There is an out-of-balance force of $700 - 150 = 550$ N. Thus an upward reaction of 550 N must develop between the ground and the student if she is not to move.

In figure (b), a rope passing over a frictionless pulley carries a load of 10 kN at each end. What is the reaction at the ceiling? The important thing to realise is that, when a rope passes over a frictionless pulley, the internal force in the rope does not change. If you look at the left-hand load first, you will realise that there will be a tensile force of 10 kN developed in the rope. If there is a tensile force of 10 kN in the rope to the left of the pulley, there will also be a tensile force of 10 kN in the rope to the right of the pulley. There are thus two forces acting on the right-hand load, 10 kN up and a weight force of 10 kN down. The system is thus in equilibrium. To determine the reaction in the ceiling, consider the equilibrium of the pulley. There are two downward forces of 10 kN in the rope, and the reaction, all acting on the pulley. For equilibrium, therefore, the reaction R must be 20 kN upwards.

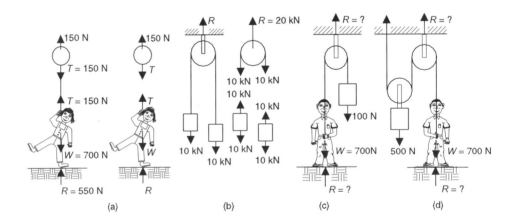

(a)   (b)   (c)   (d)

Now determine the magnitude and direction of the reactions below the engineer and securing the pulley to the ceiling in figures (c) and (d).

Draw free-body diagrams of each part of each problem and consider the equilibrium of each free body in turn. (Hint: in (d), start by considering the equilibrium of the left-hand pulley.)

(c) 600 N up and 200 N up;   (d) 450 N up and 500 N up

The following diagram shows a more complex situation, where the student is supporting a load using a rope passing over an inclined pulley. One rope is no longer vertical. We want to know the magnitude and direction of the unknown reaction R at the ceiling, as shown in the diagram.

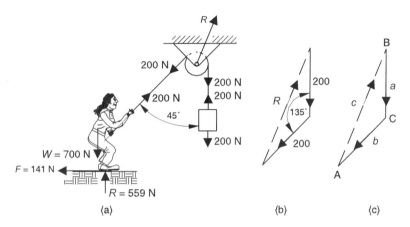

(a)   (b)   (c)

If we start at the load we see that there must be a tensile force of 200 N in the vertical rope. Since the pulley can be assumed to be frictionless there is an equal force of 200 N in the rope on the left-hand side of the pulley. The reaction R can be determined using a triangle of forces as in figure (b), which represents the three forces acting on the pulley. As the pulley is in equilibrium, R must be the *equilibrant* of the other two forces.

As the forces in the rope either side of the pulley are known in magnitude and direction, the triangle could be drawn to scale, but since sides a, b and angle C of the triangle are known (figure (c)) the reaction can be found using the *cosine rule*:

$$c^2 = a^2 + b^2 - 2ab \cos C$$
$$R^2 = 200^2 + 200^2 - 2 \times 200 \times 200 \cos(135°)$$
$$\therefore \quad R = 369.55 \text{ N}$$

Angles A and B are equal and have a value of $(180° - 135°)/2 = 22.5°$. It follows that the angle of the reaction R to the horizontal is $22.5° + 45° = 67.5°$.

An alternative approach to the calculation of R is to use the tabulated analytical method introduced in Programme 1. You will recall that we used the principle that when a set of forces is in equilibrium, then the *algebraic sum of the horizontal and vertical components of the forces must be in equilibrium*.

Can you calculate the reaction at the ceiling using this alternative approach? Check your calculations against the solution given in the next frame.

26

Check your calculations:

Force	θ	V	H
200 (inclined)	225°	−141.42	−141.42
200 (vertical)	270°	−200.00	0
R	θ	$R\sin\theta$	$R\cos\theta$

The sum of the vertical components $= -141.42 - 200.00 + R\sin\theta = 0$

$$R\sin\theta = +341.42$$

The sum of the horizontal components $= -141.42 + R\cos\theta = 0$

$$R\cos\theta = +141.42$$

Dividing these two equations we get:

$$\frac{R\sin\theta}{R\cos\theta} = \tan\theta = \frac{341.42}{141.42} = 2.41$$

$$\therefore \quad \theta = \tan^{-1} 2.41 = 67.5°$$

and

$$R\sin 67.5° = 341.42$$

$$\therefore \quad R = \frac{341.42}{\sin 67.5°} = 369.55 \text{ N}$$

Look back at the diagram in Frame 25. Considering the vertical equilibrium of the student, we note that she is subject to the tension in the rope and her own weight. If we resolve these forces we obtain a total vertically downward force on the ground of value $700 - 141 = 599$ N. This will be resisted by an upward reaction of 559 N.

Resolving the forces acting on the student horizontally, we see that there is also a horizontal out-of-balance force of 141 N.

What effect will this force tend to have on her and what reaction will be required at ground level to maintain her equilibrium?

27

> It will tend to pull her to the right, causing her to slide along the ground.
> A frictional resistance is required between her feet and the ground.

Frictional forces will develop to resist sliding between any two surfaces in contact. The value of such a force depends on the nature of the materials in contact, the state of the surfaces (rough or smooth) and on the value of the normal force pressing the surfaces together. For any two surfaces, there is an upper limit to the value of frictional force that can be developed in response to a given value of normal force, and this relationship is quantified by the *coefficient of friction* (μ) defined as the ratio (maximum frictional force)/(normal force between the surfaces).

In the above example, there is a normal force of 559 N between the student and the ground. We need a horizontal frictional force of 141 N to prevent her sliding. This is only possible if the coefficient of friction is at least $141/559 = 0.25$, otherwise she will slide along the ground and will not be in a state of equilibrium.

In this type of problem it may be convenient to quote the reaction in terms of the vertical component (V) and the horizontal component (H), or it may be more useful to quote the total reaction R, as we did at the pulley.

28

PROBLEMS

1. Figure Q1 shows a plan view of a ship's capstan which consists of a circular drum onto which is wound a coil of rope connected to the ship's anchor. The capstan rotates about a spindle at B. The anchor is raised by applying a force F to the leverage bar AB. For the situation shown, where the anchor is just on the point of being raised, calculate (i) the applied force F; (ii) the moment induced in the bar at B; (iii) the magnitude and direction of the reaction at the spindle

Ans. (i) 1.25 kN; (ii) 1.25 kN m; (iii) 6.25 kN at 90° anticlockwise from the X axis.

2. Repeat question 1. If the capstan is rotated through 45° from the position shown and held in that position.

Ans. (i) 1.25 kN; (ii) 1.25 kN m; (iii) 5.95 kN at 98.54° anticlockwise from the X axis.

3. Calculate the reactions at (i) A; (ii) B; (iii) C and (iv) the value of the load at D, in figure Q3. (**Hint**: start by looking at the free-body diagram of the load W_1.)

Ans. (i) 14.64 N upwards 30° to the left of vertical; (ii) 25.36 N vertically upwards; (iii) 10.35 N upwards 45° to the right of vertical; (iv) load at D = 25.36 N.

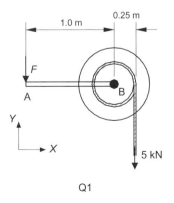

Q1

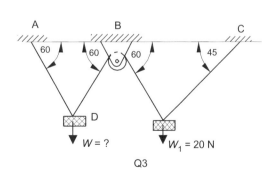

Q3

29

BEAM SUPPORTS

Simple supports

You should now be aware of the nature of reactions required to keep a component or system in equilibrium. Since beams are an important type of component, it is essential, for subsequent design and analysis, that we are able to evaluate the reactions at the beam's supports.

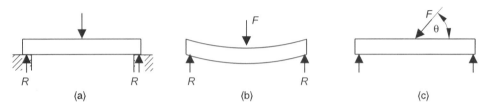

(a)   (b)   (c)

The simplest way to support a beam is to place it directly on top of the supports, as shown in figure (a). This means that the supports provide vertical reactions only, and allow a certain amount of rotation so that the beam can bend, as shown in figure (b). This is a reasonable assumption, as any rotation would in practice be very small, also the material of both beam and support have elastic properties and can change shape under load.

Suppose the loads on a beam are not vertical, but are applied at an acute angle, as shown in figure (c).

Is the beam in figure (c) in equilibrium?

30

$$\boxed{\text{No}}$$

The applied force can be resolved into a vertical component ($F\sin\theta$) and a horizontal component ($F\cos\theta$). The vertical component will be resisted by vertical reactions in the supports, but the horizontal component will cause the beam to move to the left.

A beam having supports that provide vertical reactions only is called *simply supported*. Such a beam will be in equilibrium and must satisfy the conditions for static equilibrium:

$\sum V = 0$ (the sum of all vertical forces must be zero)

$\sum H = 0$ (the sum of all horizontal forces must be zero)

$\sum M = 0$ (the sum of the moments of all forces about *any point* must be zero)

Since a simply supported beam has no horizontal reactions at the supports, it follows that all the applied horizontal forces must sum to zero. In practice, it is sufficient to consider vertical forces only as acting on a beam, although occasionally these can take the form of a couple. Therefore, the calculation of the reactions at the supports can be performed using the two conditions of $\sum V = 0$ and $\sum M = 0$. Since the application of these conditions will result in two equations, it is possible to calculate just two unknown support reactions. Hence, using these equations, we can solve beam problems with no more than two unknown support reactions – such types of problem are referred to as *statically determinate*.

As a first example, let's look at the beam AD shown below which is loaded with two concentrated loads of 5 kN and 7 kN. The support reactions are indicated by vertically upwards arrows at A and D marked V_A and V_D respectively.

To determine the reactions it is convenient to take moments since, if we choose the point about which we take moments correctly, we can eliminate one of the unknowns and simplify the calculations. In this case we shall take moments about A and thus eliminate V_A from the calculation.

Why will V_A be eliminated from the calculation?

31

Because V_A passes through A and therefore has no moment about A

Calculate the values of the reactions at D by taking moments about A

32

$V_D = 6.5$ kN

Take moments of *all* forces about A with clock-wise moments as positive:

$$\sum M_A = 0: \qquad (5 \times 2) + (7 \times 6) - (V_D \times 8) = 0$$

$$\therefore \quad V_D = \frac{10 + 42}{8} = 6.5 \text{ kN}$$

Our choice of where to take moments about was based on the wish to produce an equation with a single variable, V_D, which can be solved directly. Hence we took moments about A. We could equally well have taken moments about D to determine V_A.

Calculate V_A by taking moments of all forces about D (be careful with the signs of your moments).

33

$$V_A = 5.5 \text{ kN}$$

$$\sum M_D = 0: \quad -(5 \times 6) - (7 \times 2) + (V_A \times 8) = 0$$

$$\therefore \quad V_A = \frac{30 + 14}{8} = 5.5 \text{ kN}$$

Having previously obtained V_D can you think of another way that we could have calculated V_A?

34

We could have used the equation of vertical equilibrium $\sum V = 0$

This would have given us:

$$\sum V = 0: \quad V_A + V_D - 5 - 7 = 0$$

$$\therefore \quad V_A + 6.5 - 5 - 7 = 0$$

$$\therefore \quad V_A = 5.5 \text{ kN}$$

Which is the same answer as obtained previously. However, if we had calculated the value of V_D incorrectly, we would have compounded our error by using this incorrect value to calculate an incorrect value of V_A. It is therefore better to calculate the two reactions independently by taking moments and then using the expression $\sum V = 0$ as a *check* on the accuracy of our calculations. In other words:

$$\sum V: \quad V_A + V_D - 5 - 7 = 5.5 + 6.5 - 5 - 7$$

$$= 0$$

which is correct.

Suppose we now modify the loading to include a uniformly distributed load of 2 kN/m between B and C:

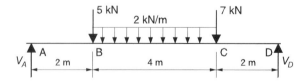

What are the new reactions at A and D?

$$\boxed{V_A = 9.5 \text{ kN} \quad V_D = 10.5 \text{ kN}}$$

As in Frame 32, take moments about A and considering the uniformly distributed load as an equivalent point load through the centre of the load distribution diagram:

$$\sum M_A = 0: \quad (5 \times 2) + (\{2 \times 4\} \times 4) + (7 \times 6) - (V_D \times 8) = 0$$

$$\therefore \quad V_D = \frac{10 + 32 + 42}{8} = 10.5 \text{ kN}$$

Taking moments about D:

$$\sum M_D = 0: \quad - (5 \times 6) - (\{2 \times 4\} \times 4) - (7 \times 2) + (V_A \times 8) = 0$$

$$\therefore \quad V_A = \frac{30 + 32 + 14}{8} = 9.5 \text{ kN}$$

and as a *check* on the accuracy of our calculations:

$$\sum V: \quad V_A + V_D - 5 - (2 \times 4) - 7 = 9.5 + 10.5 - 5 - 8 - 7 = 0$$

which is correct.

It is not always the case that simple supports are located at the extreme ends of the beam as the following loading diagram illustrates:

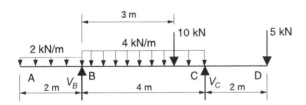

*Calculate the reactions at C by taking moments about B. (**Hint**: replace both the uniformly distributed loads by their equivalent resultants acting through the centre of their respective load distribution diagrams.)*

$$\boxed{V_C = 22 \text{ kN}}$$

$$\sum M_B = 0: \quad - (\{2 \times 2\} \times 1) + (\{4 \times 4\} \times 2) + (10 \times 3) + (5 \times 6) - (V_C \times 4) = 0$$

$$\therefore \quad V_C = \frac{-4 + 32 + 30 + 30}{4} = 22 \text{ kN}$$

Did you take the *signs* of the moments into account?

Calculate V_B and check the accuracy of your calculations by considering the overall vertical equilibrium of the beam.

37

$$\boxed{V_{\rm B} = 13 \ \text{kN}}$$

Taking moments about C:

$$\sum M_{\rm C} = 0: \quad -(\{2 \times 2\} \times 5) - (\{4 \times 4\} \times 2) - (10 \times 1) + (5 \times 2) + (V_{\rm B} \times 4) = 0$$

$$\therefore \quad V_{\rm B} = \frac{20 + 32 + 10 - 10}{4} = 13 \ \text{kN}$$

and as a *check* on the accuracy of our calculations:

$$\sum V: \quad V_{\rm B} + V_{\rm C} - (2 \times 2) - (4 \times 4) - 10 - 5 = 13 + 22 - 4 - 16 - 10 - 5 = 0$$

which is correct. If you had difficulty calculating the moments of the two uniformly distributed loads then go back and study Frame 11 again.

Fixed supports

Not all beams are simply supported. There is an important class of beam that has only one support, as illustrated in figure (a) below. The end of the beam, at **B**, is unsupported, while the supported end A is firmly fixed to prevent vertical movement and rotation at the support. Figure (b) shows the vertical reaction, $V_{\rm A}$, and the fixing moment $M_{\rm A}$ necessary to maintain equilibrium. $M_{\rm A}$ is shown as an anti-clockwise moment as the effect of the 10kN load is to tend to rotate the beam in a clockwise direction about A, and this must be resisted by a moment in the opposite direction.

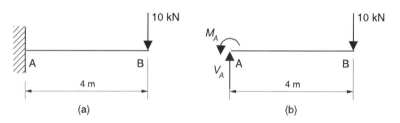

$$(a) \qquad\qquad (b)$$

For this beam to be in equilibrium, what are the values of the reactions that must be provided by the fixed support?

38

$$\boxed{\begin{array}{c} \text{A vertical force of 10 kN} \\ \text{An anticlockwise moment of 40 kN m} \end{array}}$$

Taking the support reactions acting in the directions shown in figure (b) and resolving the forces vertically:

$$\sum V: \quad V_{\rm A} - 10 = 0$$

$$\therefore \quad V_{\rm A} = 10 \ \text{kN}$$

and taking moments about A:

$$\sum M_A = 0: \qquad -M_A + (10 \times 4) = 0$$

$$\therefore \quad M_A = 40 \text{ kN m}$$

A beam with one fixed support is called a *cantilevered* beam. To achieve the rigidity required of a fixed support, the beam must be firmly attached to a supporting structure either using bolts and rivets or by welding.

Figure (a) below shows the wing of an aircraft subject to a uniform lift of 5 kN/m. It must be firmly attached to the fuselage so that the wing can be assumed to act as a cantilevered beam.

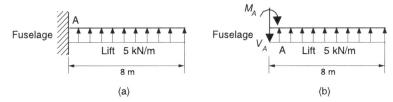

Fuselage — A — Lift 5 kN/m — 8 m — (a)

Fuselage — M_A — V_A A — Lift 5 kN/m — 8 m — (b)

Determine the loads on the fuselage.

39

> Downward force of 40 kN; Clockwise moment of 160 kN m

Taking the support reactions acting in the directions shown in figure (b) and resolving the forces vertically:

$$\sum V: \qquad -V_A + (5 \times 8) = 0$$

$$\therefore \quad V_A = 40 \text{ kN}$$

and taking moments about A:

$$\sum M_A = 0: \qquad M_A - \{(5 \times 8) \times 4\} = 0$$

$$\therefore \quad M_A = 160 \text{ kN m}$$

Some light aircraft have an additional support provided by a strut mounted between the wing and the fuselage, as shown in the figure below. The force in the strut can be resolved into a vertical and a horizontal component: the horizontal component being transmitted through the wing section, AB, and resisted by an equal and opposite horizontal reaction at the fuselage at A:

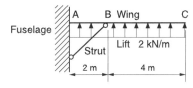

Fuselage — A B Wing C — Strut — Lift 2 kN/m — 2 m — 4 m

Can you determine the vertical reactions at A and B?

40

```
┌─────────────────────┐
│         No          │
└─────────────────────┘
```

Strictly speaking the answer is 'not by using the laws of statics'. The reason is apparent when we consider the loading on the wing (beam):

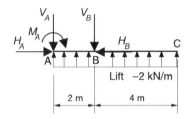

We can write down only three equations of equilibrium. The equation of horizontal equilibrium $\sum H = 0$ will enable us to consider the horizontal forces acting on the beam. In addition, there are three unknowns V_A, V_B and M_A to be solved, but only two further equations of equilibrium ($\sum V = 0$ and $\sum M = 0$). Hence, we cannot solve this problem by applying the simple equations of equilibrium we have considered so far.

This type of structural component is known as *statically indeterminate*. To solve this type of problem, a further criterion must be used. A realistic criterion would be to assume that the deflections at A and B are both zero. Programme 10 discusses the deflection of beams, and using the principles that you will study in Programme 10 it would then be possible to analyse the loading on the wing. Statically indeterminate problems are outside the scope of this programme, but they are mentioned here to make you aware that they exist in practice.

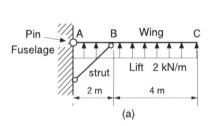

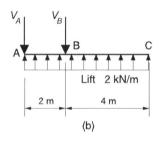

Suppose we change the above problem such that the wing is attached to the fuselage by a pinned connection so that the wing is no longer rigidly fixed at A. A pin joint is assumed to be frictionless so that there is no longer a fixing moment at A.

Assuming that the vertical support reactions act in the directions shown in figure (b), calculate the values of V_A and V_B (for clarity the horizontal forces, which are not required for this calculation, have been omitted from the diagram).

$$\boxed{V_A = -6 \text{ kN}; \; V_B = 18 \text{ kN}}$$

Check your calculations:

The two unknowns are now the reactive forces at A and B. Taking moments about A:

$$\sum M_A = 0: \qquad (V_B \times 2) - \{(2 \times 6) \times 3\} = 0 \qquad \therefore \quad V_B = 18 \text{ kN}$$

Taking moments about B:

$$\sum M_B = 0: \qquad -2(\{2 \times 6\} \times 1) - (V_A \times 2) = 0 \qquad \therefore \quad V_A = -6 \text{ kN}$$

The negative sign indicates that V_A acts in the opposite direction to that assumed; that is, it is acting upwards. As a *check* on the accuracy of our calculations:

$$\sum V: \qquad -V_A - V_B + (2 \times 6) = +6 - 18 + 12 = 0$$

which is correct. Typical examples of a beam pinned at one end include the arms of an excavator and the front suspension unit of a motor car. A further example of the application of pin joints is given in the next frame.

42

PIN JOINTED FRAMES

A pin jointed frame is fabricated from a number of straight component parts, called members, connected together at their ends by frictionless pinned joints to form a stable system that is capable of supporting applied loads at some or all of the joints.

In practice, the members will be connected by bolts, possibly several bolts at each joint, or they may be welded together. Such joints cannot act as though they were held by perfect frictionless pins. However, experience shows that, even when a frame does not contain pinned joints, the forces acting on the components do not vary significantly from a similar frame with pinned joints. It is therefore convenient and sufficiently accurate to analyse frames on the assumption that the joints are pinned.

It follows that, if a member has a pinned joint at each end, the rest of the frame cannot exert a *moment* on that member. A member can have a *force* transmitted from the rest of the frame. Such a force can be resolved into components acting along the longitudinal axis of the member (F_1) and a force acting at right angles to the member (F_2) as shown below.

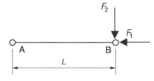

Write down an expression for the moment of the two component forces about A. As A is a pin, what conclusions do you draw about the forces in the member?

43

> The member is subject only to an axial force (F_2) acting along its longitudinal axis

Since the member will be in equilibrium, we can apply the laws of statics. Taking moments about A:

$$\sum M_A: \qquad M_A = F_2 \times L$$

But as A is a pinned joint it cannot have a moment acting on it. It therefore follows that:

$$\sum M_A: \qquad M_A = F_2 \times L = 0$$
$$\therefore F_2 = 0$$

Using this knowledge we now have the basis for analysing the forces in the members of a *plane frame*; that is, a frame that exists or is idealised as existing in a 2-dimensional plane. We now know each member of the frame is subject to an axial force only: either a tensile or a compressive force. We would normally wish to know the magnitude of the force and its nature (tensile or compressive)

Consider the simple frame ABC shown in figure (a). A load of 100 kN is applied at joint B which will create forces in the members F_{AB} and F_{BC}. We don't know whether these are tensile or compressive forces, so for calculation purposes let's assume they are tensile. The 'open' arrows shown on the members in figure (b) are shown accordingly. If we end up with a negative value for a force this simply means that the force is in fact a compressive one.

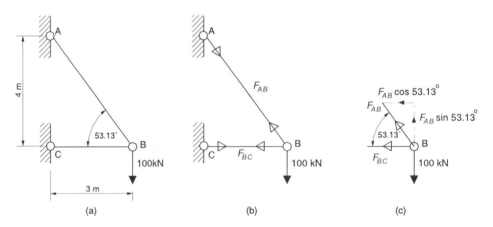

Since the frame will be in equilibrium, it follows that each joint will be in equilibrium. Figure (c) shows the free body diagram of joint B. Since the joint is in equilibrium, we can apply to the joint the principle that we saw before, that when a set of forces is in equilibrium then the *algebraic sum of the horizontal and vertical components of the forces must be in equilibrium.*

Figure (c) also shows the inclined force F_{AB} resolved into its horizontal and vertical components. Resolving forces vertically (taking forces acting *upwards* as positive) we can write:

$$\sum V: \qquad + F_{AB} \sin 53.13° - 100 = 0$$

$$F_{AB} = \frac{100}{\sin 53.13°} = 125 \text{ kN}$$

Determine the forces in member BC by resolving in the horizontal direction.

44

$$\boxed{F_{BC} = -75 \text{ kN}}$$

$$\sum H: \qquad - F_{BC} - F_{AB} \cos 53.13 = 0$$

hence: $\qquad F_{BC} = -F_{AB} \cos 53.13° = -125 \times \cos 53.13° = -75 \text{ kN}$

Did you take forces acting to the *right* as *positive*?
What is the nature of the forces in AB and BC?

45

$$\boxed{\begin{array}{c} \text{A tensile force in AB} \\ \text{A compression force in BC} \end{array}}$$

The negative sign in the calculation in Frame 44 indicates that BC is in compression. The nature of these forces is what common sense should assume. The result is that member AC will extend and member BC will shorten, such that joint B will move downwards and to the left, until it reaches a new position of equilibrium, thus changing the overall geometry of the frame. The actual movements will, however, be very small and the change in geometry negligible, so that the above analysis is still valid for the frame.

Would it have been possible to solve this problem if there had been three members meeting at joint B?

46

$$\boxed{\text{No}}$$

In analysing joint B we were able to write down *two* independent equations of statics $\sum V = 0$ and $\sum H = 0$. These equations allowed us to determine *two* unknown member forces. Hence, if we have more than two members of unknown member force meeting at a joint we cannot solve for those forces at that joint. Let's make use of this fact to solve a more complex problem.

47

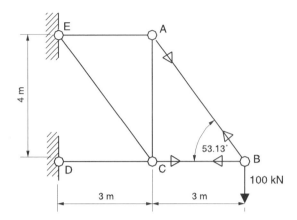

Let us now consider a slightly more complex frame, ABCDE. Members AB and BC are identical to the corresponding members in the previous example, so it follows that $F_{AB} = 125$ kN and $F_{BC} = -75$ kN. We can now analyse joints A and C to determine the forces in the rest of the members.

What joint would you next choose to analyse?

48

$$\boxed{\text{Joint A}}$$

Joint C has three unknown forces, F_{AC}, F_{DC} and F_{EC}. Therefore, as we can only write down two independent equations of statics, it cannot be solved at this time. However, joint A has just two unknowns: F_{AC} and F_{AE}, and can be solved.

Consider joint A and resolving vertically:

$$\sum V = 0: \qquad -F_{AC} - F_{AB} \sin 53.13° = 0$$

$$\text{But we know that} \quad F_{AB} = 125 \text{ kN}$$

$$\therefore \quad -F_{AC} - (125)\sin 53.13° = 0$$

$$F_{AC} = -100 \text{ kN}$$

Resolving horizontally:

$$\sum H = 0: \qquad -F_{AE} + F_{AB} \cos 53.13° = 0$$

$$\therefore \quad -F_{AE} + (125)\cos 153.13° = 0$$

$$F_{AE} = 75 \text{ kN}$$

Can you now calculate the remaining forces in the frame by considering joint C?

$$F_{CE} = 125 \text{ kN}; \ F_{CD} = -150 \text{ kN}$$

Check your calculations:

Consider joint C and resolving vertically:

$$\sum V = 0: \qquad + F_{AC} + F_{CE} \sin 53.13° = 0$$

But we know that $\quad F_{AC} = -100 \text{ kN}$

$$\therefore \quad -100 + F_{CE} \sin 53.13° = 0$$

$$F_{CE} = 125 \text{ kN}$$

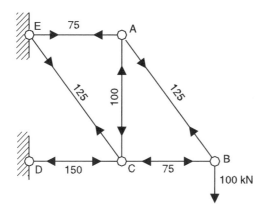

Resolving horizontally:

$$\sum H = 0: \qquad F_{BC} - F_{CD} - F_{CE} \cos 53.13° = 0$$

$$\therefore \quad -(75) - F_{CD} - (125) \cos 53.13° = 0$$

$$F_{CD} = -150 \text{ kN}$$

Did you allow for the correct sign convention that we have adopted for the direction of forces? When resolving vertically, forces (and components of force) acting upwards are taken as positive, and downwards as negative. Similarly, when resolving horizontally forces acting to the right are positive; to the left negative.

The complete frame can now be drawn showing the magnitude and correct direction of each of the forces acting in each member:

A more detailed discussion of the analysis of frames, including alternative methods of analysis, is given in the companion volume of *Structural Mechanics*.

50

TO REMEMBER

A mechanical system is made up of a number of interacting parts

Forces acting on mechanical systems can be classified as (i) concentrated loads (N); (ii) distributed loads (N/m), (iii) pressure loads (N/m^2 or bar) (iv) couples (Nm) and (v) torsional moments (Nm)

The moment of a couple is the same about any point.

For equilibrium of any part of a mechanical system the equations of statics must be satisfied:

$$\sum V = 0; \ \sum H = 0; \text{ and } \sum M = 0$$

A simple support provides one component of reaction.

A fixed support provides two components of reaction and a fixing moment.

To calculate either of the support reactions in a simply supported beam take moments about the point through which the other support reaction acts.

To determine the forces in a pin-jointed frame resolve the forces both vertically and horizontally at any joint at which there are no more than two unknown member forces.

51

FURTHER PROBLEMS

1. A rope passes over a frictionless pulley as shown in figure Q1. If the tension in the rope is 50 kN calculate the vertical and horizontal components of the resultant force acting on the pulley.

Ans. 75.44 kN downwards, 13.30 kN to the right.

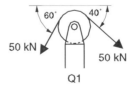

Q1

2. Determine the values of reaction at A and B for figures Q2(a) to Q2(c).

Ans. Q2(a): $V_A = +8.33$ kN, $V_B = +5.67$ kN; Q2(b): $V_A = +12.0$ kN, $V_B = +29.0$ kN; Q2(c): $V_A = +13.25$ kN, $V_B = +8.75$ kN.

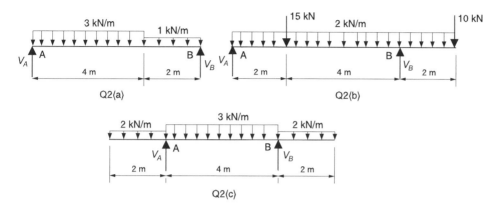

Q2(a)   Q2(b)

Q2(c)

3. Determine the values of reactions and fixing moment at A for figures Q3(a) and Q3(b).

Ans. Q3(a): $V_A = +6.0$ kN, $H_A = 0$ kN, $M_A = 9.0$ kNm anticlockwise; Q3(b): $V_A = 0$ kN, $H_A = -5.0$ kN, $M_A = 10.0$ kNm anticlockwise.

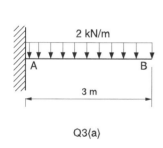

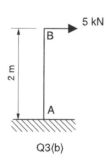

Q3(a)   Q3(b)

4. A vehicle crosses a simply supported bridge. The loading on the front axle is 6 kN and on the rear axle 9 kN. Its wheel base is 5 m. The bridge spans 20 m between supports. If the vehicle stops with its rear axle on the centre of the bridge, calculate the reactions at the supports caused by the vehicular weight.

Ans. 9.0 kN, 6.0 kN.

5. A pin-jointed frame forming an overhead gantry carrying signalling equipment above a railway line is shown in figure Q5. Calculate the magnitude and sense of the forces in all the members of the frame resulting from the loading system shown.

Ans. See diagram on page 56.

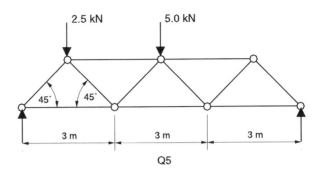

Q5

6. A crane hoist is constructed as shown in figure Q6. It is supported at A and B in such a way that the reaction at A has both horizontal and vertical components while that at B is in the horizontal direction only as shown. Calculate the magnitude and sense of the forces in all the members of the frame when the crane raises a load of 5.0 kN.

Ans. See diagram below.

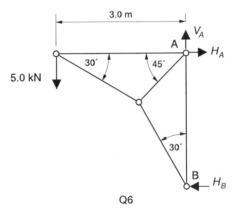

Q6

Solutions for problems Q5 and Q6

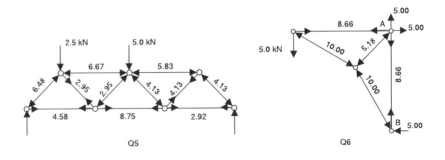

Q5   Q6

Programme 3

SHEARING FORCES AND BENDING MOMENTS

On completion of this programme you will be able to:

- Define the term 'bending moment'
- Define the term 'shearing force'
- Draw deflected shape diagrams for simple beams
- Calculate the value and sense of shearing force at different sections along a beam
- Calculate the value and sense of bending moment at different sections along a beam
- State the formula for maximum bending moment in a simply supported beam carrying a central point load
- State the formula for maximum bending moment in a simply supported beam supporting a uniformly distributed load (UDL) over the whole span
- Draw shearing force diagrams for simply supported and cantilevered beams, subject to combinations of point loads and distributed loads
- Draw bending moment diagrams for simply supported and cantilevered beams, subject to combinations of point loads and distributed loads
- Identify and calculate the position of points of contraflexure

1

In the previous programme we studied the loading on beams and the resulting reactions at the supports. We found that the external loading could be in the form of concentrated loads, distributed loads and couples or any combination of such loads acting together. The beams we analysed were either simply supported or cantilevered, and the reactions could be determined using the conditions of static equilibrium.

In this programme we shall begin to investigate the ways in which beams respond to such loads. The reasoning we shall adopt could be applied to any component, regardless of whether or not it is a horizontal beam or a component inclined at any angle to the horizontal. For convenience, however, initially we shall confine ourselves to the consideration of horizontal beams.

How many support reactions has (a) a simply supported beam; and (b) a cantilevered beam?

2

(a) 2; (b) 3

A simply supported beam has one support reaction at each support (a total of two reactions). A cantilevered beam has a horizontal and vertical support reaction together with a fixing moment at the support (a total of three reactions). We have shown previously how these reactions can be calculated by taking moments and resolving forces. Ensure that you are familiar with these techniques before proceeding further.

BENDING MOMENTS

Let's start this programme by considering a simply supported beam AB as shown. The beam is loaded only by a single concentrated load W acting at the mid-span point C. We shall for the moment ignore the self-weight of the beam. You should be able to visualise that the beam is likely to respond to the load by bending, as in figure (b). The underside would be stretched and would be in tension. Equally, the top surface will be subject to compression.

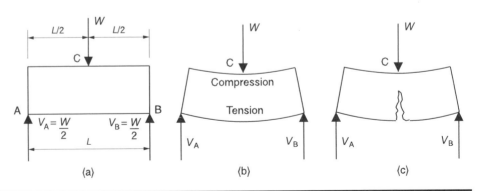

If the load was large enough the beam *could* fail in bending because of the development of excessive tension resulting in fracture at C, as indicated in figure (c). The bending is, of course, initiated by the load, but all the forces, including the reactions, should be taken into consideration when analysing the response of the beam to loading. Thus, if you look at the part of the beam to the right of C, you could visualise that, relative to C, the reaction is apparently forcing the beam to bend in a concave manner upwards.

You will realise that, in order to carry out a numerical analysis, it is necessary to be able to quantify the bending effect at any point in a beam. Let's see how we do this. Look again at the part of the beam to the right of C. To quantify the bending effect at the point C we can say that the *bending moment* at C is the moment about C of the reaction V_B. The value of this *bending moment* is $W/2 \times L/2 = WL/4$ anticlockwise.

Looking to the left of C, what is the bending moment at C caused by the reaction V_A?

3

$$W/2 \times L/2 = WL/4 \text{ clockwise}$$

You will notice that this is the same numerically as the bending moment about C caused by the reaction V_B but the sense is reversed. Hence we can quantify the magnitude of the bending effect at C by calculating the moments of all the forces to the left or right of C, but we cannot base a sign convention on the sense of the moments because the sense is different depending on which side we consider. What we can do is to say that bending moments that cause *sagging* of a beam (see figure (a) below) are positive, while bending moments that cause *hogging* of a beam (figure (b)) are negative. Note that, when the beam is subjected to positive bending, the bending moment to the right of the point under consideration is anticlockwise, and the bending moment to the left of the point under consideration is clockwise. The reverse is true for a beam that is hogging.

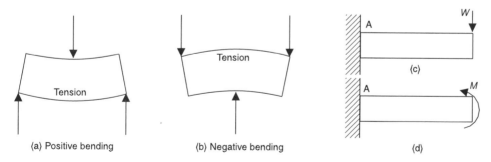

(a) Positive bending   (b) Negative bending   (c) (d)

End A of each of the two beams shown in figures (c) and (d) is rigidly fixed. Beam (c) is loaded by a single concentrated load and beam (d) is subjected to an external couple of moment M. By visualising the way in which the beams will bend, determine whether the bending is positive or negative.

4

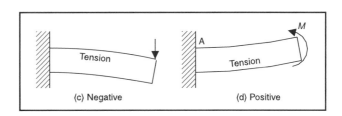

In case (d) the effect of the couple will be to extend the bottom of the beam and compress the top. The only way such deformations can take place is if the beam bends upwards as indicated.

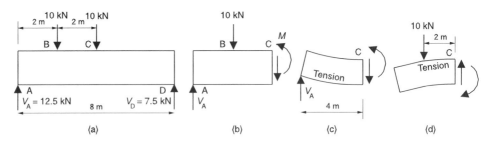

Now look at the beam AD with a concentrated load of 10 kN at the mid-span point C, and another concentrated load of 10 kN at B. In this example, the values of the two reactions have already been calculated to be as indicated. In future problems you will have to start by determining the values of the reactions, as explained in Programme 2.

In order to calculate the bending moment at C, try to visualise the left-hand side of the beam, as in figure (b). Figure (b) also shows the force and moment that must be developed within the beam at C to maintain the free body of this part of the beam in equilibrium. This moment is the bending moment at C. To the left of C, and viewed relative to C, the reaction V_A, if considered to be acting alone, would apparently tend to bend the beam upwards as in figure (c) and cause tension on the bottom face. This shape of bending has been defined as positive, thus V_A produces a positive bending moment about point C, the numerical value being $(V_A \times 4)$ kN m. In a similar way, the load at B, if considered to be acting alone, produces a negative bending moment about C of numerical value (10×2) kN m and causes tension on the top face. The total net bending moment at C caused by the forces to the left of C is given by the algebraic sum of the separate bending moments. Thus:

$$\text{Bending moment at C} = +(V_A \times 4) - (10 \times 2)$$
$$= +(12.5 \times 4) - (10 \times 2)$$
$$= +30 \text{ kN m}$$

In the calculation just completed, we considered the left-hand side of the beam. Now calculate the bending moment at C by considering the side of the beam to the right of C.

5

$$+30 \text{ kN m}$$

V_D is the only force to the right of C and relative to C, this reaction will apparently tend to bend the beam in a similar way to V_A (see figure (c) of Frame 4). This is positive (sagging) bending, and thus V_D produces a bending moment at C of value $+(V_D \times 4) = 7.5 \times 4 = +30$ kN m. You should have anticipated this result from the work done in Frame 3. Summarising what we have learnt so far about the bending moment in a beam, we can state:

The bending moment at any section in a beam is the algebraic sum of the moments about that section of all the forces to the right, or to the left, of that section.

It has been suggested in the previous frames that you try to visualise the way in which a beam bends under the action of loads. You will find, as an engineer, that it is a very useful ability to be able to visualise how components deform when loaded. Beams are perhaps one of the most straightforward components to visualise, and hence to sketch their deformed shape. Tackle the following problems to help you start to develop this ability. You may find it helpful to use a flexible plastic rule which you can hold and bend to simulate the effect of loading and support restraint.

6

PROBLEMS

The following sketches show a series of beams subjected to different loading conditions. In each case, visualise the way in which the beam will bend, and sketch the shape of the deflected beam. Show the loads and the reactions on your sketches, and mark the lengths of the beam (top or bottom) where compression develops because of bending.

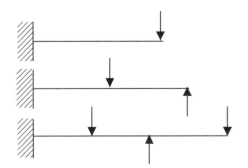
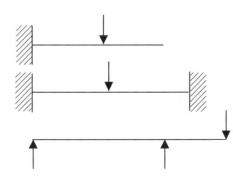

7

Check your solutions against
the following diagrams.

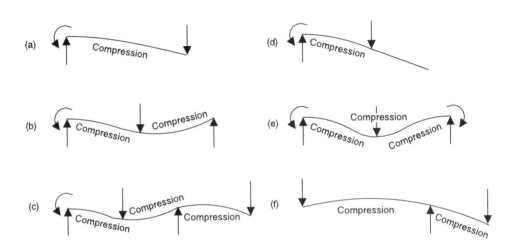

8

SHEARING FORCES

Now let's consider another way in which the beam of Frame 2 could fail. For convenience, the beam is shown below:

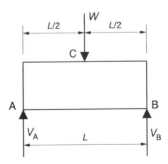

Can you suggest another possible mode of failure?

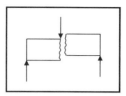

You might have suggested that the beam could fail as indicated in the sketch above. Such a failure is as if the beam had been cut in two by a guillotine. The failure is described as a *shear failure*, and the forces producing such failures are described as *shearing forces*. In the case of horizontal beams carrying vertical loads, the shearing forces will be vertical.

Look at figure (a) below and try to visualise the shearing effect at C of all the forces to the left of C.

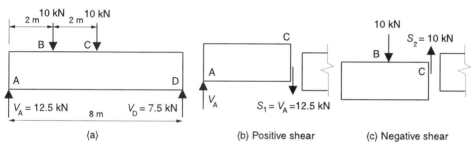

(a)   (b) Positive shear   (c) Negative shear

The reaction V_A, if acting alone, will tend to push the left-hand side of the beam upwards as in figure (b). Relatively, the right-hand side of the beam will tend to be pushed downwards. Shearing forces that cause upward shear deformation to the left (or downwards to the right) of the section under consideration are defined as positive. Hence a positive shearing force (S_1) is developed at C because of the reaction V_A as shown in figure (b). For vertical equilibrium of the length AC, this shearing force must equal the reaction V_A. That is, $S_1 = V_A = +12.5$ kN.

In the same way, the load at B, if considered to be acting alone, will tend to push the left-hand side of the beam downwards. Thus the load at B produces a negative shearing force (S_2) at C, of value -10.0 kN. The total net shearing force at C is given by the algebraic sum of the separate shearing forces. Thus, shearing force at C $= +12.5 - 10.0 = +2.5$ kN.

What value of shearing force do you get if you look at the forces to the right of C?

10

$$-7.5 \text{ kN}$$

The negative sign is as a result of our sign convention given in Frame 9. When you did the same sort of calculation for the bending moment you got the same answer working from the left as from the right. Why is it not the case for the calculation of shearing force?

11

In order to understand the apparent anomaly in the previous frame you must remember that while we talk about concentrated loads acting at a point, they do in fact act over a definite area or finite length of beam. In the figure below it is assumed that the 10 kN load at C is applied uniformly over a length of, say, 100 mm.

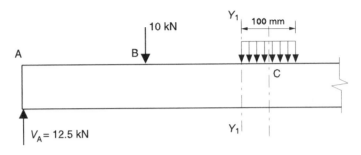

What is the value of the shearing force at section Y_1–Y_1?

12

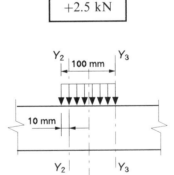

The shearing force at the section Y_1–Y_1 is the algebraic sum of all the forces to the left of Y_1–Y_1: that is, $+12.5 - 10.0 = 2.5$ kN. If we now move 10 mm to the right, to section Y_2–Y_2, you will see that the forces to the left of section Y_2–Y_2 have been changed by the addition of part of the 10 kN load. This is tending to push the left-hand part of the beam downwards and is thus providing an additional negative shearing force at section Y_2–Y_2. If the 10 kN load is uniformly applied over a length of 100 mm, then in a length of 10 mm a load of 1 kN will be applied and the total net shearing force at section Y_2–Y_2 will be $+2.5 - 1.0 = +1.5$ kN.
What will be the shearing force at the section Y_3–Y_3?

13

$$+2.5 - 10.0 = -7.5 \text{ kN}$$

This now agrees with the value in Frame 10. You will have realised that the shearing force in a beam changes abruptly at the point of application of a concentrated load. It is necessary to calculate the shearing force just to the left and just to the right of such a load. Thus:

The shearing force just to the left of C = the algebraic sum of all forces to the left of C
$$= +12.5 - 10.0 = \underline{+2.5 \text{ kN}}$$

The shearing force just to the right of C = the algebraic sum of all forces to the left of C plus the load force at C
$$= +12.5 - 10.0 - 10.0 = \underline{-7.5 \text{ kN}}$$

Summarising what we have learnt so far about the shearing forces in a beam, we can state:

The shearing force at any section in a horizontal beam is the algebraic sum of all the vertical forces to the left, or to the right, of that section.

Now on to the next frame.

14

BENDING MOMENT AND SHEARING FORCE DIAGRAMS

You should now understand the meaning of *bending moment* and *shearing force*, and realise that the values of these vary along the length of a beam. It is useful to show this variation by plotting graphs in which the length of the beam represents the horizontal axis and the values of shearing force or bending moment are plotted vertically from this axis. Let's plot such graphs for the beam shown below.

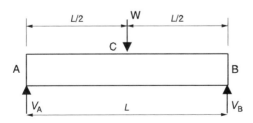

What are the values of the reactions V_A and V_B?

15

Since the load W is acting at mid-span, the reactions are equal and of value $W/2$.

We shall start with the *shearing force diagram*, which is the graph of shearing force variation. Since we are going to plot on a horizontal axis representing the length of the beam, it is convenient to draw the shearing force diagram directly below and as a projection from the diagram of the loaded beam (see the figure below).

Starting at the left-hand end, we see at A a concentrated load in the form of the reaction V_A. If we then consider a section just to the right of A and look at forces to the left of this section, then reaction V_A provides a positive shearing force of value $+W/2$. Plot this as line ad on the diagram. If you look along the beam to the right of A you will realise that the value of the shearing force cannot change until point C. Why not? Because no forces act on the beam between A and C, and hence the shearing force is constant over this length. At point C, remembering the argument in Frame 13, we reason as follows:

Just to the left of C the shearing force $= +V_A = +W/2$ kN

Plot this as line fe.

Just to the right of C the shearing force $= +V_A - W = -W/2$ kN

Plot this as line fg.

You will appreciate that the line efg should, strictly speaking, not be vertical. However, the distance over which the load is applied is very small compared with the length of the beam, and consequently it is sufficiently accurate to draw efg vertically. If you cannot understand this, refer back to Frames 11 and 12. Points d and e are joined by a straight line because the shearing force is constant over the length AC.

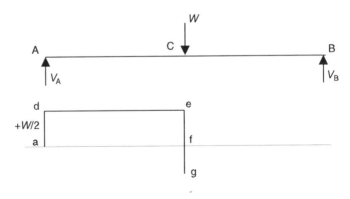

Complete the construction of the shearing force diagram.

16

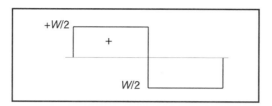

Having completed the shearing force diagram, we shall now plot the bending moment diagram for the same beam. Look at the diagram below and consider a point X on the beam distance x from the end A. If you look to the left of X you will see one force only, the reaction V_A, which produces a bending moment at X of value $M_x = +(W/2) \times x$. The moment has a positive sign as it is a sagging moment (see Frame 3 if in doubt).

This is the equation for a straight line and is valid for the length of beam between A and C, for all values of x between zero and $L/2$. If, however, we wish to calculate the value of bending moment at a point such as X_1 which is to the right of C, the equation must be modified by the addition of a term related to the load W. Thus the bending moment at X_1:

$$= +(W/2) \times x_1 - W \times (x_1 - L/2)$$

This also is the equation for a straight line which is in this case valid for the length CB of the beam. We now know that the bending moment diagram will consist of straight lines and by substituting values of x and x_1 in the appropriate equations we can derive values of bending moment to plot the required diagram. Thus:

At A: $x = 0$ and from the first equation $M_x = 0$.

Plot this at point a.

At C: $x = L/2$, ∴ from the first equation $M_x = +(W/2) \times (L/2) = +WL/4$

Plot this at point b.

Note that if we substitute $x_1 = L/2$ in the second equation:

$$M_x = +(W/2) \times (L/2) - W \times (L/2 - L/2) = +WL/4$$

The value of bending moment at C must be the same whichever equation we use, thus the calculation we have just done provides a useful check on our work.

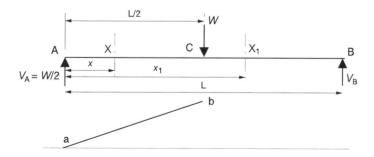

Complete the bending moment diagram.

17

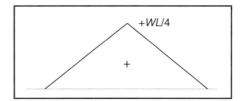

Note that we have plotted positive bending moments above the base line. This is to comply with the usual convention of plotting positive values upwards from the base line. If you imagine the base line to represent the beam, the positive values are plotted *on the side of the beam that is in compression* as the beam bends. When considering more complex situations, sketching the shape of the deflected beam, as in Frame 6, to locate those zones in which compression will develop will give you guidance as to which side of the base line to draw the bending moment diagram. *Always remember to draw the bending moment diagram on the side of the beam that is in compression.*

In the diagram below, the shearing force (SF) and the bending moment (BM) diagrams have been drawn below and in projection with the free body diagram of the beam. Plotting in this way enables the values of shearing force and bending moment at any point in the beam to be determined rapidly by vertical projection. Thus, at Q distance $L/4$ from B, you can see that the shearing force is $-W/2$ and the bending moment is $+WL/8$.

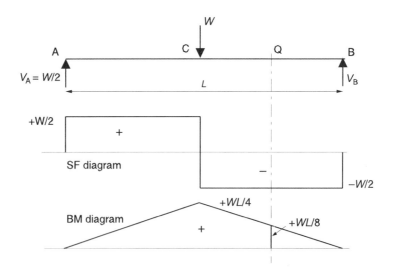

What is the value of the shearing force at the point in the beam where the bending moment is a maximum?

18

Zero at C

If you didn't give the answer of zero, look back at frames 11 and 12. When plotting bending moment diagrams it is a useful fact that, at beam sections where the shearing force is zero, the bending moment will always be either a maximum or a minimum. We shall now show that the relationship is always true.

Figure (a) below is the free body diagram for a beam simply supported at A and B and carrying a non-uniform distributed load indicated by the irregular figure drawn on top of the beam. Let the intensity of loading be w N/m (note that this is not necessarily constant).

Figure (b) shows an enlarged view of a small segment abcd of the beam at a section X–X, the length cd being δx. To the right of the face bc there is a downward-acting load, the value of which is given by the area of the load distribution diagram.

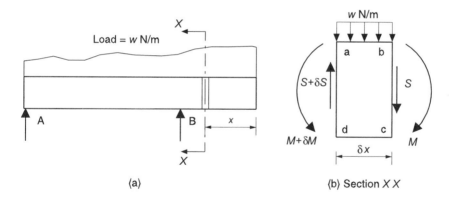

(a)   (b) Section $X X$

The load to the right of section X–X produces a positive shearing force S at the face bc and to resist this there must be an upward shearing force $S + \delta S$ on the face ad. This shearing force on face ad is bigger than the shearing force on face bc because there is a load $w\delta x$ on the length of beam between those two faces and the segment abcd must be in equilibrium.

Now consider the bending moments. The load to the right of section X–X will produce a bending moment at the face bc. Let's call this moment M. To resist this moment there will be a bending moment $M + \delta M$, at the face ad in the opposite direction.

Look at figure (b) above and by taking moments about the left face (ad) write down an equation relating the moments and shearing forces acting on the portion of beam abcd.

19

$$M + \delta M = M + S\delta x + (w\delta x)\delta x/2$$

From the above relationship and by ignoring second-order terms (δx^2) we obtain:

$$M + \delta M = M + S\delta x$$

thus: $\qquad\qquad\qquad\qquad \delta M/\delta x = S$

and as $\delta x \to 0$ then: $\qquad\qquad dM/dx = S$

The bending moment M is a maximum or minimum if dM/dx equals zero. Hence it follows that as $dM/dx = S$, then the bending moment is a maximum or a minimum if $S = 0$.

Can you suggest why a knowledge of this relationship will be of assistance to you when plotting bending moment diagrams?

20

Determining the point of zero shearing force will locate the point of maximum bending moment: a critical point in the bending moment diagram.

SHEARING FORCE AND BENDING MOMENT DIAGRAMS FOR UNIFORMLY DISTRIBUTED LOADS

The figure at the top of the next page shows a beam AB simply supported at A and B and carrying a uniformly distributed load of w kN/m. This is a very common loading situation. For example, the self-weight of a beam usually constitutes such a load although the cross-section of a beam may not always be constant throughout its length. If this is the case, the value of w will vary along the length of the beam. To draw the SF diagram, consider a section X–X at a distance x from A:

The total load on the beam $\qquad\qquad\qquad\qquad W = wL$

and, by symmetry, the reactions are equal and $\qquad\quad = wL/2$

The shearing force at X–X $\qquad = +wL/2$ because of the reaction V_A

and $\qquad\qquad\qquad\qquad\quad = -wx$ because of the load to the left of X–X

Thus the net shearing force: $\quad$ SF $= +wL/2 - wx$

This is the equation of a straight line with a slope of $-w$ and is applicable to all points between A and B. To plot the SF diagram, only two points are required:

when $x = 0$ $\qquad\qquad\qquad$ SF $= +wL/2$

when $x = L$ $\qquad\qquad\qquad$ SF $= +wL/2 - wL = -wL/2$

These values are plotted to give the shearing force diagram as shown.

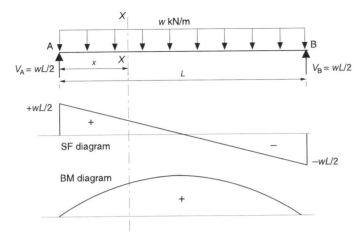

Now let's consider bending moments. The bending moment at a section X–X distance x from A is obtained by taking moments of forces to the left of X–X:

$$= +V_A \times x \text{ because of the reaction } V_A$$

and

$$= -(wx) \times x/2 \text{ because of the load to the left of } X\text{–}X$$

Thus the net BM at X–X

$$= +(wL/2)x - wx^2/2$$

This is the equation of a parabola and will apply for all values of x between zero and L. Why? Because there is no change in the load system along the length of the beam. In order to plot the bending moment diagram it would be useful to locate the point of maximum bending moment. You can probably guess, correctly, that this will be at the mid-span position. If you did not guess this, look at the shearing force diagram and identify the point at which the shearing force is zero.

To plot the bending moment diagram we need the value of the maximum bending moment. What is the value of the maximum bending moment?

21

$$\boxed{wL^2/8}$$

Substituting $x = L/2$ into the equation for bending moment derived in Frame 20, the bending moment at mid-span is given by:

$$M = +(wL/2)L/2 - w(L/2)^2/2$$
$$= +wL^2/4 - wL^2/8$$
$$= +wL^2/8$$

Thus the maximum bending moment in a beam simply supported at each end and carrying a uniformly distributed load is $wL^2/8$ (or $WL/8$, where $W = w \times L$ equals the *total* load on the beam).

Do you remember the expression for the maximum bending moment in a similar simply supported beam with a single central concentrated load?

22

$$\boxed{WL/4}$$

The expressions $WL/4$ and $WL/8$ (or $wL^2/8$) for the maximum bending moment in a simply supported beam subject to either a single central concentrated load or to a uniformly distributed load, respectively, are in common use and should be remembered.

Now go to the next frame.

23

In the next few frames we shall construct shearing force and bending moment diagrams for beams with multiple loads. We shall develop a standard procedure that can be used to solve any problem.

The beam shown below is simply supported at A and D. It carries concentrated loads at B, C and E.

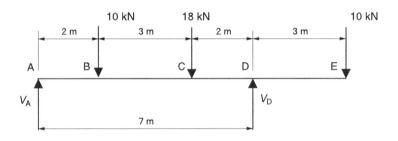

The first step is to determine the values of the reactions.
Calculate the values of V_A and V_D.

24

$$\boxed{\begin{array}{l} V_A = \ \ 8 \text{ kN} \\ V_D = 30 \text{ kN} \end{array}}$$

If you did not get these values, revise the methods used in Programme 2 for calculating beam reactions.

Now let's derive the information to plot the shearing force diagram. We shall work from left to right. To follow the calculations you will need to refer to the diagram below. In this and subsequent problems you may find it useful to cover the free-body diagram with a piece of paper and move it slowly from left to right progressively to uncover those forces causing shear at the section being considered.

$$\begin{aligned}
\text{SF just to the right of A} = +V_A && = +8 \text{ kN} \\
\text{left of B} = +V_A && = +8 \text{ kN} \\
\text{right of B} = +8 - 10 && = -2 \text{ kN} \\
\text{left of C} = +8 - 10 && = -2 \text{ kN} \\
\text{right of C} = +8 - 10 - 18 && = -20 \text{ kN} \\
\text{left of D} = +8 - 10 - 18 && = -20 \text{ kN} \\
\text{right of D} = +8 - 10 - 18 + 30 && = +10 \text{ kN} \\
\text{left of E} = +8 - 10 - 18 + 30 && = +10 \text{ kN}
\end{aligned}$$

These values are plotted to give the shearing force diagram. Note that the plotted points are joined by horizontal straight lines between the load positions with 'steps' in the diagram at the point of application of each concentrated load. This is always the case when only concentrated loads act on a beam. When distributed loads are acting, however, the lines of the shearing force diagram will be sloping, as for the example given in Frame 20.

Now for the bending moment diagram. We shall take moments of all forces to the left of the point considered and calculate the values of bending moment at the load points, since we know from previous work that when a beam is subjected to concentrated loads only the bending moment diagram consists of straight lines with critical points (changes of direction) occurring at load positions.

$$\begin{aligned}
\text{BM at A} && = 0 \\
\text{at B} = +(8 \times 2) && = +16 \text{ kN m} \\
\text{at C} = +(8 \times 5) - (10 \times 3) && = +10 \text{ kN m} \\
\text{at D} = +(8 \times 7) - (10 \times 5) - (18 \times 2) && = -30 \text{ kN m} \\
\text{at E} = +(8 \times 10) - (10 \times 8) - (18 \times 5) + (30 \times 3) && = 0
\end{aligned}$$

These values are plotted to give the BM diagram.

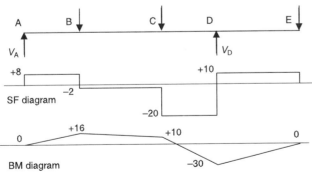

Note that there is a maximum sagging bending moment under the load at B and a maximum hogging bending moment at the reaction point at D.

Repeat the above calculations but take moments of all forces to the right of each point.

25

You should have obtained the same values.

You should now realise that, when calculating bending moments, you can take moments of all forces to the left or right of the point considered. You will also appreciate that if, in the previous frame, we had taken moments to the left for part ABC of the beam and to the right for part ED we would have simplified the calculations. However, when calculating shearing forces it is better to work systematically from left to right. Now for another example.

Beam ABCD, in Frame 26, is simply supported at A and C. It carries concentrated loads at B and D, a uniformly distributed load of 2 kN/m between A and C, and a uniformly distributed load of 1 kN/m between C and D.

By taking moments about A, the reactions are determined as:

$$V_A = 13.2 \text{ kN and } V_C = 25.8 \text{ kN}$$

Then for the SF diagram working from left to right:

$$
\begin{aligned}
\text{SF just to the right of A} &= V_A & &= +13.2 \text{ kN} \\
\text{to the left of B} &= +13.2 - (2 \times 4) & &= +5.2 \text{ kN} \\
\text{to the right of B} &= +13.2 - (2 \times 4) - 10 & &= -4.8 \text{ kN} \\
\text{to the left of C} &= +13.2 - (2 \times 10) - 10 & &= -16.8 \text{ kN} \\
\text{to the right of C} &= +13.2 - (2 \times 10) - 10 + 25.8 & &= +9.0 \text{ kN} \\
\text{to the left of D} &= +13.2 - (2 \times 10) - 10 + 25.8 - (1 \times 4) &&= +5.0 \text{ kN}
\end{aligned}
$$

These values are plotted to give the shearing force diagram. Note that the lines joining the plotted points are sloping because the beam is, in this case, carrying distributed loads over its whole length.

Now for the bending moment diagram: BM at A = 0.

What is the value of the bending moment at B?

26

+36.8 kN m

Taking moments of all forces to the left of B:

The bending moment at B $= +(13.2 \times 4) - (2 \times 4) \times 4/2 = +36.8$ kN m

Did you remember to take into account only that part of the UD load to the left of B?

Continuing: the BM at C $= + (13.2 \times 10) - (2 \times 10) \times 10/2 - (10 \times 6)$
$$= -28.0 \text{ kN m}$$

Alternatively, taking moments to the right:

BM at C $= - (5 \times 4) - (1 \times 4) \times 4/2 = -28.0$ kN m

The shearing force is zero at B and C, thus the values of BM calculated at those points are local maximum values.

The calculated values of bending moment are plotted and joined by parabolic curves. The lines are curved because distributed loads are acting on the beam (see Frame 20). You may find it necessary to calculate intermediate values in order to plot the curves more precisely. For example, you could calculate the value of bending moment at a point half way between A and B in order to determine the precise shape of the curve between A and B.

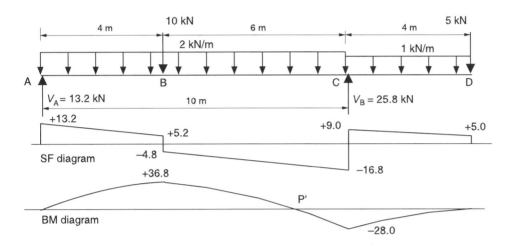

Now sketch the shape of the deflected beam and mark the lengths of the beam (top or bottom) where compression develops.

27

You should have sketched the beam as shown above being curved downwards at the left-hand end and curved upwards at the right-hand end. The direction of curvature changes at the point P to the left of the support C. Point P is called a **point of contraflexure** and coincides with point P' on the BM diagram, where the bending moment changes sign from positive bending (sagging) to negative bending (hogging). Note that the deflected shape of the beam indicates which part of the beam is in tension or compression at different locations along the span. The BM diagram should always be drawn on the side that is in compression at all points along the beam span. You should always sketch the deflected shape *before* doing any calculations and use this as a guide to the correct shape of the BM diagram.

Now calculate the distance from A to the point of contraflexure.

28

8.12 m

The bending moment at a point of contraflexure is zero. You should have tackled this question by writing the equation for bending moment at a point between B and C and distance x from A, then equating to zero and solving for x. See below.

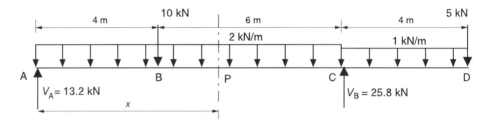

Bending moment at P is given by:

$$M_P = +(13.2 \times x) - 10 \times (x - 4) - (2 \times x) \times x/2$$
$$= +13.2x - 10x + 40 - 2x^2/2$$
$$= +3.2x + 40 - x^2$$

then if $\qquad M_P = 0$

$$x^2 - 3.2x - 40 = 0$$

from which $\qquad x = 8.12 \text{ m}$

Note that to perform this calculation it was necessary to determine, by inspection, the approximate region of the beam where the point of contraflexure occurs so that the correct bending moment equation could be written down and equated to zero.
Now calculate the position of the point of contraflexure in the beam of Frame 23.

29

5.5 m from A

You should have derived the equation:

$$8x - 10 \times (x - 2) - 18 \times (x - 5) = 0$$
$$8x - 10x + 20 - 18x + 90 = 0$$
$$\therefore \quad -20x + 110 = 0$$

and $\qquad x = 5.5 \text{ m from A}$

30

PROBLEMS

In the following problems you are required to sketch the shearing force and bending moment diagrams, marking the values of all important points. First sketch the shape of the deflected beams and hence sketch the shape of the bending moment diagrams before attempting any calculations. For question Q5, work from right to left.

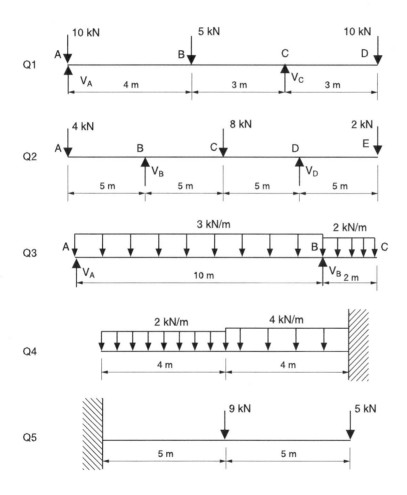

Check your solution against the sketches in Frame 31.

31

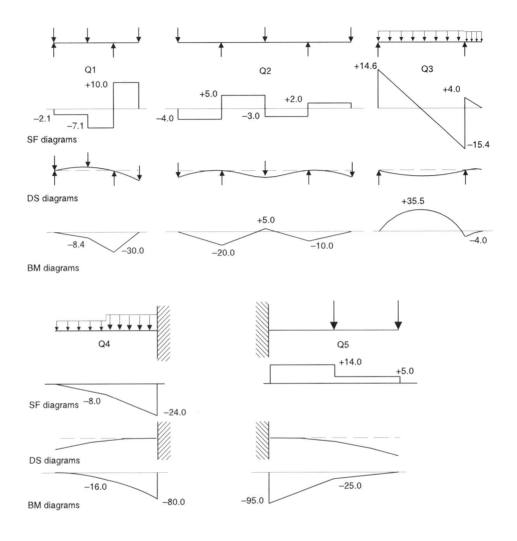

32

TRIANGULAR LOADING

The previous problems indicate the principles of drawing shearing force and bending moment diagrams and we can apply these principles to beams loaded with combinations of concentrated and uniformly distributed loads. You should be able to draw such diagrams for simply supported beams with or without cantilevers at either end or both ends. Now let's look at some slightly more complicated examples of loading such as the cantilevered wing shown below. The wing is assumed to be delta in shape and the self-weight loading on the wing approximates to the triangular loading shown. The maximum intensity of loading is 12 kN/m.

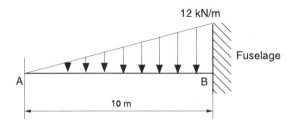

Can you calculate the vertical reaction and the fixing moment at B?

33

$$V_B = 60 \text{ kN}; \ M_A = 200 \text{ kN m}$$

You should have calculated that the *average* loading intensity acting on the wing is 6 kN/m, and hence the total downward load on the wing is $6 \times 10 = 60$ kN. This load must be resisted by the upward reaction at B, which must therefore have the value of 60 kN.

The downward load of 60 kN must act through the centroid of the triangle which is at a distance of $10/3 = 3.33$ m from B. Therefore, taking moments to the left of B, the fixing moment at B must have a value of $60 \times 3.33 = 200$ kN m.

Now let's calculate the shearing force at C, which is at a variable distance x from the left-hand end of the span:

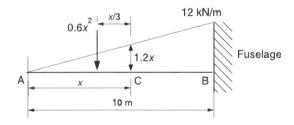

By similar triangles, the load intensity at C is given by $12/10 \times x = 1.2x$ kN/m. The *average* load intensity between A and C is therefore given by $0.6x$ kN/m. The total *downward* load to the left of C is given by $0.6x \times x = 0.6x^2$ kN. This must represent the shearing force to the left of C, which therefore has a value of $-0.6x^2$ kN.

What do you think is the shape of the shearing force diagram?

34

A parabolic curve

Can you draw the shearing force diagram for this wing?

35

A   B

−60 kN

Looking back at the diagram in Frame 33 can you write down an expression for the bending moment at C?

36

$$BM_C = -0.2x^3 \text{ kN m}$$

Did you reason that the load acting to the left of C, has a magnitude of $0.6x^2$ and acts at a distance of $x/3$ from C (that is, at the centroid of the triangular load). Hence, by taking moments about C :

$$M_C = -0.6x^2 \times \frac{x}{3} = -0.2x^3$$

Did you visualise the deflected shape of the wing and realise that it is hogging under the self-weight load? Hence the bending moments must have a negative sign.

The bending moments, in this case, vary according to a cubic equation. In plotting the shape of the diagram values of x could be inserted into the equation, but as we are normally interested in the maximum values of moment it is only necessary to calculate the maximum moment at the support of the cantilever where the wing meets the fuselage.

Calculate the maximum moment and sketch the bending moment diagram

37

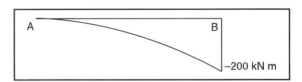

A   B

−200 kN m

This example indicates that both the maximum bending moment and the maximum shearing force occur at the root of the cantilever where the wing meets the fuselage. Hence, in designing the wing, the connection between the wing and fuselage is critical when ensuring that the wing does not fail in either bending or shear.

Can you think of another design criterion that would have to be considered when designing this wing?

38

Deflection at the tip of the wing

Excessive deflection at the tip of the wing could render it unserviceable in use. We shall consider how to calculate deflections in Programme 10.

COUPLES

You will recall that in Programme 2 we introduced the concept of loading from a *couple* system. Let's look at the effect of a couple acting on a beam. The beam shown is supported at A and E. Concentrated loads act at B and D, and an external couple applies a clockwise moment of 10kNm at the mid-point C.

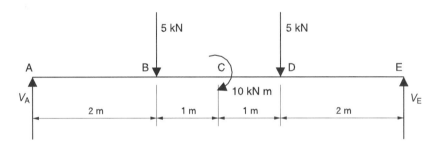

First we determine the reactions:
By moments about A:

$$\sum M_A = 0: \quad -(V_E \times 6) + (5 \times 4) + (5 \times 2) + 10 = 0$$

$$\therefore \quad V_E = 40/6 = 6.67 \text{ kN}$$

By moments about E:

$$\sum M_E = 0: \quad (V_A \times 6) - (5 \times 4) - (5 \times 2) + 10 = 0$$

$$\therefore \quad V_E = 20/6 = 3.33 \text{ kN}$$

You should, of course, *check* that the two reactions summate to the total downward load on the beam. Did you realise that the couple exerts a clockwise moment about both A and E? If not, look back at Programme 2.

Calculate the shearing force at A,B,D and E

39

Right of A	+3.33 kN	Left of B	+3.33 kN
Right of B	−1.67 kN	Left of D	−1.67 kN
Right of D	−6.67 kN	Left of E	−6.67 kN

Check your calculations:

Just to the right of	A	SF = +V_A	= +3.33 kN
to the left of	B	SF = +V_A	= +3.33 kN
to the right of	B	SF = +3.33 − 5.0	= −1.67 kN
to the left of	D	SF = +3.33 − 5.0	= −1.67 kN
to the right of	D	SF = +3.33 − 5.0 − 5.0	= −6.67 kN
to the left of	E	SF = +3.33 − 5.0 − 5.0	= −6.67 kN

Now let's calculate the bending moment values at critical points along the beam. Taking moments of forces to the *left* of each point:

BM at	A = 0	
BM at	B = +(3.33 × 2)	= +6.66 kN m
BM just to the left of	C = +(3.33 × 3) − (5 × 1)	= +5.0 kN m
BM just to the right of	C = +(3.33 × 3) − (5 × 1) + 10	= +15.0 kN m

and taking moments to the right:

BM at	D = +(6.67 × 2)	= +13.33 kN m

If you are still having trouble with the signs, look at the figure below. When calculating the bending moment at C you can see in figure (a) that, relative to C, reaction V_A (3.33 kN) tends to bend the beam upwards (positive bending) and in figure (b) you can see that the couple is also tending to bend the beam upwards (positive bending).

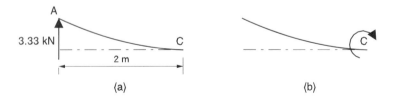

(a)   (b)

Using the values calculated above, can you draw the shearing force and bending moment diagrams?

40

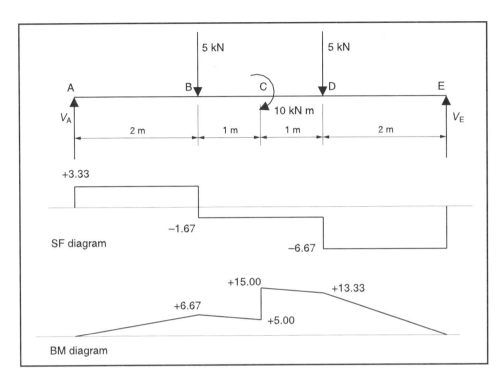

Note that the shearing force does not change at point C. The couple applies a moment at C but no vertical force. This moment is shown on the bending moment diagram as a sudden change of 10 kNm at C.

THE PRINCIPLE OF SUPERPOSITION

You should now be able to construct shearing force and bending moment diagrams for beams subject to any form of loading. It is appropriate at this stage to introduce a concept known as the *Principle of Superposition*, which can help in the more rapid construction of such diagrams when a beam is subject to complex loading. Phrasing the *Principle of Superposition* to suit the context of this programme, we may say:

If a component is made of linear elastic materials and is loaded by a combination of loads which do not strain the component beyond the linear elastic range, then the resulting shearing force and bending moments are equal to the algebraic sum of the shearing forces and bending moments which would have been produced by each of the loads acting separately.

A simply supported beam of 3 m span supports a central point load of 10 kN and a load of 2 kN/m over the whole span. By considering the effect of the two loads acting separately, and then using the Principle of Superposition, calculate the shearing force at the left-hand end of the span.

41

$$\boxed{8 \text{ kN}}$$

This should have been a simple and fairly intuitive application of the *Principle of Superposition.* You should have reasoned that:

The reaction at the left-hand end caused by the point load $= \frac{1}{2} \times 10 = 5$ kN

The reaction at the left-hand end caused by the UDL $= \frac{1}{2} \times (3 \times 2) = 3$ kN

Hence the total end-reaction $= 5 + 3 = 8$ kN, which must also be equal to the value of the shearing force at this position.

What is the value of the maximum bending moment in this beam caused by the combined load system?

42

$$\boxed{9.75 \text{ kN m}}$$

If you had recalled the expressions for the mid-span maximum bending moment for (a) a point load located at the centre of a simply supported beam; and (b) a load uniformly distributed over a simply supported beam (see Frames 21 and 22) you should have simply written down:

Maximum bending moment caused by the point load $= \dfrac{WL}{4} = \dfrac{10 \times 3}{4} = 7.5$ kN m

Maximum bending moment caused by the UDL $= \dfrac{wL^2}{8} = \dfrac{2 \times 3^2}{8} = 2.25$ kN m

Hence, using the *Principle of Superposition* the maximum bending moment is given by:

$$BM_{\max} = \frac{WL}{4} + \frac{wL^2}{8} = 7.5 + 2.25 = 9.75 \text{ kN m}$$

Before we continue to demonstrate a more complex application of the principle let's just note that in the definition of the principle given in Frame 40 we used the term 'linear elastic'. Do not worry if you do not see the full implication of this term as it will be explained in Programme 4. For the present, we can assume that we can use the *Principle of Superposition* provided that the total load on a component is significantly less than the critical value at which it would fail. We can also apply the principle to behavioural properties other than shearing forces and bending moments. For example, you will realise in later programmes that the principle can be used to help determine the deflection of components under complex load systems.

Now let's look at a more complex problem such as the beam shown on page 85. The beam is supported at A and C; length AB weighs 3 kN/m while length CD weighs 1 kN/m. There are concentrated loads of 10 kN and 2 kN acting at B and D respectively.

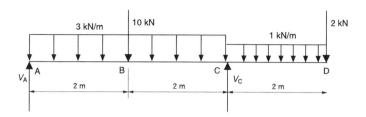

Draw the shearing force diagram for each of the four loads acting separately on the beam, and then use the Principle of Superposition to combine the four diagrams into a single shearing force diagram. Compare your answer with the diagrams given in the next frame.

43

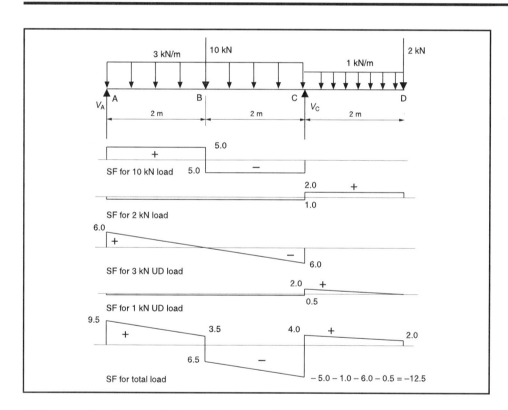

Did you realise that to calculate the shearing force at any location you simply had to combine (superimpose) algebraically the separately calculated values at that location? For example, to the right of C, the shearing force is given by $(-5.0 - 1.0 - 6.0 - 0.5)$ $= -12.5$ kN m.

Now use the Principle of Superposition to derive the bending moment diagram for the total loading system, having first drawn the diagram for each of the loads acting separately.

44

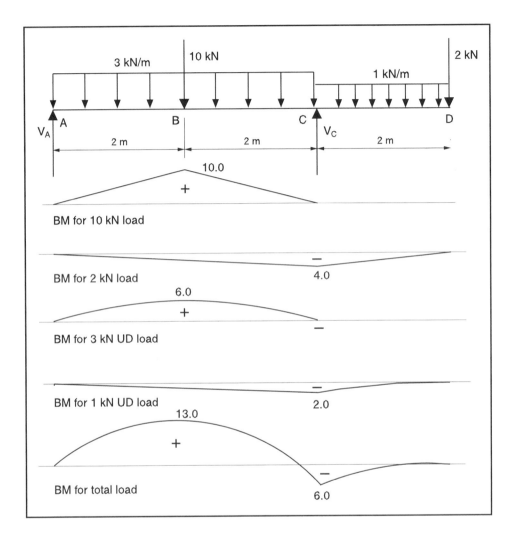

The above example illustrates the application of the *Principle of Superposition* to the drawing of shearing force and bending moment diagrams for beams subject to more complex loading. It is not necessary to do it this way, as we could have drawn the diagrams directly as illustrated in previous problems. However, in cases where loading is complex you may find this approach a little easier.

You will see the further application of the *Principle of Superposition* to other situations later in this text. For the time being, you should appreciate that the analysis of a component under any complex loading system can be accomplished by considering the loading effects separately then combining the results algebraically to give the net loading effect.

Finally, you must practise the drawing of shearing force and bending moment diagrams until you have gained confidence in your ability to draw accurate diagrams. These diagrams form the basis of the analysis of stress within mechanical components resulting from both bending and shear. We shall cover this in Programmes 5 and 6.

45

TO REMEMBER

The bending moment at a section in a beam is the algebraic sum of the moments about that section of all the forces to the right, *or to the left*, of that section.

Bending moments that cause a beam to sag are taken as positive.

Bending moments that cause a beam to hog are taken as negative.

Bending moment diagrams showing the variation of bending moment along a beam are plotted on the compression face of the beam.

Bending moment diagrams resulting from the action of concentrated point loads consist of straight lines with changes of direction at the point of application of the loads.

Bending moment diagrams resulting from the action of uniformly distributed loads consist of parabolic curves.

At the point of application of a couple there is a sudden change in the shape of the bending moment diagram of height equal to the magnitude of the couple.

The shearing force at a point in a beam is the algebraic sum of all vertical forces to the right, *or to the left*, of that point. It is, however, better to sum all forces systematically *to the left* of all points when drawing a shearing force diagram.

Shearing force diagrams resulting from the action of concentrated point loads on horizontal beams consist of horizontal straight lines with vertical changes at the point of application of the loads.

Shearing force diagrams resulting from the action of uniformly distributed loads on horizontal beams consist of sloping straight lines.

The maximum bending moment occurs at a point where the shearing force is zero.

The maximum bending moment in a simply supported beam of span L carrying a single concentrated load W at mid-span is $WL/4$.

The maximum bending moment in a simply supported beam of span L carrying a uniformly distributed load w per metre length is $wL^2/8$ (or $WL/8$).

46

FURTHER PROBLEMS

In the following problems, try to sketch the deflected shapes and hence visualise the shape of the BM diagrams before attempting any calculations of bending moment values. The solutions to all problems are given at the end of the programme.

1. Draw the shearing force and bending moment diagrams for the beam shown in figure Q1, marking all important values.

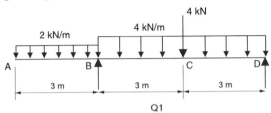

Q1

2. Draw the shearing force and bending moment diagrams for the beam shown in figure Q2, marking all important values.

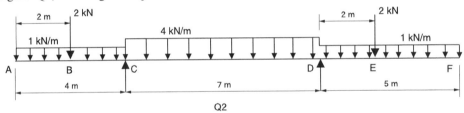

Q2

3. Construct the shearing force and bending moment diagrams for the two beams shown in figures Q3(a) and Q3(b).

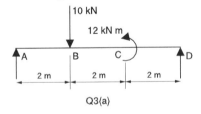

Q3(a)

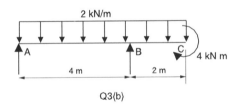

Q3(b)

4. Figure Q4 shows the loading acting on a propeller blade. Draw the shearing force and bending moment diagrams.

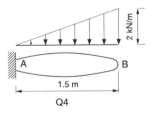

Q4

SOLUTIONS TO PROBLEMS

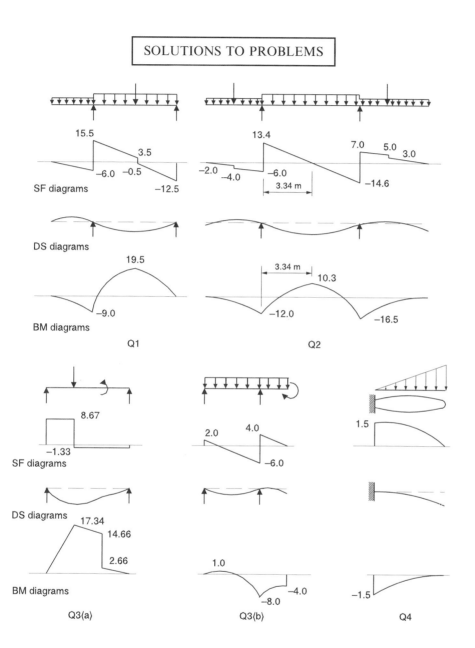

SF diagrams

DS diagrams

BM diagrams

Q1

Q2

SF diagrams

DS diagrams

BM diagrams

Q3(a)

Q3(b)

Q4

Programme 4

STRESS ANALYSIS
(DIRECT STRESS)

On completion of this programme you will be able to:

- Define 'stress'
- Calculate tensile stress values for a range of simple axial stress problems
- Calculate compressive stress values for a range of simple axial stress problems
- Define 'strain'
- Calculate strain values for a range of simple axial stress problems
- Describe the concept of linear elastic behaviour
- State the relationship between stress and strain
- Define and calculate lateral strain
- Explain the terms 'Young's Modulus' and 'Poisson's ratio'
- Calculate volumetric strain
- Analyse the effect of temperature variation on axially loaded composite bars

1

In Programme 2 we considered different types of loading on mechanical components. In Programme 3 we saw how external loads induced shearing forces and bending moments in beams. We now begin to look more closely at the way in which the material of which the component is made reacts to the effects of loading. We start in this programme by considering in detail the behaviour of components subjected only to axial tensile or compressive forces. The effect of shearing forces and bending moments will be considered in subsequent programmes.

We have already noted in previous programmes that components subjected to tensile forces increase in length, and those subjected to compressive forces decrease in length. It is true to say that whenever a force is applied to a piece of material, that material will change shape. The change may only be microscopic but in all cases a loading is accompanied by deformation. Thus all components, when loaded, will deform, the amount of deformation depending on factors such as the magnitude of the load and the type of material used in the component. In this programme we shall learn how to calculate the effect of axial loading on some simple mechanical components.

2

DIRECT TENSILE STRESS

Consider a component having a cross-sectional area A and which is in equilibrium under the action of external forces F which are applied at the ends of the member in a direction parallel to the longitudinal axis of the member and thus at right-angles to the cross-section. The internal force developed in the member is also F as shown on the free-body diagram (figure (b)) which is obtained by taking any section through the member and considering the equilibrium of the part of the member to the left of that section.

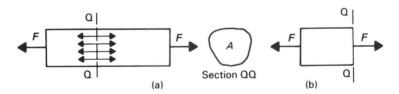

The force F is transmitted along the length of the component through the material fibres of which it is made. The material is resisting the tendency to pull apart and is said to be in a *state of stress*. The small arrows shown on the section Q–Q indicate those internal stresses which develop over the entire area of a cross-section and which act in a direction at right angles to the plane of the cross-section. In order to quantify the state of stress, normally denoted by σ (sigma), we calculate the force acting on each unit of area of the cross-section, and say that the average *magnitude of stress* is given by: $\sigma = F/A$. The term *magnitude of stress* is abbreviated to *stress*. Thus, for any section Q–Q, we can say that there is a *direct (tensile) stress* acting on the section, given by:

$$\text{average stress } \sigma = F/A$$

The term *direct* implies that the member is subject to an axial force only, and that the stress is normal (at right angles) to the plane on which it acts. In this programme we shall denote tensile stresses as positive.

We have derived the value of *average* stress by dividing the total force by the total area. Does this mean that the stress is necessarily uniform over the entire area? It does not. We have no justification to make such an assumption. A uniform distribution of stress would, however, be desirable, since all fibres would then be evenly stressed to resist the external force, and the material would be utilised in the most efficient manner.

Can you suggest how the external force should be applied to the component to ensure that the stress in the component is uniformly distributed across a cross-section?

3

> The force should be applied so that it acts along
> an axis through the centroid of the cross-section.

You may have arrived intuitively at this conclusion. If not, look at the figure below. The stress on section Q–Q is shown as being uniform across the section and of value σ. The resultant total internal tensile force will thus be given by $F = \sigma \times A$

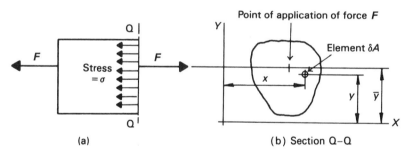

(a)　　　　　　　　　　(b) Section Q–Q

To determine the line of action of the resultant force, F, we calculate the moment of F about the X-axis and equate to the sum of the moments about the X-axis of the forces ($\sigma \times \delta A$) on each elemental area (δA) of the cross-section. Thus, referring to figure (b):

$$F \times \bar{y} = \Sigma(\sigma \times \delta A) \times y$$

but $F = \sigma \times A$ 　　$\therefore$　$\sigma \times A \times \bar{y} = \sigma\Sigma y \times \delta A$

$\therefore$　　　$A\bar{y} = \Sigma y \delta A$

Similarly, it can be shown that:　　$\bar{x}$　　$= \Sigma x \delta A$

You will remember these relationships from Programme 1. What do they suggest to you?

4

You should recognise these relationships from Programme 1 as defining the position of the centroid of an area.

It follows that, if the direct stress in a component is distributed uniformly across any section, then the resultant internal tensile force acts at the centroid of the cross-section. For equilibrium, the external force F must be collinear with the internal force. Thus, if the stress is to be distributed uniformly, the external force must be applied at the centroid of the cross-section.

What would happen if the external force was not applied at the centroid of the cross-section?

5

The stress distribution across the section would not be uniform. The component would be subject to bending in addition to direct loading.

The first answer follows from the reasoning of the previous frames, but you may not have made the second observation. Figure (a) below shows a bar on which the loading is eccentric (that is, the load is not collinear with an axis through the centroid). The bar bends as shown by the broken lines, and the stresses on a cross-section are a combination of the results of direct tension and bending. We shall study the effects of combined tension and bending in Programme 5. For the time being, however, we shall confine our attention to components subject to direct loading only, and in which the stress is distributed uniformly across the cross-section. We now know this means that we are considering situations where loads are applied at the centroids of cross-sections, as shown in figures (b), (c) and (d).

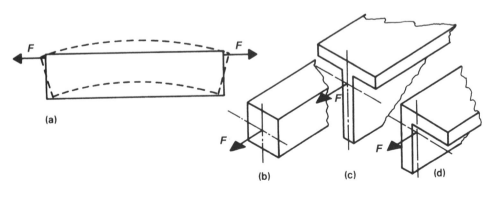

Note that, while in figures (b) and (c) the line of action of the force F passes through the component, in figure (d) the line of action of force F lies outside the component. In practice it is not always easy to provide end connections to ensure that external forces (loads) are transmitted to components at the centroids of their cross-sections. This is particularly so in the case of frameworks, where components are often fabricated from angles with cross-sections as in figure (d). It is nevertheless normally sufficiently accurate to assume that the members of frameworks are subject only to direct stress (no bending).

Now let's look at some examples of members subject to direct tensile stress:

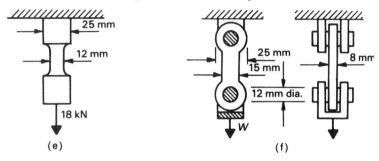

(e) (f)

In figure (e) a vertical bar of circular cross-section 25 mm diameter has its central length reduced to 12 mm diameter. If a load of 18 kN is attached to the lower end, determine the tensile stresses in the bar.

6

> Stress in the central length $= 159.16$ MN/m^2
> Stress in the end lengths $\quad= 36.67$ MN/m^2
> Note the units of stress!

The cross-sectional area in the central length $= \pi 12^2/4 = 113.09$ mm^2
$$= 113.09 \times 10^{-6} \text{ m}^2$$
and at the ends $= \pi 25^2/4 = 490.87$ mm^2
$$= 490.87 \times 10^{-6} \text{ m}^2$$

The tensile stress $\sigma = $ force/area

∴ the stress in the central length $= (18 \times 10^3/113.09 \times 10^{-6}) = 159.16$ MN/m^2

and in the end lengths $= (18 \times 10^3/490.87 \times 10^{-6}) = 36.67$ MN/m^2

The central length is the most heavily stressed part of the bar, and if the load is increased sufficiently, fracture will take place somewhere along that central length. The strength of the bar is determined by the strength of the central length, since that length is the weakest part of the bar.

Now try the following problem.

The suspension link, figure (f), is fabricated from steel plate 8 mm thick. If the tensile stress is not to exceed 165 MN/m^2, determine the maximum allowable value of load W. The load is transmitted to the link by steel pins passing through the 12 mm diameter holes.

7

$$\boxed{17.16 \text{ kN}}$$

The cross-sectional area of the link at its narrowest part $= (15 \times 8) \times 10^{-6}$
$$= 120 \times 10^{-6} \text{ m}^2$$

Now stress $\sigma = \text{load/area}$ $\therefore$ load $(W) = \text{stress} \times \text{area}$

Thus if the stress in the link at its narrowest part is not to exceed 165 MN/m^2, then the maximum load on the link is given by:
$$W = (165 \times 10^6) \times (120 \times 10^{-6}) = 19800 \text{ N} = 19.80 \text{ kN}$$

But, in this example, the narrowest part is not the weakest part of the link. The weakest parts are at the ends, where the drilling of the holes has reduced the area of material under stress considerably. At a section through the centre line of the hole, the effective width of the link is reduced to:
$$25 - 12 = 13 \text{ mm}$$

Thus the effective area of cross-section $= (13 \times 8) \times 10^{-6} = 104 \times 10^{-6} \text{ m}^2$ and if the stress at this section is not to exceed 165 MN/m^2, then the maximum load on the link is given by:
$$W = (165 \times 10^6) \times (104 \times 10^{-6}) = 17160 \text{ N} = \underline{17.16 \text{ kN}}$$

8

DIRECT COMPRESSIVE STRESS

Now look at the figure here showing a component 300 mm square resting on a base 500 mm square. A load of 1500 kN acts vertically on the centre of a steel plate 150 mm square set symmetrically on the top of the component.

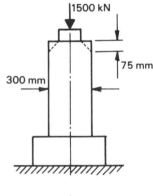

Since the load is axial along an axis of symmetry through the centroid of cross-section, then the stress will be uniformly distributed across any section. Thus, in the column, the direct compressive stress is given by:
$$\sigma = \text{load/area} = \left(-1500 \times 10^3 / [0.3 \times 0.3]\right)$$
$$= \underline{-16.67 \text{ MN/m}^2}$$

Similarly, the stress in the base is given by:
$$\sigma = \text{load/area} = \left(-1500 \times 10^3 / [0.5 \times 0.5]\right)$$
$$= \underline{-6.0 \text{ MN/m}^2}$$

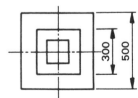

What is the direct compressive stress

(i) in the steel plate? and

(ii) in the component immediately below the steel plate?

9

> (i) -66.67 MN/m^2
> (ii) -66.67 MN/m^2

$$\sigma = \text{load/area} = \left(-1500 \times 10^3/[0.15 \times 0.15]\right) = -66.67 \text{ MN/m}^2$$

The stress in the component immediately below the steel plate will be the same as in the steel plate, because the load is applied over an area of 150×150 mm^2 only. The load, however, spreads rapidly over the entire area of the component. In design, it is often assumed that the broken lines, drawn at an angle of 45°, indicate the way in which the load is distributed into the component. Thus, at a distance of 75 mm below the top of the component, the entire cross-sectional area is under stress and the direct compressive stress at that level will be:

$$\sigma = \text{force/area} = \left(-1500 \times 10^3/[0.3 \times 0.3]\right) = -16.67 \text{ MN/m}^2$$

The figure below shows a bar subjected to a compressive force F applied through steel pins passing through 12 mm diameter holes drilled in the bar.

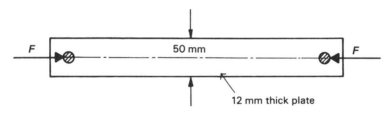

If the maximum permissible compressive stress in the bar is 150 MN/m^2, calculate the maximum value of F.

10

> 90 kN

Force $(F) = \text{stress} \times \text{area} = (150 \times 10^6) \times (50 \times 12) \times 10^{-6} = 90\,000 \text{ N} = 90 \text{ kN}$

Note that, unlike in the tensile case, the holes drilled in the bar do not reduce its load-carrying capacity. This is because the contact surface between pin and bar, through which the load is transmitted, is on the side of the pin towards the centre of the bar. If you take a section through the bar which also cuts the pin, you will see that this reduced area of section is not stressed and therefore does not reduce the strength of the bar.

11

1. A bar with a circular cross-section of diameter 12 mm is subjected to a longitudinal tensile force of 10 kN. Determine the value of the direct tensile stress in the bar.

Ans. 88.42 MN/m².

2. A concrete cube 150 mm × 150 mm × 150 mm is loaded in a compression testing machine. If the compressive force acting normal to one face of the cube is 250 kN, calculate the compressive stress in the concrete.

Ans. −11.11 MN/m².

3. A length of steel having a rectangular cross-section 50 mm × 12 mm is subject to a tensile force of 60 kN. Calculate the tensile stress in the steel: (a) if the ends of the member are welded to the rest of the system, and (b) if the member is bolted to the rest of the system by one bolt through a 10 mm diameter hole at each end. The hole is drilled through the 50 mm width of the section.

Ans. (a) 100 MN/m² (b) 125 MN/m².

4. An L-shaped steel angle section has a cross-sectional area of 1200 mm². If the permissible tensile stress in the steel is not to exceed 165 MN/m², calculate the maximum permissible force in the component. The connection at each end of the component consists of one bolt through a 13 mm diameter hole drilled in one of the two 6 mm sides of the angle section.

Ans. 185.13 kN.

12

STRAIN

Now we shall consider the deformation of materials under stress. You already appreciate that materials in tension increase in length in the direction of the applied force, and that materials in compression decrease in length. For example, figure (a) on the next page shows a bar of length L_a, which extends a distance δL_a because of the application of a tensile axial load. Figure (b) shows a bar of original length L_b which shortens by a distance δL_b because of the application of a compressive axial load. Let's think about the relationship between the change in length and the original length of bars that are stressed in this way.

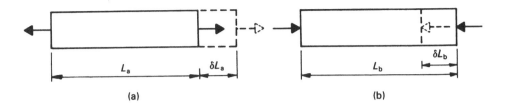

(a)   (b)

Figure (c) shows two bars made from identical material, having the same cross-sectional area, and acted upon by forces of equal magnitude. One bar is, however, twice the length of the other.

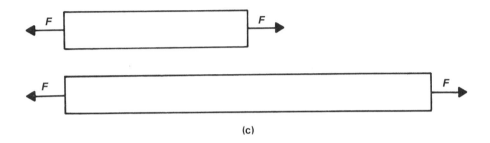

(c)

Can you guess what the relationship is between the magnitude of the extension of the longer bar and the extension of the other bar?

13

> The longer bar would extend
> twice as much as the shorter.

Intuitively, you should realise that the longer bar will extend further than the shorter. The extension of a given bar under a given load will depend on the original length and is in fact directly proportional to the original length. If a bar of original length L changes in length by an amount δL, then the fractional change in length is $\delta L/L$.

This dimensionless parameter is used to define the strain in the material. That is:

$$\text{Strain} = \frac{\text{change in length}}{\text{original length}}$$

Strain is normally denoted by the symbol ε (epsilon).

You should now appreciate that the effect of a load acting on a component is to cause both stress and strain in that component. In the next frame we shall examine the relationship between stress and strain.

14

THE STRESS–STRAIN RELATIONSHIP

If specimens of material are tested in a laboratory so that corresponding values of strain and stress can be recorded, then graphs may be plotted to show the relationship between strain and stress. The following figures show graphs typical of those which result from tensile tests on commonly used metals.

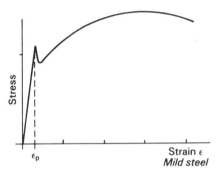

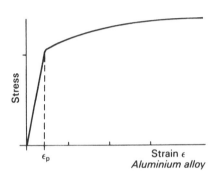

The important feature of each graph is the straight line with which each starts. Stress is seen to be directly proportional to strain, provided the strain does not exceed some value ε_p, the limit of proportionality. You can see the limit of proportionality marked on the graphs shown above. If the materials had been tested in compression instead of tension, the first part of the resulting graphs would similarly have been straight lines, although the later part of each graph would differ from that of the tensile test. We see then that, provided the limit of proportionality is not exceeded, *stress is proportional to strain*. This relationship is known as Hooke's law and is written as:

$$\sigma = E\varepsilon \text{ (or stress } \sigma/\text{strain } \varepsilon = E)$$

where E is known as *Young's Modulus of Elasticity* and is usually quoted, for a given material, in units of N/m^2 (or other SI multiples such as GN/m^2).

ELASTICITY

Another common feature of the behaviour of metals, and some other materials, under test is that when the stress is reduced the strain also reduces. This phenomenon of recoverable strain is known as *elasticity*. You will be familiar with elastic bands and appreciate their behaviour when stretched and then released.

It can be shown experimentally that, provided an elastic material is not strained beyond the limit of proportionality, if the load is reduced to zero the strain similarly reduces to zero and the material reverts to its original length. If a material is loaded so that the strain is in excess of the limit of proportionality, then the material suffers a permanent deformation.

LINEAR ELASTICITY

When a metal is loaded so that the strain does not exceed the limit of proportionality it behaves in a *linear elastic* fashion; strain is recovered completely on unloading, and stress is directly proportional to strain. Such behaviour is termed *linear elasticity*. In addition to metals, other common materials may, under some conditions, be considered to act in a *linear elastic* fashion.

The rest of this book will be based on linear elasticity.

15

CALCULATION OF LINEAR DEFORMATION

Figure (a) below shows a steel bar subjected to a tensile force of 100 kN. Let's determine the increase in length of the bar under load.

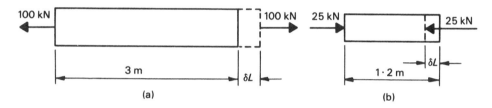

(a)　　　　　　　　　　　　(b)

If the original, unloaded, length of the bar is 3 m, the cross-sectional area 645 mm^2, and if E for steel is 200 GN/m^2 then:

The stress in the bar $\sigma = $ force/area $= (100 \times 10^3)/(645 \times 10^{-6}) = 155$ MN/m^2

Stress/strain $= E$　that is　$\sigma/\varepsilon = E$

or　$\varepsilon = \sigma/E$

$\therefore$　in this example, the strain $\varepsilon = (155 \times 10^6)/(200 \times 10^9) = 0.775 \times 10^{-3}$

But, the strain $\varepsilon = $ change in length/original length

$\therefore$　the change in length (extension) $= \varepsilon \times$ original length

$$= (0.775 \times 10^{-3}) \times 3$$

$$= 0.00233 \text{ m} = \underline{2.33 \text{ mm}}$$

The positive sign indicates an extension in length corresponding to a (positive) tensile stress. Throughout these calculations did you note the factors used to convert all units to either Newtons or m? Correct conversion to consistent units is important!

Figure (b) above shows an aluminium bar 1.2 m long which is subjected to a compressive force of 25 kN. Calculate the strain in the bar and determine the change in length.

(Area of cross-section = 220 mm^2, E for aluminium = 70 GN/m^2)

16

$$\varepsilon = -1.6 \times 10^{-3}$$
Decrease in length $= 1.94$ mm

Stress $\sigma = \text{force/area} = -\left(25 \times 10^3\right)/\left(220 \times 10^{-6}\right) = -113.64$ MN/m^2
Strain $\varepsilon = \text{stress}/E = -\left(113.64 \times 10^6\right)/\left(70 \times 10^9\right) = -1.62 \times 10^{-3}$
Change in length $= \varepsilon \times \text{original length} = -\left(1.62 \times 10^{-3}\right) \times 1.2$
$= -0.00194$ m
$= \underline{-1.94 \text{ mm}}$

LATERAL STRAIN

Now look at the following figures showing (a) a bar of circular cross-section and (b) a member having a rectangular cross-section, both being subject to direct tensile forces. We know that the bars will extend in length under the action of the external forces F.

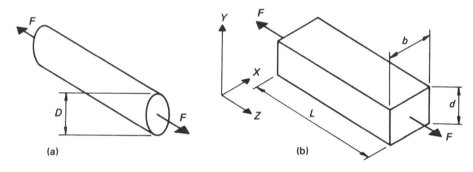

(a)   (b)

Can you visualise the effect of the forces F on the lateral dimensions b, d and D?

17

The lateral dimensions will decrease.

Common experience, perhaps the stretching of a piece of elastic with a rectangular cross-section, should have led you to make the above general observation. It is indeed true that all lateral dimensions decrease if any component is stretched longitudinally. Similarly, it is true that all lateral dimensions increase if a component is compressed longitudinally. Thus longitudinal strain is always accompanied by lateral strain. Experiments show us that lateral strain (ε_L) is directly proportional to the longitudinal stress (σ) in the same way that longitudinal strain (ε) is directly proportional to (σ).

The lateral strain is thus proportional to the longitudinal strain and we say that:

Lateral strain $= -v \times$ longitudinal strain

where v is a constant for a particular material and is known as *Poisson's Ratio*.

Experimental evidence also shows that the lateral strain is the same in all directions for materials that are homogeneous and isotropic (having the same elastic properties in all directions). Many materials are isotropic or can be assumed to be so.

Thus in figure (b) of Frame 16, if the breadth b of the member decreases by δb, the strain in the X direction $= -\delta b/b$ and this will be numerically the same as $-\delta d/d$, the lateral strain in the Y direction. The longitudinal strain, in the Z direction, is $+\delta L/L$, thus:

$$\delta b/b = \delta d/d = -v(\delta L/L)$$

The negative sign implies that if the longitudinal strain is an extension, then the lateral strains are contractions, and vice versa.

18

Now look at the following figure which shows a component of rectangular cross-section subjected to a tensile force of 78 kN. Assuming that Young's Modulus of Elasticity (E) $= 200$ GN/m^2 and that Poisson's ratio $v = 0.33$, we shall calculate the changes in the linear dimensions of the component.

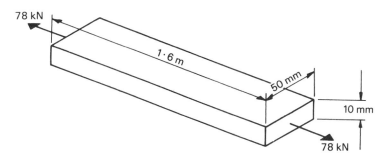

The cross-sectional area $= 50 \times 10 = 500$ mm$^2 = 500 \times 10^{-6}$ m^2

direct tensile stress, $\sigma = (78 \times 10^3)/(500 \times 10^{-6}) = 156$ MN/m^2

The longitudinal strain is given by $\varepsilon = \sigma/E$

$$= 156 \times 10^6/(200 \times 10^9)$$

$$= 0.78 \times 10^{-3}$$

the lateral strain $= -v \times \varepsilon = -0.33 \times 0.78 \times 10^{-3} = -0.257 \times 10^{-3}$

change in length $= \varepsilon \times$ original length $= +0.78 \times 10^{-3} \times 1.6 \times 10^3 = +1.25$ mm

change in width $= \varepsilon_L \times$ original width $= -0.257 \times 10^{-3} \times 50 \qquad = -12.85 \times 10^{-3}$ mm

change in depth $= \varepsilon_L \times$ original depth $= -0.257 \times 10^{-3} \times 10 \qquad = \underline{-2.57 \times 10^{-3}}$ mm

19

PROBLEMS

1. A steel bar is 1.4 m long, has a cross-sectional area of 110 mm^2 and carries a tensile load of 10.5 kN. If the value of Young's Modulus of Elasticity (E) is 200 GN/m^2 and Poisson's ratio $v = 0.3$, calculate: (i) the direct tensile stress, (ii) the longitudinal strain, (iii) the lateral strain and (iv) the change in length.

Ans. (i) 95.45 MN/m^2; (ii) 0.48 × 10^{-3}; (iii) −0.14 × 10^{-3}; (iv) 0.67 mm.

2. A hollow cylindrical steel tube with an outer diameter of 300 mm is to carry a vertical load of 2000 kN. If the direct stress in the steel is not to exceed 120 MN/m^2, calculate: (i) the thickness of metal required in the wall of the tube (*Hint*: calculate the internal diameter); and (ii) the change in external diameter under load.
   Assume that $E = 200$ GN/m^2 and $v = 0.3$.

Ans. (i) 18.87 mm; (ii) +0.054 mm.

3. A steel bar of 25 mm diameter has its central length reduced in diameter to 12 mm. If $E = 200$ GN/m^2 and $v = 0.33$ determine the reduction in diameter of (i) the ends and (ii) the central length of the bar under the action of a tensile force of 25 kN.

Ans. (i) 2.10 × 10^{-3} mm; (ii) 4.38 × 10^{-3} mm.

4. A bar is 1.0 m long, has a circular cross-section of 25 mm diameter and is subjected to a force of 125 kN. If $E = 200$ GN/m^2 and $v = 0.3$, determine the change in volume of the bar when loaded. (*Hint*: calculate the original volume, the changes in dimensions and hence the volume after loading.)

Ans. 249 mm^3.

20

VOLUMETRIC STRAIN

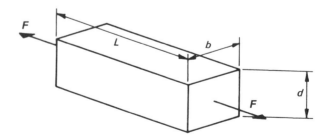

You may have been surprised by the answer to the fourth problem in Frame 19. The volume of the bar changed under load. We shall now make a more detailed study of this effect. Consider the element of material shown in the figure on the previous page.

The longitudinal stress $\sigma = F/bd$

The longitudinal strain $\varepsilon = +\delta L/L$ where δL is the increase in length

The lateral strain $\varepsilon_L \quad = -\delta b/b$ and $= -\delta d/d$ where δb and δd are the decreases in b and d respectively

The original volume $\quad = L \times b \times d$

The volume after loading and the subsequent deformation

$$= (L + \delta L)(b - \delta b)(d - \delta d)$$
$$= L(1 + \varepsilon)b(1 + \varepsilon_L)d(1 + \varepsilon_L)$$
$$= Lbd(1 + \varepsilon)(1 + 2\varepsilon_L + \varepsilon_L^2)$$

If we expand the brackets and neglect second-order terms in ε and ε_L because they are small in magnitude then:

The volume after loading $= Lbd(1 + \varepsilon + 2\varepsilon_L)$

The change in volume is thus $=$ final volume $-$ original volume

$$= Lbd(1 + \varepsilon + 2\varepsilon_L) - Lbd = Lbd(\varepsilon + 2\varepsilon_L)$$
$$= Lbd\varepsilon(1 - 2v) \text{ since } \varepsilon_L = -v\varepsilon$$

For the majority of engineering materials, v has values between 0.35 and 0.25. Thus in the case of most applications there will be a change in volume as a result of loading. The ratio (change in volume/original volume) is termed the *volumetric strain*.

$\therefore \quad$ Volumetric strain $= \delta V/V = Lbd\varepsilon(1 - 2v)/Lbd = \varepsilon(1 - 2v)$

The expression $\delta V/V = \varepsilon(1 - 2v)$ may be used to determine the volumetric strain for any body for any shape of cross-section. Thus, for problem 4 of Frame 19

the longitudinal stress $\sigma = $ load/area $= [(125 \times 10^3)/(\pi 25^2/4 \times 10^{-6})]$
$$= 254.65 \text{ MN/m}^2$$

the longitudinal strain $\varepsilon = \sigma/E = 254.65 \times 10^6/200 \times 10^9 = 0.001\,27$

the volumetric strain $\quad = \varepsilon(1 - 2v) = 0.00127(1 - 2 \times 0.3) = 0.000508$

The original volume $\quad = (1 \times 10^3) \times \pi 25^2/4 = 490.87 \times 10^3 \text{ mm}^3$

$\therefore \quad$ the change in volume $\quad = $ volumetric strain $\times$ original volume
$$= 0.000508 \times 490.87 \times 10^3 = 249 \text{ mm}^3$$

This agrees with your previous answer to this problem.

21

MULTI-AXIAL STRESS

In the last few frames we have considered problems involving a single direct stress situation resulting from the application of an external load which acts in a uni-axial direction. However, in practice, there are situations where two, or even three, stresses may act on a component in two or three mutually perpendicular directions. These stresses may have identical or, more probably different magnitudes. Such situations will be discussed later in the text (see Programme 8).

Move to the next frame where we shall look at a situation where uni-axial stress can be developed in a component although there may be no externally applied axial load.

22

THERMAL STRESS

So far in this programme we have considered direct stress arising in a component as a result of the application of an external axial load. However, there is a further situation where direct stress can arise, not from physical loading, but as a result of temperature variations across a component or within a mechanical system.

A typical example is a continuously welded rail on a railway which will be subject to the variation of temperature from a hot summer day to below freezing in the winter. The resulting expansion and contraction of the rail, which will be partially restrained against such movement by the adjacent lengths of rail, will give rise to an internal stress system within the rail. This stress could be tensile or compressive depending on the ambient temperature conditions.

To complete this programme we are going to look at the elementary principles of such problems and learn how to analyse simple thermal stress problems.

What is the property of a material that would enable you to calculate its change of length when it is subjected to a temperature change?

23

> The coefficient of expansion α

The coefficient of expansion of a material is 'the change of length per unit length per degree rise in temperature', and is a term that should be familiar to you from your previous studies.

Now look at the figure below, showing a bar which is sitting on a smooth surface and restrained from moving at one end. The bar is subjected to a temperature rise of $T°C$ and is allowed to expand freely. It has a coefficient of expansion α.

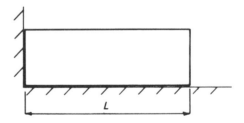

Write down an expression for the change in length of the bar, the strain in the bar and, if the Young's Modulus of Elasticity of the bar is E, state what the stress is in the bar.

24

Change in length $\delta = \alpha LT$

Strain $= \alpha T$

Stress $=$ zero

The expression for the change in length of the bar follows from the definition of the coefficient of expansion (α) given in Frame 23. The expression for strain follows from the definition of strain as change in length divided by original length ($\alpha LT/L = \alpha T$).

You should have obtained the first two answers without difficulty. Did you write down an expression for the stress in the bar based on the relationship that stress divided by strain is Young's Modulus, E? In this case, that is wrong. If there are internal stresses there has to be an external force system to maintain equilibrium. There is no such system, and hence the internal stress must be zero.

It is important to recognise that, if the bar is allowed to expand freely without any external restraint, then it will strain without any corresponding stresses taking place.

Now let's look at the expanded bar as shown in figure (a) and let's apply a force F to the bar which is large enough to return the bar to its original length (figure (b)).

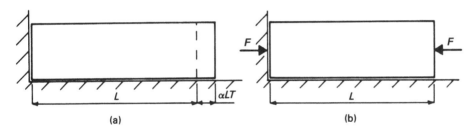

(a)   (b)

Write down an expression for F in terms of the cross-sectional area of the bar, A and Young's Modulus, E. Hence write down an expression for the stress (σ) in the bar.

25

$$F = AE\alpha T \qquad \sigma = E\alpha T$$

From Hooke's Law: $\qquad \dfrac{\sigma}{\varepsilon} = E \quad$ where $\quad \sigma = \dfrac{F}{A}$

Hence: $\qquad F = A\sigma = AE\varepsilon = AE\alpha T$

and: $\qquad \sigma = F/A = AE\alpha T/A = E\alpha T$

If a bar is subjected to a temperature change, what additional condition do you think must exist for stress to be set up in the bar?

26

> Restraint against expansion
> or contraction

What the equations in Frame 25 show us is that, if the bar is restrained against expansion by some sort of restraining system capable of developing a restraining force (F), then stress ($E\alpha T$) will develop in the bar. If the bar is completely unrestrained, it will strain without being stressed. This is an important observation.

The logic of the steps we have just followed can be applied in reverse order to the analysis of a restrained bar system subjected to a temperature rise. Consider the restrained bar shown in figure (a) where the supports are sufficiently rigid to prevent movement. Figure (b) shows the bar released at one end and allowed to expand freely. The amount of expansion can be calculated (αLT). Figure (c) shows the bar subjected to an applied force $F (= AE\alpha T)$ which is large enough to return the bar to its original length and induces a stress ($E\alpha T$) in the bar. The final figure (c) represents the completely analysed situation where the deformations are known (zero) and the internal stress and external forced have been calculated.

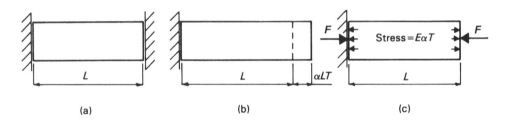

(a)   (b)   (c)

A steel beam, 4 metres long and forming part of a building structure, is firmly built into solid walls at either end. If the temperature rise in the beam on a summer day is 15°C, what stress is induced in the beam? Take $\alpha = 12 \times 10^{-6}$ per degree centigrade and $E = 200$ GN/m^2.

27

> 36 MN/m^2

The solution follows from the equation that we have just developed and ensuring, as in all problems, that the units are correct:

$$\sigma = E\alpha T = (200 \times 10^9) \times (12 \times 10^{-6}) \times 15 = 36 \text{ MN/m}^2$$

This is a compressive stress caused by a temperature rise. If the stress was induced by a temperature fall, it would be a tensile stress. It is interesting to note that this is independent of the cross-sectional area of the beam. Now let's turn to another type of problem: an engine cylinder head restrained by steel bolts. As the engine heats up there will be differential expansion, causing stresses in the components. Such a situation can be modelled as a bar (material 1) contained within a tube (material 2), as shown in the figure below.

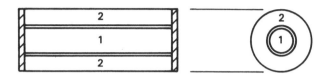

If the bar and the tube are subjected to a temperature rise T, will there be stress induced in the bar if the coefficients of expansion (α_1 and α_2) are (a) the same, or (b) different?

28

(a) No   (b) Yes

If the materials have identical coefficients of expansion they will expand the same amount, and because there is no external restraint no stresses will be set up.

However if they have different coefficients of expansion they will attempt to expand by different amounts, but because they are fastened together they must expand together. Hence an *internal restraint* system will be set up as the material that is trying to expand the most pulls the other with a force (F_2) in the direction of expansion. Equally, the material trying to expand the least will pull back on the other with a force (F_1) against the direction of expansion. This is shown in the figure below, where it is assumed that the internal bar has the larger coefficient of expansion.

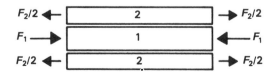

What is the relationship between F_1 and F_2?

29

$$F_1 = F_2 = F$$

As F_1 and F_2 are the only forces acting on the bar and tube, they must represent a set of forces in equilibrium. The above equation therefore represents our *equilibrium expression*.

To analyse this system to determine the internal stresses arising from the temperature rise, let's adopt a similar approach to that used in Frame 26 to analyse the restrained bar made of one material. In other words, we shall release one end of the system and allow both components to expand freely without restraint. This is shown in figure (a), where the free expansions δ_1 and δ_2 are given by:

$$\delta_1 = \alpha_1 LT \qquad \text{and} \qquad \delta_2 = \alpha_2 LT$$

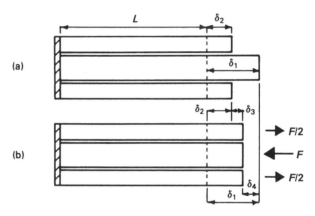

The final position of the ends of both bar and tube must lie at the same point somewhere between the two extremities shown in figure (a). To bring them to the same position we will apply a compressive force F to the bar, and an equal opposite tensile force to the tube, as shown in figure (b).

Using the notation shown in figure (b), can you write down an expression of displacement compatibility that relates the overall displacement of the bar to that of the tube?

30

$$\delta_2 + \delta_3 = \delta_1 - \delta_4$$

This equation follows from the geometry of figure (b). The displacement δ_3 and δ_4 are attributable to the application of the force F and can be expressed in terms of F by the equations:

$$\delta_3 = \frac{FL}{A_2E_2} \quad \text{and} \quad \delta_4 = \frac{FL}{A_1E_1}$$

Hence our equilibrium and compatibility equations for this problem are:

(a) *Equilibrium* $\qquad F_1 = F_2 = F$

and

(b) *Compatibility* $\qquad \delta_2 + \delta_3 = \delta_1 - \delta_4$

where:

$$\delta_1 = \alpha_1 LT \qquad \delta_2 = \alpha_2 LT \qquad \delta_3 = \frac{FL}{A_2E_2} \qquad \delta_4 = \frac{FL}{A_1E_1}$$

Rearrange the above equations to eliminate the displacements δ_1 to δ_4 and produce an equation for the internal force F.

31

$$F = \frac{(\alpha_1 - \alpha_2)TA_1E_1A_2E_2}{(A_1E_1 + A_2E_2)}$$

From the compatibility equation:

$$\delta_2 + \delta_3 = \delta_1 - \delta_4$$

Substituting:

$$\alpha_2 LT + \frac{FL}{A_2E_2} = \alpha_1 LT - \frac{FL}{A_1E_1}$$

which rearranges to give:

$$F = \frac{(\alpha_1 - \alpha_2)TA_1E_1A_2E_2}{(A_1E_1 + A_2E_2)}$$

This equation gives the internal force between the bar and the tube. How would you calculate the stresses in the bar and the tube?

32

$$\sigma_1 = \frac{F}{A_1}, \ \sigma_2 = \frac{F}{A_2} \quad \text{where } F \text{ comes from the equation in Frame 31}$$

This should be fairly obvious (stress = force/area).
   How would you calculate the final elongation of the system? Write down the equation that would enable you to determine this.

33

$$\boxed{\begin{array}{l} \text{Elongation} = \delta_2 + \delta_3 = \alpha_2 LT + \dfrac{FL}{A_2 E_2} \\[2mm] \text{where } F \text{ comes from the equation in Frame 31} \end{array}}$$

In Frame 30 and figure (b) in Frame 29 we identified the elongation as $\delta_2 + \delta_3$. Substituting the appropriate terms from Frame 30 gives the above equation. A corresponding equation in terms of material 1 would be obtained by taking the elongation as $\delta_1 - \delta_4$ and making the appropriate substitution.

The equations that we have identified above enables us to analyse any system where *axial stress* is induced by temperature changes. In other types of system, such as composite beams, temperature variations will induce flexural stresses and flexural deformations. The analysis of this situation is beyond the scope of this book, although the principles involved are similar. Now try a problem, the solution to which is in the next frame:

A steel rod 20 mm in diameter is fitted inside an aluminium tube with internal and external diameters of 22 mm and 30 mm respectively. The ends of the rod are fastened to the tube by screwed connections. Calculate the stress induced in the rod if the temperature of both rod and tube is raised by $80°C$. Take $E_{steel} = 200 \ GN/m^2$, $E_{alum} = 70 \ GN/m^2$, $\alpha_{steel} = 10 \times 10^{-6}/°C$ and $\alpha_{alum} = 23 \times 10^{-6}/°C$.

34

$$\boxed{\sigma_s = 55.49 \ \text{MN/m}^2}$$

Using subscripts 's' and 'a' to indicate the steel rod and aluminium tube respectively:

Area $A_s = \pi \times 20^2/4 = 314.3 \ \text{mm}^2$: Area $A_a = \pi(30^2 - 22^2)/4 = 326.9 \ \text{mm}^2$

From the equation in Frame 31 and working in units of GN and m:

$$\begin{aligned} F &= \frac{(\alpha_a - \alpha_s)TA_aE_aA_sE_s}{(A_aE_a + A_sE_s)} \\[2mm] &= \frac{(23-10)10^{-6} \times 80 \times 326.9 \times 10^{-6} \times 70 \times 314.3 \times 10^{-6} \times 200}{[(326.9 \times 10^{-6} \times 70) + (314.3 \times 10^{-6} \times 200)]} \\[2mm] &= 0.00001744 \ \text{GN} = 17.44 \ \text{kN} \end{aligned}$$

Hence:

$$\sigma_s = \frac{F}{A_s} = \frac{17.44 \times 10^3}{314.3 \times 10^{-6}} = 55.49 \ \text{MN/m}^2$$

A little bit of thought will tell you that this must be a tensile stress, as the steel has the lowest coefficient of expansion (look back at the diagram in Frame 29).

35

┌─────────────────────┐
│   TO REMEMBER   │
└─────────────────────┘

Direct stress is the normal force acting on a surface divided by the area of that surface ($\sigma =$ force/area) (units $=$ N/m^2).

A direct stress is uniform over a surface (or section) only if the normal force passes through the centroid of the surface (or section).

A direct stress acts at right angles to the surface under consideration.

Tensile stresses are produced by tensile forces which tend to lengthen components.

Compressive stresses are produced by compressive forces which tend to shorten components.

Strain is the ratio of change to original length ($\varepsilon = \delta L/L$) and is a small, dimensionless measurement.

Longitudinal strain is the strain in the direction of the force acting on a component.

Provided that an elastic material is not strained beyond the limit of proportionality, stress is directly proportional to strain. The strain is completely recovered when the load is removed.

Young's Modulus of Elasticity (E) $=$ stress/strain $= \sigma/\varepsilon$ (units $=$ N/m^2).

Lateral strain is the strain in a direction at right angles to the direction of the force acting on a member.

Poisson's ratio (v) $= -$ (lateral strain)/(longitudinal strain) and is dimensionless.

Thermal stresses: $F = \dfrac{(\sigma_1 - \sigma_2)TA_1E_1A_2E_2}{(A_1E_1 + A_2E_2)}$

36

FURTHER PROBLEMS

---

1. A tie bar is 2 m in length, has a circular cross-section of 19 mm diameter and carries a longitudinal load of 35 kN. Calculate the stress in the bar and the change in length ($E = 200$ GN/m^2).

Ans. 123.44 MN/m^2, 1.23 mm.

2. A draw bar between a tractor and a trailer is made from a length of steel with a rectangular cross-section 100 mm by 12 mm. The load is transmitted to the bar via a pin through a 25 mm diameter hole drilled through the bar at each end. If the maximum permissible stress in the steel is 150 MN/m^2, determine the maximum load that can be taken by the bar.

Ans. 135 kN.

3. Figure Q3 shows one end of a beam resting upon a bearing pad made of a rubber compound and which is 250 mm square in plan area. If the vertical reaction at the end of the beam is 3000 kN, calculate the compressive stress in the bearing pad.

Ans. -48.0 MN/m^2.

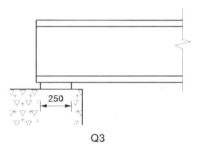

Q3

4. Figure Q4 shows a 'strong back' device for use in lifting long heavy castings. The loading is such that the load is shared equally by the lower links. The twin links connecting the device to the crane hook are each made from 75 mm by 12 mm steel strip and have 20 mm diameter holes to the connecting pins. The lower links are each made from 50 mm by 12 mm steel and have 18 mm diameter holes. Considering only the tensile strength of the links, determine the maximum load that can be lifted safely. Assume that the maximum permissible tensile stress is 150 MN/m^2.

Ans. 198.0 kN.

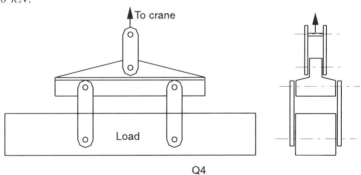

Q4

5. A steel tie bar 1.1 m long and 50 mm diameter is subjected to a tensile stress of 120 MN/m². Determine:

(i)   the extension
(ii)   the change in lateral dimension; and
(iii)   the change in volume.

Assume that $E = 200$ GN/m² and Poisson's Ratio $v = 0.3$.

Ans. (i) 0.66 mm, (ii) −0.009 mm, (iii) 518 mm³.

6. A steel rod 20 mm in diameter is placed inside a copper tube with external and internal diameters of 30 mm and 25 mm, respectively. The ends of the rod and tube are connected together firmly. When the temperature of the compound bar is raised by 250°C, the length of the bar is found to increase by 700×10^{-6} metres. Calculate the length of the original bar and the stress induced in both steel and copper.

$E_{steel} = 200$ GN/m²; $E_{copper} = 120$ GN/m²; $\alpha_{steel} = 10 \times 10^{-6}/°C$; and
$\alpha_{copper} = 17 \times 10^{-6}/°C$

Ans. 232.5 mm, 102.21, 148.67 MN/m²; steel in tension, copper in compression.

7. If the bar in Q6 is maintained at the elevated temperature, determine what axial force would have to be applied to the compound bar to reduce the stress in the steel rod to zero.

Ans. 45.37 kN.

8. Determine the stresses in the compound bar shown in figure Q8 if the temperature of the bar is raised by 50°C. The left-hand part of the bar is made of a solid steel circular section of diameter 20 mm and the right-hand part of solid copper of diameter 30 mm. Take the material properties from Q6.

Ans. 155.13 (steel), 68.95 (copper) MN/m², both in compression.

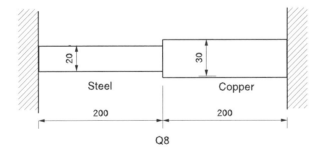

Q8

Programme 5

BENDING STRESS

On completion of this programme you will be able to:

- Explain the term 'neutral axis'
- Calculate the 'second moment of area' of regular and irregular shapes
- State and apply the parallel axis theorem
- Calculate the elastic section modulus of regular and irregular shapes
- State the formulae for the second moment of area and elastic section modulus of a solid rectangular section
- State the formulae for the second moment of area and elastic section modulus of a solid circular section
- Recognise the state of bending stress and strain within a beam's cross-section
- Calculate stress values at different levels in a beam's cross-section
- State the standard equation of bending
- Recognise and describe the terms in the equation of bending
- Apply the equation of bending to the solution of a range of simple beam problems
- Carry out simple design procedures for beams in bending
- Carry out simple design and analytical procedures for components subject to both bending and axial stress
- Define and identify the 'principal axis' of a beam's cross-section

1

In Programme 3 you learnt how to determine the shear force and bending moment at any section of a loaded beam. In future programmes you will learn how to design beams capable of withstanding the effects of shear force and bending moment.

As an introduction to beam design we will, in this programme, develop and study the equations that can be used to analyse the bending stresses resulting from the application of bending moment. Although the theory we shall develop can be applied to other types of mechanical components, we shall restrict our study to a consideration of beams only.

2

When a beam is loaded, strains and stresses are introduced internally at every cross-section and we must be able to determine their magnitude and distribution. Are the strains and stresses uniform, or do they vary along the length of a beam and throughout the depth of a cross-section? Experience based on our previous work should tell you that a typical simply supported beam deflects under load, as shown below.

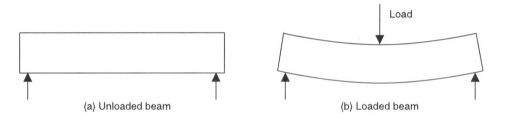

(a) Unloaded beam   (b) Loaded beam

Now look at figure (b). Which face (top or bottom) of the loaded beam is in tension and which is in compression? (Hint: remember that material which increases in length is in tension, and material which decreases in length is in compression.)

3

> The top is in compression.
> The bottom is in tension.

You should have decided that the top of the beam is in compression and the bottom in tension. This implies that the strain and stress at any section in a beam will vary from compressive to tensile across the depth of the beam. To help us understand what happens in the material of a beam, it is useful to imagine the beam as made up of several layers of fibres as shown below in figures (a) and (b). When bending under load takes place, such a beam could deflect in one of two ways, either as in figure (c) or as in figure (d).

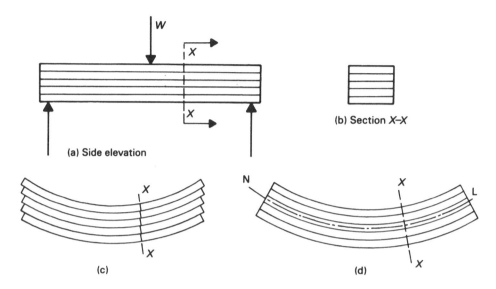

(a) Side elevation

(b) Section *X–X*

(c)

(d)

In case (c), each layer deforms independently and slipping takes place along the interface between adjacent layers. Because each layer is deforming independently, compressive stresses will occur at the top surface and tensile stresses will occur at the bottom surface of each layer. This would happen if our beam was indeed made up of many separate layers with no adhesion or bond between them. If our beam was built up using separate layers and we wished to prevent it bending and slipping along the interfaces as in (c), the layers would have to be securely bonded together by glue, bolts or similar means before the load was applied.

A real beam, which is solid and assumed to be homogeneous (having the same composition throughout) would deflect as in figure (d) without any relative slipping between layers. A section *X–X* in the elevation in figure (a) is in the vertical plane at right angles to the longitudinal axis of the beam and is a plane (flat) surface. You can see in figure (d) that, after bending, section *X–X* remains plane and at right angles to the longitudinal axis, although no longer vertical. It is therefore assumed that all plane sections normal to the longitudinal axis of the beam remain plane after bending.

For bending to take place as in figure (d), fibres towards the top of the beam shorten and are in compression, while those fibres towards the bottom of the beam lengthen and are in tension. Somewhere between the top and bottom is a layer which is neither compressed nor stretched, and hence the fibres along this layer do not change in length. This layer is called the *neutral layer* and is shown by the line N–L in figure (d).

4

Now look at the beams sketched below:

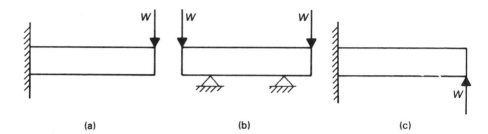

(a)   (b)   (c)

Can you state:
(i) for each beam: is the top or the bottom face in tension? and
(ii) for all beams: at what level are the fibres of the beam subjected to the greatest
*   extension or the greatest shortening?*

5

| (i) (a) top; (b) top; (c) bottom |
| (ii) At the top or bottom face of the beam |

In all cases, the layer of fibres at the top or bottom face of a beam will be subject to the greatest extension if that face is in tension. If the top or bottom face is in compression, then the fibres at that level will be subjected to the greatest shortening. You will find it helps to see this if you visualise the way in which the beam deflects. The following figures show the deflected shape of the beams considered in Frame 4.

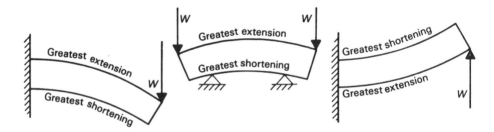

If a beam under load deflects in the shape of a circular arc, we can identify a centre of curvature O and a radius of curvature R as shown in the next figure (a). We shall define R as the radius from the centre of curvature to the neutral layer.

In practice, the radius of curvature of a deflected beam will not necessarily be the same throughout the length of the beam. We shall discover why later in this programme. We can, however, consider a beam as comprising several elements of such a short length that the radius of curvature can be considered to be constant over an element. Such an element is shown in figures (b) and (c).

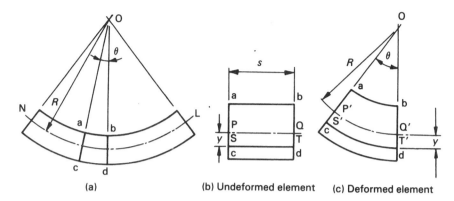

(a)　　　　　　　(b) Undeformed element　　　(c) Deformed element

In figure (b), PQ is the neutral layer and ST is a typical layer at a distance y from the neutral layer and on the tension side of the beam. In figure (c) these layers are shown as P'Q' and S'T', respectively.

Can you state the relationship between the length of PQ and P'Q'?

6

$$\boxed{\text{Length PQ} = \text{length } P'Q'}$$

In Frame 3 we defined the neutral layer as the layer where the fibres do not change in length when the beam deflects. Hence as PQ is the neutral layer, its length when the beam is unloaded must be the same as when it is loaded.

$$\text{Let the length of } PQ = s$$
$$\text{Then from figure (c), PQ} = P'Q' = s = R \times \theta$$

where θ is the angle subtended at O as shown.

All layers of fibres in the element from the top face ab to the bottom face cd are of the same length ($s = R \times \theta$) when the beam is unloaded. If we now consider the layer ST we can see that, whereas the length of this is s in the unloaded beam, its length is greater in the loaded beam and equal to the length of the arc S'T' in figure (c).

$$\text{From figure (c), the length of layer } S'T' = (R + y)\theta$$
$$\text{The original length of ST} = s = R\theta$$
$$\text{Hence the increase in length of layer ST} = (R + y)\theta - R\theta = y\theta \qquad (5.1)$$

From Equation (5.1) the increase in the length of layer ST is seen to be directly proportional to the distance (y) of layer ST from the neutral layer.

Can you sketch a diagram to show how the change in length of a layer of fibres varies across the section of the element from the top face ab to the bottom face cd?

7

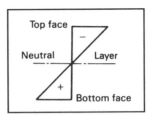

You should have realised from Equation (5.1) that the change in length of any layer throughout the depth of the element is directly proportional to its distance (y) from the neutral layer. For any value of y on the tension side of the element, the fibres will extend (shown as positive on the diagram above). Similarly for values of y on the compressive side of the element, the fibres will shorten (shown as negative on the diagram above).

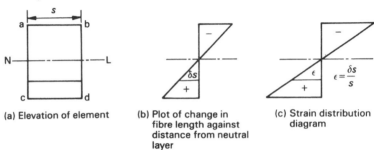

(a) Elevation of element (b) Plot of change in fibre length against distance from neutral layer (c) Strain distribution diagram

Rather than plot a diagram showing the change in length of the fibres throughout the depth of the element, it is more useful to plot a diagram showing the variation of strain throughout the depth of the element. The strain in any layer of fibres is the change in length of the layer (δs) divided by the original length of that layer. All layers of fibres in the undeformed element are, however, of the same original length (s). Hence the strain distribution diagram (figure (c)) can be obtained from figure (b) by dividing each ordinate of figure (b) by the original length (s), thus giving a strain diagram of the same shape. The maximum tensile and compressive strains are seen in figure (c) to occur in the outer fibres at the bottom and top faces of the element. As the small element we have been considering is representative of any point along a beam, we can draw similar strain distribution diagrams to show the strain condition across the depth of any beam at any cross-section along the length of that beam.

Now sketch the strain distribution diagrams at section X–X for each of the beams shown below, and mark the zones of tensile strain and the zones of compressive strain. Indicate the position of the neutral layer in each case.

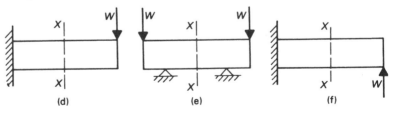

(d) (e) (f)

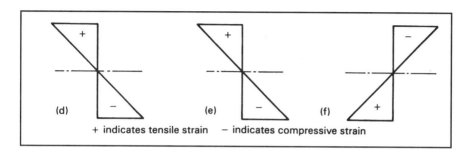

+ indicates tensile strain   − indicates compressive strain

We have already seen that for a *linearly elastic* material, stress is directly proportional to strain and:

$$\frac{\text{stress}}{\text{strain}} = \frac{\sigma}{\varepsilon} = E$$

that is:

$$\sigma = E\varepsilon$$

You will realise consequently that if we multiply the ordinates of a strain diagram by the *elastic modulus E* for the material of which the beam is made, we shall obtain a *stress distribution diagram* as shown in figure (c) below. Note that, when deriving figure (c) we have assumed that the value of E is the same in the tension zone as in the compression zone. Also, since we have previously defined tensile strains as being positive we have now, to be consistent, shown tensile stresses as being positive.

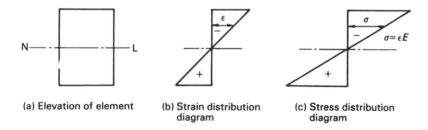

| (a) Elevation of element | (b) Strain distribution diagram | (c) Stress distribution diagram |

For the small element we have been considering, stresses above the neutral layer are compressive and stresses below the neutral layer are tensile. The maximum compressive and maximum tensile stress can be seen to occur in the outer fibres at the top and bottom faces of the element.

The stress diagram we have just developed is triangular in shape. This is not always the case and later in your studies you may encounter stress diagrams of different shape. The programmes in this book will, however, refer to triangular stress distribution. In other words our analysis is based on the assumption that materials behave in a truly linear elastic manner.

9

In this frame we shall look at the stress distribution diagram in greater detail so that we can further develop the theory of bending in beams.

For simplicity, initially we shall look at beams that have a rectangular cross-section. Not all beams, however, will have a rectangular section, and we shall discover in subsequent frames how to analyse such beams.

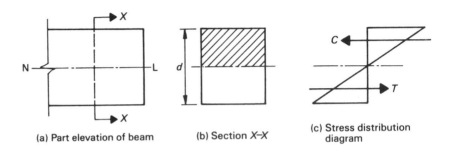

(a) Part elevation of beam   (b) Section X–X   (c) Stress distribution diagram

Look at the cross-section (b) above, which is subjected to the stresses shown in the stress diagram in figure (c). We see that the cross-hatched area is under compressive stress. All fibres above the neutral layer are subject to compressive stress, ranging from zero at the neutral layer to a maximum at the top of the beam. The fibres thus react to external loading by developing reactive forces acting in a direction parallel to the longitudinal axis of the beam. In figure (b) all fibres within the compressive zone are exerting reactive forces in the same direction. These forces can be combined into a single resultant as indicated by the arrow C in figure (c). C represents the resultant of all compressive forces in the beam above the neutral layer. Similarly T represents the resultant of all tensile forces in the beam below the neutral layer.

Now, and with reference to figure (c) above, consider the following question: does your present understanding enable you to predict the position of the line of action of the resultant force C and the line of action of the resultant force T?

10

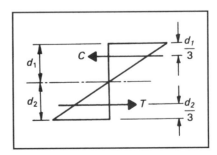

You may have predicted that C and T act through the centroid of their respective *stress blocks*, as shown here. This is a reasonable prediction based on work done in previous programmes and is true in this case, but would not be true if the beam was not rectangular in cross-section. Why not? Because the line of action of a resultant *force* passes through the centroid of a *force* distribution diagram, whereas we have been considering *stress* distribution diagrams. The two diagrams are only the same shape if the beam is of uniform width.

Now look at figure (a) below. The line X–X, which is the line of intersection between the neutral layer and the plane of the cross-section, is known as the *neutral axis* (NA) of the cross-section. We shall prove later that the neutral axis always passes through the geometric centre of the cross-section. Consequently, in the case of a rectangular section, the neutral axis is at mid depth. The neutral axis is, however, not necessarily at mid-depth in the case of more complicated shapes of cross-section.

Figure (b) below shows the stress distribution diagram for the rectangular cross-section (a), and we see that the tension and compression stress blocks are of identical shape. Now consider the part of the beam above the neutral axis. The stress varies from zero to maximum value σ_{max} so that the average stress is $\sigma_{max}/2$. This average stress acts over the hatched area $b \times d/2$ so that the resultant force C is given by:

$$C = \text{average stress} \times \text{area} = \frac{\sigma_{max}}{2} \times \frac{b \times d}{2}$$

$$= \frac{\sigma_{max}bd}{4}$$

$$\text{Similarly } T = \frac{\sigma_{max}bd}{4}$$

$$\text{Hence } \underline{T = C}$$

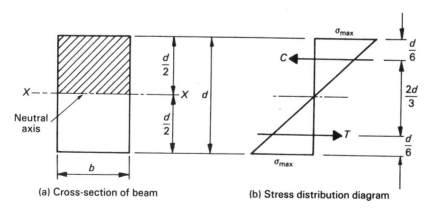

(a) Cross-section of beam **(b) Stress distribution diagram**

Notwithstanding the calculations we have just done, you should realise that the tensile force (T) has to equal the compressive force (C). Why should $T = C$?

11

> Because, for equilibrium of the section, the sum of the
> horizontal forces acting on it must be zero, and as there is no
> external force acting on the section, then T must equal C.

Having decided that $T = C$, we see that now we have two equal forces acting on the cross-section which form a couple. This couple exerts a moment of C (or T since they are equal) times the distance between their lines of action $(2d/3)$.

This *internal* moment provides the beam's resistance to the *external* bending moment resulting from the external loads, and is consequently called the *moment of resistance* (M). For equilibrium of the section, the internal moment of resistance must be equal in magnitude and opposite in sense to the external moment acting on the section.

From the stress diagram in Frame 10 it can been seen that:

$$\text{Moment of resistance} = M = C \times \frac{2d}{3}$$
$$= \frac{\sigma_{max} \times bd}{4} \times \frac{2d}{3}$$
$$= \frac{\sigma_{max}bd^2}{6} \tag{5.2}$$

Given a permissible value for the maximum stress σ_{max}, you should now be able to determine the size of the beam required to resist a given bending moment. But remember that the above derivation applies only to a beam of rectangular cross-section.

A timber beam of solid rectangular cross-section is required to withstand an external bending moment of 11.25 kNm. If the maximum permissible bending stress is 5.0 MN/m² and the beam has a breadth b = 150 mm, calculate the minimum required depth (d) of the beam.

12

> 300 mm

To resist a bending moment of 11.25 kNm the beam must be able to develop a moment of resistance of 11.25 kNm. Then using Equation (5.2):

$$M = \frac{\sigma_{max}bd^2}{6} \qquad \therefore \quad 11.25 \times 10^3 = 5.0 \times 10^6 \times \frac{(150 \times 10^{-3})d^2}{6}$$
$$\therefore \quad d^2 = \frac{11.25 \times 6}{5.0 \times 10^3 \times 150 \times 10^{-3}}$$
$$\therefore \quad \underline{d = 0.3 \text{ m} = 300 \text{ mm}}$$

Now answer the following questions:

(i) Bearing in mind the shape of the stress distribution diagram, do you consider that for a beam of fixed length and for a given weight of material, a rectangular cross-section provides the greatest possible moment of resistance?

(ii) For the same length and weight of material, could a beam of different shape cross-section be stronger?

13

> (i) No (ii) Yes

In fact, a rectangular section does not utilise the material of which a beam is made to the best advantage. A rectangular section may be the easiest shape to make, but for a given weight of material does not give the greatest possible moment of resistance. Nor would such a shape provide the most economic beam to withstand a given loading.

In design we normally need to keep the weight of a component as low as possible, since this will lead to economy of material and the lowest cost. This will be achieved if, where feasible, we use beams in which as much of the beam section as possible is stressed as highly as possible, hence ensuring an efficient use of the available material. Therefore, as much of the material as possible should be located near the top and bottom faces of the beam, where the maximum compressive and tensile stresses occur.

Now assume that we have a given quantity of material to make a beam of a certain fixed length, and that we have a choice of three cross-sections, as shown below. (Note that the areas of all three sections are identical.)

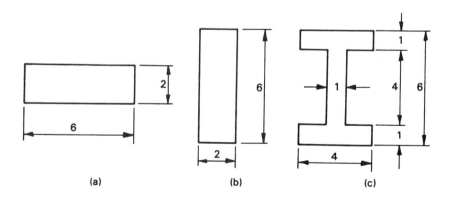

Which of the sections would give the greatest moment of resistance? (Assume that the maximum permissible stress (σ_{max}) is the same in each case.)

14

The best section is (c).

You should have reasoned as follows:

From Equation (5.2) the moment of resistance $M = \dfrac{\sigma_{max}bd^2}{6}$

$\therefore$ for section (a) $M = \sigma_{max} \times 6 \times 2^2/6 = 4\sigma_{max}$

for section (b) $M = \sigma_{max} \times 2 \times 6^2/6 = 12\sigma_{max}$

Hence section (b) is stronger than section (a).

Although you cannot as yet calculate the moment of resistance of section (c), you can see that more material is positioned near the outer fibres and is concentrated in the regions of greatest stress. Thus section (c) is stronger that section (b).

We can now learn how to calculate the moment of resistance for a beam with a cross-section other than rectangular. To do this we consider the general case of a beam with irregular cross-section as shown below:

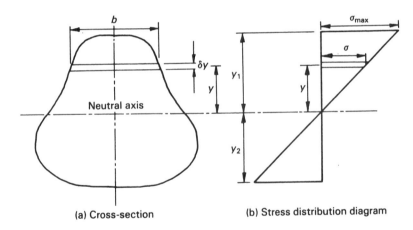

(a) Cross-section   (b) Stress distribution diagram

Consider a thin strip of the cross-section of width b, thickness δy and at distance y from the neutral axis. Let the stress in this strip $= \sigma$.

Then the longitudinal force acting on the strip $=$ stress $\times$ area

$= \sigma \times (b\delta y)$

And hence the longitudinal force acting on the cross-section $= \displaystyle\int_{-y_2}^{y_1} \sigma b \, dy$

But as there can be no resultant longitudinal force acting on the section, this force must be zero if static equilibrium is to be assured.

thus $\quad \int_{-y_2}^{y_1} \sigma b\, dy = 0 \qquad (5.3)$

By similar triangles in figure (b) you will see that:

$$\frac{\sigma}{y} = \frac{\sigma_{max}}{y_1}$$

thus $\quad \sigma = \dfrac{\sigma_{max}}{y_1} \times y$

and Equation (5.3) becomes:

$$\frac{\sigma_{max}}{y_1} \int_{-y_2}^{y_1} by\, dy = 0$$

But σ_{max} and y_1 cannot be zero, thus $\int_{-y_2}^{y_1} by\, dy$ must be zero.

This integral expression is the first moment area of the cross-section about the neutral axis, and we know from Programme 1 that if the first moment of area about an axis is zero, then that axis must pass through the centroid of that area.

What does this tell you about the position of the neutral axis?

15

> The neutral axis passes through
> the centroid of the cross-section.

This is a very important conclusion and enables us to identify where the neutral axis of the cross-section of a beam is located.

Now consider four horizontal beams, each carrying vertical loads and having cross-sections as shown below:

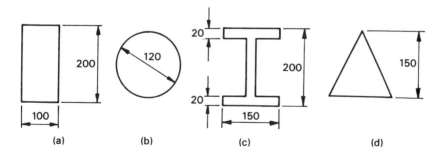

(a)   (b)   (c)   (d)

Identify the position of the neutral axis in each case. (Note that, since the loads are vertical, the beams will bend about a horizontal axis. Consequently, you are looking for a neutral axis that is horizontal in each case.)

16

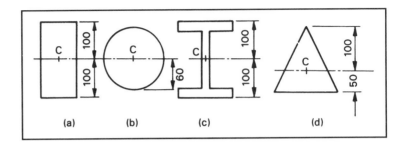

(a)   (b)   (c)   (d)

You should have found this straightforward, since you can identify the centroids of (a), (b) and (c) by symmetry, and you know that the centroid of a triangle is one third of the height above the base. For some other sections, however, you may need to use the method used in Programme 1 to locate the centroid, and hence the neutral axis.

SECOND MOMENT OF AREA

Now refer to the diagram in Frame 14.

The longitudinal force in the thin strip	$= \sigma b \delta y$

The moment of this force about the neutral axis $= \text{force} \times \text{distance } (y)$

$$= \sigma b \delta y \times y$$

The total moment of the resultant force about the neutral axis $= \displaystyle\int_{-y_2}^{y_1} \sigma b y \, \mathrm{d}y$

But, as before (Frame 14) $\qquad\qquad\qquad\qquad \sigma = \dfrac{\sigma_{\max} \times y}{y_1}$

Thus the total moment about the neutral axis $= \text{the Moment of Resistance}$

$$= M$$

$$= \frac{\sigma_{\max}}{y_1} \int_{-y_2}^{y_1} b y^2 \, \mathrm{d}y \qquad (5.4)$$

The integral expression in Equation (5.4) is termed the *second moment of area* of the cross-section about the neutral axis, and for convenience is given the symbol I. I has units of $(\text{length})^4$ and typically would be calculated in m^4. Equation (5.4) can now be written more simply as

$$M = \frac{\sigma_{\max} I}{y_1} \qquad \text{where } I = \int_{-y_2}^{y_1} b y^2 \, \mathrm{d}y$$

but $\dfrac{\sigma_{max}}{y_1} = \dfrac{\sigma}{y}$ (see Frame 14). Thus $M = \dfrac{\sigma I}{y}$

or

$$\frac{\sigma}{y} = \frac{M}{I} \qquad (5.5)$$

Where: M is the moment of resistance
I is the second moment of area about the neutral axis; and
σ is the bending stress in any fibre at a distance y from the neutral axis.

The second moment of area of a beam section is 10×10^{-6} m^4. If the section is subjected to a bending moment of 2 kN m, calculate the bending stress at a distance of 50 mm from the neutral axis.

17

$$\boxed{10 \ \text{MN/m}^2}$$

$$\sigma = \frac{M \times y}{I} = \frac{2 \times 10^3 \times 50 \times 10^{-3}}{10 \times 10^{-6}} = 10 \ \text{MN/m}^2$$

Equation (5.5) can be used to calculate the stress at any level in the cross-section of a beam. The stress will be tensile or compressive depending on which side of the neutral axis is being considered, and whether the beam is being subjected to a hogging or sagging bending moment. This can always be determined by inspection. You should note that, in other studies, you may encounter the use of symbol I to represent moment of inertia, whereas here we are using it to represent the second moment of area. The two uses are not identical: moment of inertia has units of mass $\times$ length^2, whereas the second moment of area is a geometrical property of an area and has units of length^4.

Let's now calculate the second moment of area for a rectangular beam section. We have now shown (as previously assumed) that the neutral axis passes through the centroid of the section which is at mid-depth.

For a beam b wide and d deep we can consider an elemental strip as shown in the figure below.

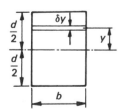

$$I = \int_{-y_2}^{y_1} by^2 \, \mathrm{d}y = \int_{-d/2}^{d/2} by^2 \, \mathrm{d}y = b\left[\frac{y^3}{3}\right]_{-d/2}^{d/2}$$

$$= b\left[\frac{d^3}{24} + \frac{d^3}{24}\right] = \frac{bd^3}{12} \qquad (5.6)$$

You should remember this formula, as it is widely used in mechanical analysis and design.

Calculate the I value for a rectangular section 50 mm wide and 100 mm deep.

18

$$\boxed{4.17 \times 10^{-6} \text{ m}^4}$$

$$I = bd^3/12 = \left(50 \times 100^3\right)/12 = 4.17 \times 10^6 \text{ mm}^4$$
$$= 4.17 \times 10^{-6} \text{ m}^4$$

ELASTIC SECTION MODULUS

Frame 16 introduced the concept of second moment of area. We now consider an equally useful parameter in design: the *elastic section modulus* (Z). This is defined as the second moment of area of a section about the neutral axis divided by the distance (y_{max}) from that axis to the furthermost fibre.

$$\text{Thus} \quad Z = \frac{I}{y_{max}}$$

For example, in the case of a *solid rectangular section b* wide and *d* deep:

$$I = bd^3/12 \text{ and } y_{max} = d/2 \quad \therefore \quad Z = \frac{I}{y_{max}} = \frac{bd^3/12}{d/2} = \frac{bd^2}{6}$$

You may recognise this from Equation (5.2) in Frame 11. You should also remember this equation as it is widely used in design. Note that, if the neutral axis is not at mid-height of the section (for example, in the case of a T-section), then the section will have two Z values: one related to the top face of the section and the other to the bottom face.

Now, from the equation developed in Frame 16:
$$\frac{\sigma}{y} = \frac{M}{I}$$

and if σ_{max} is the stress in the furthermost fibre then

$$\frac{\sigma_{max}}{y_{max}} = \frac{M}{I}$$

$$\text{or} \quad \sigma_{max} = \frac{M}{I/y_{max}}$$

$$= \frac{M}{Z}$$

Which rearranges to give:
$$M = \sigma_{max} Z \qquad (5.7)$$

Where M = the moment of resistance of the section

σ_{max} = the maximum bending stress in the outer face of the section

Z = the elastic section modulus appropriate to the face being considered.

We can use this equation:

(i) to determine the moment of resistance of a beam, since:

the moment of resistance of a beam = maximum permissible bending stress $\times$ Z or (ii) to determine the maximum bending stress induced in a beam by an externally applied bending moment, since:

$$\text{maximum bending stress} = \text{bending moment}/Z$$

'Universal' steel beams of I-shaped cross-section are widely used as structural components. They are usually specified by quoting their depth, breadth and mass per metre length. Their geometric properties can be obtained from standard steel tables.

Given two universal beams (A and B), with properties as follows, which would resist the greatest bending moment? (Note: the first two numbers are overall depth and breadth in mm; the third number is the mass per metre length in kg.)
$A\ 178 \times 102 \times 21.5,\ Z = 170.9 \times 10^{-6}\ m^3$: $B\ 127 \times 76 \times 13.4,\ Z = 74.9 \times 10^{-6}\ m^3$

19

Beam A

You should have chosen A because its Z value is the greater. This is correct provided that the maximum value of bending stress is the criterion for design. Later in your studies you will discover, however, that other criteria such as deflection or shearing stress may dictate the maximum safe load that a beam can carry.

When analysing a beam, it is important to distinguish between the terms *plane of bending* and *axis of bending*. Consider the beam shown below:

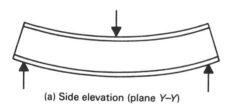

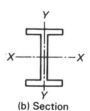

(a) Side elevation (plane *Y–Y*)   (b) Section

The beam is bending in the $Y–Y$ plane as evidenced by the fact that we see the shape of the deflected beam in the side elevation which is in the $Y–Y$ plane. The beam is bending about the $X–X$ axis passing through the centroid of the section and I_{XX} would be needed for calculations of strength and, as you will see in a later programme, deflections. In this case we are using the symbol I_{XX} to denote the second moment of area. The subscript $X–X$ indicates that bending is taking place about the $X–X$ axis. Similarly, if bending was taking place about the $Y–Y$ axis, we would use I_{YY}.

So far we have considered horizontal beams subject to vertical loading. Many structural members other than horizontal beams may however be subject to bending moments. Similarly, beams may be subject to loads in a direction other than vertical.

If the beam above was not loaded as shown, but was subject instead to a horizontal load (acting on the side face of the beam at right angles to plane Y–Y): (i) which is the plane of bending? and (ii) which is the axis of bending?

20

> (i) Bending is in the horizontal X–X plane
> (ii) Bending is about the Y–Y axis

We see this by looking at the beam in plan:

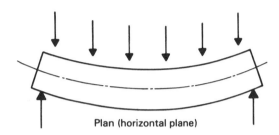

Plan (horizontal plane)

You will remember from Programme 3 that the value of bending moment will usually vary along the length of the beam. Consequently, since $M = \sigma \times Z$ (or $\sigma = M/Z$) the value of stress (and strain) in the fibres at any level will also usually vary with changing moment along the length of the beam. You will discover later in this programme that the radius of curvature of the deflected beam also usually varies along the length of the beam.

Now try some problems.

21

PROBLEMS

1. A beam has a solid rectangular cross-section 50 mm wide and 150 mm deep. Calculate I_{XX} and Z_{XX}.

 Ans. 14.06×10^{-6} m^4, 187.50×10^{-6} m^3.

2. If the maximum permissible bending stress is 10.5 MN/m^2, calculate the moment of resistance of the beam in Q1.

 Ans. 1.97 kN m.

3. If a beam 50 mm wide and 150 mm deep is used as a cantilever 0.75 m long, and if the maximum permissible bending stress is 12 MN/m^2, calculate the maximum single concentrated vertical load that can be supported at the end of the cantilever. (*Hint*: where does the maximum bending moment in a cantilevered beam occur?)

 Ans. 3.0 kN.

PARALLEL AXIS THEOREM

In the previous frame you carried out calculations for beams of solid rectangular section. Many beams, however, are not rectangular in section. We may obtain values of I and Z for such beams from standard tables used in design offices, or we may calculate them from first principles.

For sections consisting of rectangular components, we can often speed the process of calculation by dividing an area into individual rectangular parts (for which we know $I = bd^3/12$) and then translating the value of I for each part to an I value about the axis of bending of the whole section using the theorem of parallel axes. You may have developed the theorem of parallel axes in your study of mathematics but, using the case of a rectangular section as an example, we include it here for completeness.

Consider the rectangular area shown. Let I_{CC} be the second moment of area of the section about an axis through its centroid and let I_{XX} be the second moment of area about a parallel axis at a distance h from the centroidal axis. In subsequent frames this axis $(X–X)$ will be the neutral axis of the composite section of which this rectangle is part.

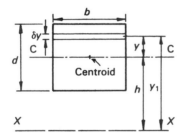

The second moment of area of the elemental strip about the $X–X$ axis $= b\delta y y_1^2$

Hence the second moment of area of the whole section about the $X–X$ axis

$$I_{XX} = \int by_1^2 \, dy$$

But: $y_1 = y + h$ $\quad \therefore \quad I_{XX} = \int b(y+h)^2 \, dy = \int b(y^2 + 2yh + h^2) \, dy$

$$= \int by^2 \, dy + \int b2yh \, dy + \int bh^2 \, dy$$

$$= \int by^2 \, dy + 2h\int by \, dy + h^2 \int b \, dy$$

But: $\int by^2 \, dy =$ the second moment of area (I_{CC}) about the centroidal axis

$\quad \int by \, dy =$ the first moment of area about an axis through the centroid

$\quad\quad = 0$ (by definition of centroid)

and $\quad \int b \, dy =$ the area of the rectangle ($A = b \times d$)

Thus: generally $I_{XX} = I_{CC} + Ah^2$, or for a solid rectangle: $I_{XX} = bd^3/12 + bdh^2$.
Now go on to the next frame.

23

We shall now use the theorem of parallel axes to help us calculate the second moment of area of a beam with an I-shaped cross-section. The second moment of area is calculated about the neutral axis which, as we have shown, passes through the centroid of the section. Many I-beams are symmetrical. In this example, however, we have selected an asymmetrical beam to emphasise that the first step is to determine the position of the centroid. In a symmetrical section, of course, the centroid is located by inspection.

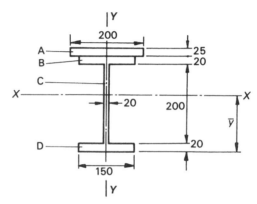

The section shown above is treated as if made of four rectangular parts A, B, C, D. First we determine the position of the centroid by taking the sum of the first moments of area of each part about a convenient axis (we take the bottom face of the beam) and equating to the total area times $\bar{y}$, where $\bar{y}$ is the height of the centroid above the bottom face.

Thus $\qquad A \times \bar{y} = \Sigma \left(A_{\text{part}} \times y_{\text{part}} \right)$ and working in mm

$$\{(200 \times 25) + (150 \times 20) + (20 \times 200) + (150 \times 20)\}\bar{y}$$
$$= (200 \times 25 \times 252.5) + (150 \times 20 \times 230) + (20 \times 200 \times 120) + (150 \times 20 \times 10)$$

Thus $\qquad\qquad\qquad\qquad \bar{y} = 164.2 \text{ mm}$

Now $\qquad\qquad\qquad\qquad I_{XX} = I_{CC} + Ah^2$
$$= bd^3/12 + bdh^2$$

Thus for part A: $\qquad I_{XX} = (200 \times 25^3)/12 + (200 \times 25)(252.5 - 164.2)^2$
$$= 39.24 \times 10^6 \text{ mm}^4$$

for part B: $\qquad\qquad I_{XX} = (150 \times 20^2)/12 + (150 \times 20)(230.0 - 164.2)^2$
$$= 13.09 \times 10^6 \text{ mm}^4$$

for part C: $\qquad\qquad I_{XX} = (20 \times 200^3)/12 + (20 \times 200)(120.0 - 164.2)^2$
$$= 21.15 \times 10^6 \text{ mm}^4$$

and part D:
$$I_{XX} = (150 \times 20^3)/12 + (150 \times 20)(10 - 164.2)^2$$
$$= 71.43 \times 10^6 \text{ mm}^4$$

For the complete section
$$I_{XX} = (39.24 + 13.09 + 21.15 + 71.43) \times 10^6$$
$$= 144.91 \times 10^6 \text{ mm}^4 = 144.91 \times 10^{-6} \text{ m}^4$$

This is an unwieldy calculation and is best done in tabular form. We shall do this in the next frame.

Now, if the beam above is to bend about the Y–Y axis (at right angles to X–X), calculate the value of I_{YY}.

24

$$\boxed{28.05 \times 10^{-6} \text{ m}^4}$$

In the figure in Frame 23, axis Y–Y passes through the centroids of each part (A, B, C and D), therefore the theorem of parallel axes is not needed in this instance, ($h = 0$ for each part).

$$\overset{\text{A}}{} \qquad \overset{\text{B}+\text{D}}{} \qquad \overset{\text{C}}{}$$
Thus $I_{YY} = (25 \times 200^3)/12 + 2(20 \times 150^3)/12 + (200 \times 20^3)/12 = 28.05 \times 10^6 \text{ mm}^4$
$$= 28.05 \times 10^{-6} \text{ m}^4$$

We will now set out the previous calculation for I_{XX} in tabular form. This shows a systematic and better way of presenting this type of calculation.

Part	Area (A) (mm^2)	y (mm)	Ay	$I_{CC}(bd^3/12)$ (mm^4)	$h = (y - \bar{y})$ (mm)	Ah^2 (mm^4)
A	200×25		$(\times 10^3)$	$(\times 10^6)$	$252.5 - 164.2$	$(\times 10^6)$
	$= 5000$	252.5	1262.5	0.26	$= 88.3$	38.98
B	3000	230.0	690.0	0.10	65.8	12.99
C	4000	120.0	480.0	13.33	44.2	7.81
D	3000	10.0	30.0	0.10	154.2	71.33
Total	15000		2462.5	13.79		131.11

Thus, $\bar{y} = \dfrac{2462.5 \times 10^3}{15000}$
$$= 164.17 \text{ mm}$$

and $I_{XX} = \begin{array}{r} 13.79 \times 10^6 \\ +131.11 \times 10^6 \\ \hline 144.90 \times 10^6 \text{ mm}^4 \\ 144.90 \times 10^{-6} \text{ m}^4 \end{array}$

Now go to the next frame.

25

COMPLETION OF THE BASIC THEORY OF BENDING

We have already seen in Frame 6 that a short layer (ST) of fibres at a distance y from the neutral layer and having a length $(R + y)\theta$ in the loaded beam has a length $R\theta$ in the unloaded beam, the change in length caused by bending being:

$$(R + y)\theta - R\theta = y\theta$$

If you have difficulty following this statement, refer back to Frames 5 and 6. For clarity, figure (c) of Frame 5, which shows the deformed element, is reproduced below:

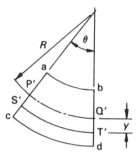

Since the change in length of $ST = y \times \theta$

then the strain in the fibre $= \dfrac{\text{change in length}}{\text{original length}}$

$$= y\theta / R\theta$$

that is:
$$\varepsilon = y/R$$

Now the Modulus of Elasticity $E = \dfrac{\text{stress}}{\text{strain}} = \dfrac{\sigma}{\varepsilon} = \dfrac{\sigma}{y/R}$

Hence: $\dfrac{E}{R} = \dfrac{\sigma}{y}$

We can combine this with the relationship of Equation (5.5) ($\sigma/y = M/I$) to give:

$$\frac{\sigma}{y} = \frac{M}{I} = \frac{E}{R} \tag{5.8}$$

These equalities summarise the basic theory of bending and should be remembered because they are used in a wide variety of analysis and design problems.

What do these equations suggest to you about the radius of curvature of a loaded beam?

26

> Since the value of bending moment will normally vary along the length of a beam, then the radius of curvature will also normally vary along the length of that beam.

Now can you remember the assumptions we made in developing the basic theory of bending?

27

> 1. The material is linearly elastic
> 2. E is the same in tension and compression.
> 3. The material is homogeneous (same physical properties throughout).
> 4. Plane sections at right angles to the longitudinal axis remain plane after bending.

These assumptions are unlikely to be fully satisfied by any engineering material. The theory does nevertheless provide a valuable tool that is widely used in analysis and in design.

Now see of you can complete the relationship: $\dfrac{?}{?} = \dfrac{M}{I} = \dfrac{?}{?}$

28

$$\frac{\sigma}{y} = \frac{M}{I} = \frac{E}{R}$$

A steel beam with an I-shaped cross-section as shown carries a single concentrated load of 30 kN at the mid-point of a simply supported span of 3 m. We wish to determine the maximum bending stress and the curvature of the beam at the point of maximum bending moment. First we must calculate the maximum bending moment.

(i) Where will the bending moment be greatest?

(ii) What is the value of the maximum bending moment (ignoring the self-weight of the beam)?

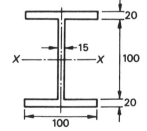

29

> At mid span
> $M = WL/4 = (30 \times 3)/4 = 22.5 \text{ kN m}$

We must now locate the neutral axis and calculate the value of I_{XX}. Since the section is symmetrical, we know that the centroid is at mid-depth, at 70 mm from the top and the bottom faces. We then calculate I_{XX} using the expression $bd^3/12$ and the parallel axes theorem.

Part	$I_{CC} = bd^3/12$ $(\times 10^6)$	Area (A)	h	Ah^2 $(\times 10^6)$
Top flange	0.07	$100 \times 20 = 2000$	60	7.2
Bottom flange	0.07	$100 \times 20 = 2000$	60	7.2
Web	1.25		0	0.0
Totals	1.39			14.4

Thus, for the complete section, $I_{XX} = (1.39 + 14.4) \times 10^6 \text{ mm}^4 = 15.79 \times 10^{-6} \text{ m}^4$.

We now use the equality $\sigma/y = M/I$ to find the maximum stress. Since the cross-section is symmetrical about the X–X axis, the maximum tensile and compressive stresses will be the same.

The maximum value of y is $140/2 = 70$ mm (distance from neutral axis to furthermost fibre), thus the maximum bending stress is

$$\sigma_{\max} = \frac{My_{\max}}{I} = \frac{\left(22.5 \times 10^3\right) \times \left(70 \times 10^{-3}\right)}{\left(15.79 \times 10^{-6}\right)}$$
$$= 99.75 \text{ MN/m}^2$$

Calculate the maximum bending stress in the web.

30

> 71.25 MN/m^2

We obtain this answer by putting $y = 50$ mm in the above expression. Why? Because the outer layer of the web is 50 mm from the neutral axis.

Now calculate the radius of curvature of the loaded beam at mid span if the elastic modulus for steel is 200 GN/m^2.

31

$$\boxed{140.36 \text{ m}}$$

If you did not get this answer, check your working:

$$\frac{M}{I} = \frac{E}{R}$$

thus

$$R = (E \times I)/M = \frac{(200 \times 10^9) \times (15.79 \times 10^{-6})}{22.5 \times 10^3} = 140.36 \text{ m}$$

Remember that this is the radius at the mid-span of the beam only, because with this loading the value of bending moment varies at all other points along the beam. The radius will therefore vary along the length of the beam.

In Frame 29 we used the parallel axis theorem to calculate the second moment of area of the I-shaped section that we used in this problem. To do this we split the section into three rectangular parts consisting of the top and bottom flange and the web.

Can you think of a simpler way of calculating the second moment of area?

32

$$\boxed{\text{By making use of the symmetry of the section.}}$$

The section in figure (a) can be considered to be equivalent to the section in figure (b) where the *I* value of the section can be calculated by subtracting the *I* value of the two shaded rectangular areas from that of the whole rectangle. This is possible because all the rectangular parts of the problem share the same centroidal axis.

Hence

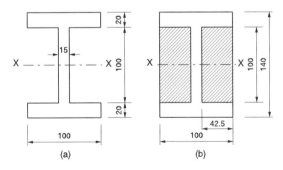

(a)   (b)

$$I_{XX} = \frac{(b \times d^3)_{\text{whole}}}{12} - \frac{(b \times d^3)_{\text{shaded}}}{12} = \left[\frac{(100 \times 140^3)}{12} - 2\frac{(42.5 \times 100^3)}{12} \right] \times 10^{-12}$$

$$= 15.79 \times 10^{-6} \text{ m}^4$$

This technique can be applied to similar shapes such as hollow rectangular box sections where there is symmetry about the axis of bending.

Now attempt the following problems.

33

| PROBLEMS |

1. A rectangular beam 50 mm wide and 150 mm deep carries a bending moment of 1.12 kNm. Determine the maximum bending stress

Ans. ± 5.97 MN/m^2

2. A beam with a symmetrical cross-section, an I_{XX} value of 25×10^{-6} m^4 and of depth 150 mm is simply supported over a span of 5 m. The beam supports a single concentrated load of 40 kN at mid-span. Determine the maximum bending stress at mid-span and at a point 1 m from one end of the beam. Ignore the self weight of the beam.

Ans. ± 150 MN/m^2, ± 60 MN/m^2.

3. A hollow box section as shown carries a bending moment of 10.0 kN m. Determine the maximum bending stress at (i) the top of the flange at A and (ii) the inside of the flange at B.

Ans. 33.70 MN/m^2; 24.07 MN/m^2.

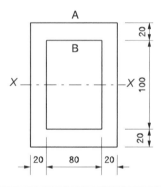

34

T SHAPED SECTIONS

Structural shapes in the form of T-sections are used widely as mechanical components. The design and analysis of such shapes, when used as beams, follows exactly the same methods as those used for the I-shaped beams we considered previously. The section properties of standard T-shapes are available from standard design tables or can be calculated using the parallel axis theorem we used in previous problems.

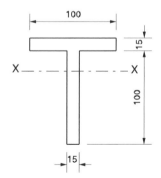

The beam shown above is simply supported and carries a bending moment of 7.0 kN m. Determine the maximum tensile and the maximum compressive bending stress. (Hint: the value of y for maximum tensile stress is not the same as that for the maximum compressive stress.)

$$\boxed{146.61 \text{ MN/m}^2 \text{ , } 67.48 \text{ MN/m}^2}$$

Check your calculations:

Part	Area (A) (mm²)	y (mm)	Ay	$I_{CC}(bd^3)/12$ (mm⁴)	$h = (y - \bar{y})$	Ah^2 (mm⁴)
			$(\times 10^3)$	$(\times 10^6)$		$(\times 10^6)$
Top flange	1500	107.5	161.25	0.03	28.75	1.24
Web	1500	50.0	75.00	1.25	28.75	1.24
Total	3000			1.28		2.48

Thus $\bar{y} = \dfrac{236.25 \times 10^3}{3000} = 78.75$ mm and $I_{XX} = (1.28 + 2.48) \times 10^6 = 3.76 \times 10^6$ mm⁴
$$= 3.76 \times 10^{-6} \text{ m}^4$$

Hence the maximum tensile stress at the bottom of the section:

$$\sigma_{\text{tension}} = \frac{My_{\text{bottom}}}{I_{XX}} = \frac{(7.0 \times 10^3) \times 78.75 \times 10^{-3}}{3.76 \times 10^{-6}} = 146.61 \text{ MN/m}^2$$

and the maximum compressive stress at the top of the section:

$$\sigma_{\text{compression}} = \frac{My_{\text{top}}}{I_{XX}} = \frac{(7.0 \times 10^3) \times (115 - 78.75) \times 10^{-3}}{3.76 \times 10^{-6}} = 67.48 \text{ MN/m}^2$$

If the maximum permitted stress in the T-beam is 175 MN/m² and it is to carry a uniformly distributed load of w kN/metre over a 3 m simply-supported span, calculate the maximum value of w.

$$\boxed{7.43 \text{ kN}}$$

From the previous calculations, the tensile stress at the bottom of the beam is greater than the compressive stress at the top and is therefore critical. Hence, by simple proportions, the maximum moment for a permissible stress of 175 MN/m² is given by:

$$M_{\text{max}} = 7.0 \times \frac{175}{146.61} = 8.36 \text{ kN m}$$

and if the beam is supporting a uniformly distributed load then:

$$\frac{wL^2}{8} = \frac{w \times 3^2}{8} = 8.36 \text{ kN m}$$
$$\therefore \quad 8.36 \times 8/3^2 = 7.43 \text{ kN/m}$$

Note that this load includes the beam's self weight which must be deducted from this figure to give the permissible load the beam can carry. Now go on to the next frame.

37

CIRCULAR SECTIONS

Solid and hollow circular sections, extruded or fabricated from a wide range of materials, are widely used as flexural members. The bending theory we have developed so far can be applied readily to such sections provided that the second moment of area about the axis of bending can be determined and used in the bending formula.

Consider the solid circular section shown in figure (a). The section is considered to be bent about the horizontal X–X axis. A small elemental area δA is located at distance x from the y-axis, a distance y from the x-axis and a radial distance r from the origin which passes through the centroid.

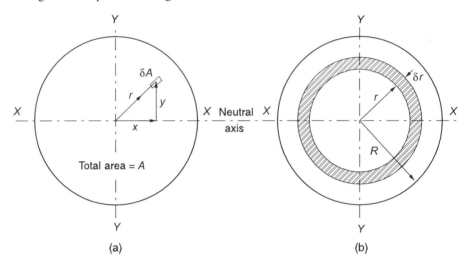

(a)   (b)

It can be seen from the diagram that:

$$r^2 = x^2 + y^2$$

Hence multiplying throughout by δA: $r^2 \delta A = x^2 \delta A + y^2 \delta A$

or, when the expression is summated over the whole area of the circular shape:

$$\int_A r^2 \, dA = \int_A x^2 \, dA + \int_A y^2 \, dA \tag{5.9}$$

the terms on the right-hand side of the equation represent the second moments of area, I_{YY} and I_{XX}, respectively. But as we are dealing with a symmetrical circular section it follows that the second moment of area of the section about any diameter of the circle must be the same, i.e. $I_{YY} = I_{XX}$. Hence, we can express Equation (5.9) as:

$$\int_A r^2 \, dA = \int_A x^2 \, dA + \int_A y^2 \, dA = 2 \int_A y^2 \, dA = 2I_{XX}$$

or

$$I_{XX} = \int_A y^2 \, dA = \frac{1}{2} \int_A r^2 \, dA$$

This expression gives us a convenient way of evaluating I_{XX} as follows. If the small elemental area is now considered to be the shaded ring of width δr (figure (b)) the area of this ring is given by $\delta A = 2\pi r \delta r$ (circumference × thickness). Hence I_{XX} can be expressed as:

$$I_{XX} = \frac{1}{2} \int_A r^2 \, dA = \frac{1}{2} \int_0^R r^2 (2\pi r dr) = \frac{1}{2} \int_0^R 2\pi r^3 \, dr$$

Can you now integrate this expression to give the second moment of area of a solid circular section about its diameter?

38

$$\boxed{\frac{\pi R^4}{4}}$$

How would this formula be expressed in terms of the diameter 'D' of the circle?

39

$$\boxed{\frac{\pi D^4}{64}}$$

This is obtained by simply replacing the radius R by $D/2$ in the formula we derived in Frame 37. You should remember this formula – you will use it in the equations of bending when analysing or designing solid circular shaped sections used as flexural members.

What is the formula for the Elastic Section Modulus (Z) of a solid circular shape?

40

$$\boxed{\frac{\pi D^3}{32}}$$

This should have been quite straightforward if you remembered that the Elastic Section Modulus (Z) is the second moment of area divided by the distance from the neutral axis to the outer fibres (top or bottom) of the section – which in this case is equal to the radius (R) or half the diameter (D).

What is the formula for the second moment of area of a hollow circular tube of outside diameter D_{out} and inside diameter D_{ins}?

41

$$\boxed{\frac{\pi\left(D_{\text{out}}^4 - D_{\text{in}}^4\right)}{64}}$$

The formula for the second moment of area of a hollow circular tube can be calculated by simply subtracting the I value of the inner circle from that of the outer circle using the formula in Frame 39 in each case.

A beam is fabricated by joining together two hollow circular tubular sections as shown in the figure. Each tube has an outer and inner diameter of 100 mm and 90 mm respectively. The beam is to be designed to carry a bending moment of 20.0 kNm and the maximum bending stress in each tube must not exceed 100 MN/m². Determine the minimum separation 'd' of the tubes if the contribution of the joining web piece to the I-value of the section is ignored. (Hint: you will have to make use of the parallel axis theorem.)

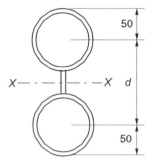

42

$$\boxed{183 \text{ mm}}$$

Check your working. This is a design question with a rather tricky solution, although the principles are straight-forward:

Cross-sectional area (A) of one tube $= \dfrac{\pi\left(D_{\text{out}}^2 - D_{\text{in}}^2\right)}{4} = \dfrac{\pi\left(100^2 - 90^2\right)}{4}$

$$= 1.49 \times 10^3 \text{ mm}^2 = 1.49 \times 10^{-3} \text{ m}^2$$

The second moment of area of one tube about its own axis (I_{CC})

$$= \frac{\pi\left(D_{\text{out}}^4 - D_{\text{in}}^4\right)}{64} = \frac{\pi\left(100^4 - 90^4\right)}{64} = 1.69 \times 10^6 \text{ mm}^4 = 1.69 \times 10^{-6} \text{ m}^4$$

The second moment of area of one tube about the centroidal axis (I_{XX}) using the parallel axis theorem

$$= I_{CC} + Ah^2 = \left[1.69 \times 10^{-6} + \left\{1.49 \times 10^{-3} \times (0.5d)^2\right\}\right] \text{ m}^4$$

Hence the second moment of area of the two tubes

$$= 2\left[1.69 \times 10^{-6} + \left\{1.49 \times 10^{-3} \times (0.5d)^2\right\}\right] \text{ m}^4$$

The maximum stress occurs at the very top and bottom of the section. Therefore, from the equation of bending:

$$\frac{\sigma}{y} = \frac{M}{I} \text{ gives } \frac{100 \times 10^6}{(0.5d + 0.05)} = \frac{20.0 \times 10^3}{2\left[1.69 \times 10^{-6} + \left\{1.49 \times 10^{-3} \times (0.5d)^2\right\}\right]}$$

This equation can be rearranged and solved as a quadratic equation to give

$$d = 0.183 \text{ m} = 183 \text{ mm}.$$

Now try some problems.

43

PROBLEMS

1. An unstayed mast for a sailing dinghy consists of a hollow circular section of outside diameter 80 mm and inside diameter 70 mm. The wind loading on the sail causes a bending moment at the base of the mast of 2.0 kN m. Calculate the maximum bending stress at the mast base.

Ans. 96.2 MN/m².

2. The tower of a wind turbine is constructed of a hollow circular section with an outside diameter of 2 m. The force of the wind on the turbine rotor causes a bending moment at the tower base of 7000 kN m. If the maximum permissible stress is 50 MN/m² calculate the minimum required wall thickness of the section.

Ans. 48 mm.

3. The extruded section shown in the figure is used as a cantilever beam and is subject to a hogging bending moment of 25kNm. Calculate the maximum bending stress developed in the section.

Ans. 80.30 MN/m².

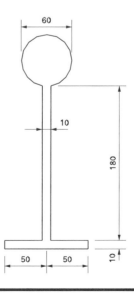

44

BENDING COMBINED WITH AXIAL LOAD

In Programme 4 we considered axial stress arising within mechanical components as a result of the application of axial loads. In this programme we have considered beam problems with bending stress resulting from the application of bending moments. There are a number of situations where both of these effects can occur together and the *combined* effect of both types of stress system must be considered. Move on to the next frame to see how to tackle such problems.

45

Consider, as an example, the cranked gear linkage of circular cross-section shown below. The tensile force F is transmitted along the length of the linkage and, at the cranked section, acts at an effective *eccentricity 'e' from the neutral axis of the cross-section at the section X–X.*

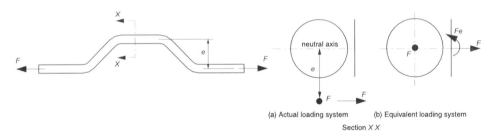

(a) Actual loading system   (b) Equivalent loading system

Section $X\,X$

Figure (a) shows the force in its actual location relative to the section X–X. This force exerts an effective tensile 'pull' on the section and, at the same time, exerts a moment $(F \times e)$ about the centroidal (or neutral) axis of the section. You should visualise that this moment effectively puts the bottom of the section into tension and the top of the section into compression because of the bending effect it induces in the section.

Figure (b) shows the *equivalent force system* where the actual force has been replaced by a force F through the centroid of the section together with a moment $F \times e$ about the axis of bending. This enables us to treat the stress system as the sum of two separate effects.

Referring to figure (b), can you write down the equation of (i) stress caused by the axial force effect; and (ii) maximum bending stress caused by the bending moment effect?

46

$$(i) \quad \sigma = \frac{F}{A}; \quad (ii) \quad \sigma = \pm\frac{M}{Z} = \pm\frac{F \times e}{Z}$$

These equations should be quite familiar to you. A is the cross-sectional area of the section and Z is its elastic section modulus. The axial stress will be uniform across the section, while the bending stress will vary from maximum tension at the bottom face of the section to maximum compression at the top face. Although we have considered a circular section, these equations are quite general and would apply to any shape of cross-section.

Although we have considered these two loading effects as being separate, they are in fact acting together. We can make use of the *Principle of Superposition* we came across earlier, and combine the effects algebraically to obtain the combined effect of both axial force and bending moment.

Hence, we can say that the stress at the bottom face of the section is given by the *addition* of the two tensile stress components. The stress at the top face is given by *subtracting* the compressive stress component caused by bending from the tensile stress component because of the axial load effect:

$$\sigma_{\text{bottom}} = \frac{F}{A} + \frac{M}{Z} = \frac{F}{A} + \frac{F \times e}{Z} \qquad \sigma_{\text{top}} = \frac{F}{A} - \frac{M}{Z} = \frac{F}{A} - \frac{F \times e}{Z}$$

The cranked linkage shown in Frame 45 is of circular section, 20 mm in diameter. The applied tensile force is 5 kN and acts at an eccentricity 'e' of 20 mm. Determine (i) the maximum tensile stress; and (ii) the minimum tensile stress in the cranked section.

47

$$\boxed{\text{(i) } 143.24 \quad \text{(ii) } -111.40 \text{ MN/m}^2}$$

The solution for maximum and minimum tensile stress is obtained by direct substitution of values into the above equations.

$$A = \pi \frac{D^2}{4} = \pi \times \frac{20^2}{4}$$

$$= 314.16 \text{ mm}^2 = 314.16 \times 10^{-6} \text{ m}^2$$

$$Z = \pi \frac{D^3}{32} = \pi \times \frac{20^3}{32}$$

$$= 785.40 \text{ mm}^3 = 785.40 \times 10^{-9} \text{ m}^3$$

$$\sigma = \frac{F}{Z} + \frac{M}{Z} = \frac{5 \times 10^3}{314.16 \times 10^{-6}} \pm \frac{5 \times 10^3 \times 20 \times 10^{-3}}{785.40 \times 10^{-9}}$$

$$= 15.92 \pm 127.32$$

$$= 143.24 \quad \text{and} \quad -111.40 \text{ MN/m}^2$$

The negative sign implies compressive stress in the top face.

What is the stress in the straight, un-cranked length of the linkage?

48

$$\boxed{15.92 \text{ MN/m}^2}$$

The stress in the straight uncranked section is simple to obtain by dividing the force by the cross-sectional area (F/A). The calculations show the very significant increase in stress by providing even a modest crank in a straight axially loaded bar.

49

PRINCIPAL AXIS

For any shape of cross-section a value for I can be calculated about any axis which passes through the centroid. The value of I will normally be different for different axes depending on the orientation of the axes, but for any section it can be shown that the maximum and minimum values of I occur about two axes at right angles to each other. These axes are the *principal axes* of the section. The maximum value of I occurs about the *major principal axis*, and the minimum value about the *minor principal axis.*

The principal axes of a section can usually be identified easily, because if the section has a geometrical axis of symmetry, then that axis is one of the principal axes and the other principal axis is at a right-angle to it. Both axes pass through the centroid of the section. In cases such as a solid rectangular beam section there will be two axes of symmetry passing through the centroid – and each will be a principal axis.

The simple theory of bending we have developed is strictly only applicable if bending takes place about either the major or minor principal axis. If this is not the case, then the calculations are more complex and beyond the scope of this book. For most cases, however, the bending of beams does take place about a principal axis and the theory we have investigated is valid. It is important for any beam, or any other component subject to bending, that it is positioned correctly to provide the greatest possible resistance to bending moments. This normally implies that the component should be positioned such that bending takes place about the major principal axis.

Identify the principal axis of the following sections:

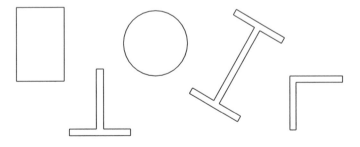

50

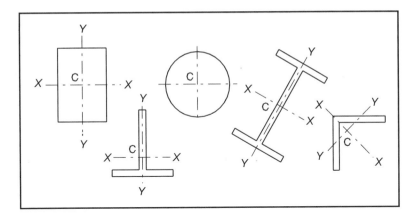

The principal axes are indicated on the above figures. X–X is the major principal axis in each case. For the circle, the I value will be the same for any axis through the centroid, all of which are axes of symmetry.

The values of I and Z about the principal axes of standard structural sections, both symmetrical and asymmetrical, and the position of these axes may be found from standard tables.

51

| TO REMEMBER |

$$\frac{\sigma}{y} = \frac{M}{I} = \frac{E}{R}$$

Maximum bending stress: $\sigma_{max} = M/Z$

Moment of resistance: $M = \sigma_{max} \times Z$

For a solid rectangular section: $I = bd^3/12$ (units $= m^4$);

$Z = bd^2/6$ (units $= m^3$)

For a solid circular section: $I = \pi D^4/64$ (units $= m^4$);

$Z = \pi D^3/32$ (units $= m^3$)

Generally: $Z = I/y_{max}$

Parallel axis theorem: $I_{XX} = I_{CC} + Ah^2$

52

FURTHER PROBLEMS

1. A beam of rectangular cross-section 75 mm wide and 225 mm deep carries a uniformly distributed load (including the self-weight of the beam) of 1.4 kN/m over a simply supported span of 4 m. Determine the maximum bending stress in the beam.

Ans. 4.42 MN/m².

2. A steel I-section joist has an I_{XX} value of 22.94×10^{-6} m⁴ and a depth of 203.2 mm. If the maximum permissible bending stress is not to exceed 165 MN/m², determine the moment of resistance of the section.

Ans. 37.25 kN m.

3. If the beam of question 2 has a self-weight of 248 N per metre length, determine the maximum uniformly distributed load which could be safely applied to the entire simply supported span of 4 m.

(*Hint*: the beam has to resist the bending moment produced both by its own weight and by the external load.)

Ans. 18.37 kN/m.

4. If the beam of question 3 is required to carry a single concentrated load at mid-span instead of the uniformly distributed load, determine the maximum value of that concentrated load.

Ans. 36.75 kN.

5. A beam is fabricated by bending and welding a 6 mm thick plate to form a hollow rectangular box section 100 mm overall width and 160 mm overall depth. If the safe permissible bending stress is 165 MN/m², calculate the moment of resistance of the section.

(*Hint*: to calculate the *I* of the section, calculate the *I* for a solid beam of the same overall dimensions and deduct the *I* of the material removed to give the hollow section.)

Ans. 21.36 kN m.

6. A hollow tube of 50 mm external diameter and 44 mm internal diameter is subjected to a bending moment of 0.75 kN m. Determine the maximum bending stress.

Ans. 152.67 MN/m².

7. If the material of the beam in question 6 can be stressed to 165 MN/m², determine the value to which the external bending moment may be safely increased.

Ans. 0.81 kN m.

8. A beam forming the main supporting girder of the chassis of a lorry has a cross-section as shown in figure Q8.

(i) Identify the principal axes and calculate I_{XX} and I_{YY}.

(ii) If the beam is positioned to bend about the $X–X$ axis and if the maximum permissible stress in tension or compression is 165 MN/m², calculate the moment of resistance of the section.

(*Hint*: the maximum tensile stress is not the same as the maximum compressive stress. The moment of resistance corresponds to that moment that would produce the maximum permissible bending stress in either the tensile or compressive zones. Neither stress may exceed 165 MN/m² but one may be less).

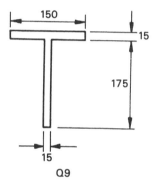

Q8

Ans. $I_{XX} = 110.80 \times 10^{-6}$ m⁴, $I_{YY} = 7.64 \times 10^{-6}$ m⁴, (ii) 132.30 kN m.

9. A horizontal cantilever beam 2 m long has a T-shaped cross-section as in figure Q9 and carries a uniformly distributed load of 11 kN/m along the entire length. Calculate the greatest tensile and compressive bending stresses. Ignore the self-weight of the beam.

Ans. Maximum tensile stress = 73.00 MN/m², compressive stress = 163.48 MN/m².

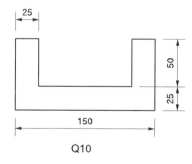

Q9

10. The steel channel section shown in figure Q10 spans 2.5 m between simple supports. It carries a single wheel of an overhead crane which traverses the span from left to right. If the maximum stress in the steel is limited to 150 MN/m² and the wheel load, W, is considered to be a concentrated point load, what is the maximum allowable value of W?

Ans. 14.28kN.

Q10

11. Figure Q11 shows the cross-section of a mechanical component which acts as a cantilevered beam. Calculate the moment of resistance of the section if the maximum permissible tensile stress is 125 MN/m^2 and the maximum permissible compressive stress is 85 MN/m^2

Ans. 35.61 kN m.

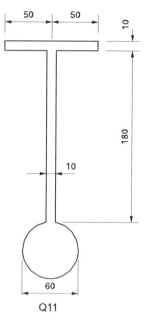

Q11

12. A bracket is formed from two steel sections welded together and supported as shown in figure Q12. If the bracket carries a load of 10 kN what are the maximum and minimum stresses in the section marked *X–X*?

Ans. 45.46, -66.06 MN/m^2.

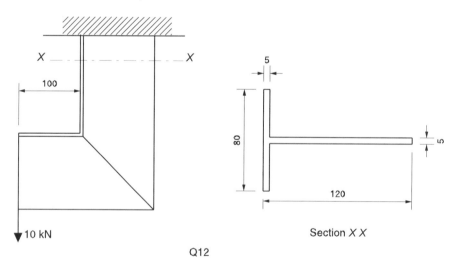

Q12

Section *X X*

Programme 6

SHEAR STRESS

On completion of this programme you will be able to:

- Define 'average shear stress'
- Calculate the average shear stress in bolts with simple bolted connections
- Design simple bolted connections with given limiting stress conditions
- Recognise the existence of and define 'complementary stress'
- Define 'shear strain'
- State the relationship between shear stress and shear strain
- Sketch the distribution of shear stress across a regular beam section
- State the relationship between average and maximum shear stress in a rectangular beam section
- State the formula for shear stress in beam sections
- Calculate the distribution of shear stress in rectangular and non-rectangular beam sections

1

So far we have shown how to calculate direct stresses arising from direct axial loading acting on mechanical components, and bending stresses within beams which are subjected to bending moments.

However, there are other stresses that can arise within a component, and in this programme we are going to examine a further type of stress. To be precise, we shall study the development of *shear stress*, and see how shear stresses can arise and how to calculate the magnitude and distribution of such stresses for a range of common problems. The development of shear stress is related to the existence of *shearing forces* and the magnitude of such stress depends on the magnitude and distribution of the shearing forces. Hence it is important that, in the case of a beam, you can sketch the shape of the shearing force diagram. If you are not confident about this, revise Programme 3 before proceeding.

Now let's see how and where shear stresses can arise.

2

As an example, consider a simple cantilevered beam of rectangular cross-section which supports a load W:

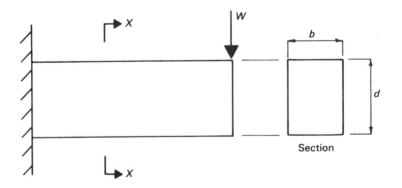

What is the magnitude of the shearing force at the section marked X–X?

3

$$\boxed{\text{Shearing force at } X\text{–}X = W}$$

If you didn't get this answer straight away, you must revise Programme 3 before going any further. In particular, remind yourself of the definition of a shearing force.

Now let's define the *average* shear stress as:

$$\textit{average shear stress} = \frac{\text{force}}{\text{area over which force acts}}$$

The reason why we have used the word *average* to define the shear stress will become more apparent later in this programme. However, let's further consider the beam in Frame 2.

If the beam has a breadth b and depth d, write down the expression for the average shear stress at section X–X.

4

$$\boxed{\text{Average shear stress} = \frac{W}{bd}}$$

You should have reasoned that the shearing force is vertical and acts on the vertical cross-section of the beam whose area is given by $b \times d$. Hence the expression given for the average shear stress. You should appreciate, however, that the nature of this stress is different from those you have studied in previous programmes as, in this case, the force acts in the same plane as the beam's cross-section. The forces that cause axial and bending stress are normal to the sections on which they act.

Now let's try a problem.

A beam is simply supported at both ends over a span of 4 metres. It carries a uniformly distributed load (inclusive of self-weight) of total magnitude 50 kN and has a breadth of 100 mm and a depth of 200 mm. Where does the largest shearing force occur, what is its magnitude and what is the average shear stress resulting from this force at the critical section?

The answer and the worked solution are given in the next frame.

5

$$\boxed{\begin{array}{c} \text{25 kN at either support} \\ \text{1.25 MN/m}^2 \end{array}}$$

If you didn't get the correct answer, check your working.

For a simply supported beam supporting a uniformly distributed load, the maximum shearing force occurs at either end. (If you didn't realise this is the case, draw the shearing force diagram. Revise Programme 3, if in doubt.)

The magnitude of the shearing force either end $= \frac{1}{2}$ the total load

$$= \frac{1}{2} \times 50$$

$$= 25 \text{ kN}$$

$$\text{The average shear stress} = \frac{W}{bd} = \frac{25 \times 10^3}{(100 \times 10^{-3}) \times (200 \times 10^{-3})}$$

$$= 1.25 \times 10^6 \text{ N/m}^2$$

$$= 1.25 \text{ MN/m}^2$$

6

Shear stresses can arise in components other than beams. For example, consider two steel plates fastened together with a single bolt and subject to two equal and opposite tensile forces F. If the equilibrium of the upper plate and the upper half of the bolt is considered, it is apparent that there must be a shearing force acting across the cross-section of the bolt at the interface of the two plates to maintain equilibrium. This shearing force must be equal in magnitude to the applied force F.

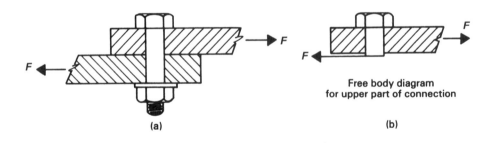

(a)

Free body diagram
for upper part of connection

(b)

If the bolt is circular in section with a diameter D, write down an expression for the average shear stress within the bolt.

7

$$\boxed{\text{Average shear stress} = \frac{F}{\pi \frac{1}{4} D^2}}$$

The expression follows directly from the definition of average shear stress given in Frame 3 and can be used to design the bolts in simple connections. Try the following example.

Calculate the strength of a single 20 mm diameter steel bolt based on an allowable average shear stress of 80 MN/m².

8

$$\boxed{25.13 \text{ kN}}$$

You should have obtained the answer as follows:

Allowable average shear stress $= \dfrac{F}{\pi \frac{1}{4} D^2} = \dfrac{F}{\pi \frac{1}{4} (20 \times 10^{-3})^2}$

$$= 80 \times 10^6 \text{ N/m}^2$$

Hence

$$F = 80 \times 10^6 \times \pi \times \tfrac{1}{4} \times \left(20 \times 10^{-3}\right)^2$$

$$= 25133 \text{ N}$$

$$= 25.13 \text{ kN}$$

The strength of a connection fabricated using a single bolt in this way depends on a number of factors other than just the bolt shear strength. The design of connections is outside the scope of this text, but the example given illustrates one of the calculations associated with such a design.

Later in this programme we shall see that the concept of an average shear stress is a simplification of what actually happens in many real components that are subjected to the action of shearing forces. We have in fact assumed that the shear stress is uniform over the shear surface which, as we will show later, is often not the case. However, in the practical design of mechanical components, *average* shear stresses are usually calculated for comparison with allowable values as this provides a simple, convenient and generally acceptably accurate method of calculation.

9

Before we move on to some problems, let's consider one further illustration of the development of shear stress. Let's look again at the connection shown in Frame 6 (figure (b)). The figure below shows the same connection, but this time is also viewed in plan.

If the force F is large enough, it is possible for the joint to 'fail' by shearing of the surfaces marked aa, resulting in the shaded area of the upper plate to the left of the bolt being 'pushed out'.

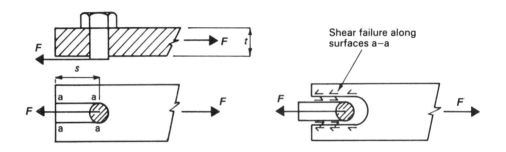

If the plate is of thickness t and the bolt is located at a distance s from the end of the plate, write down an expression for the average shear stress developed along the vertical faces of the shaded area to the left of the bolt.

10

$$\text{Average shear stress} = \frac{F}{2st}$$

Again, the expression follows from the definition of average shear stress. In this case there are two shear surfaces resisting the force F and by considering the equilibrium of the shaded area you should have written down:

$$F = \text{average shear stress} \times \text{area on which shear stress acts}$$

$$\therefore \quad F = \text{average shear stress} \times 2(s \times t)$$

Hence

$$\text{Average shear stress} = \frac{F}{2st}$$

Let's look at an example.

A 20 mm diameter bolt connects two steel plates that are both 12 mm thick and which carry a tensile load of 40 kN. Calculate the shear stresses in both the bolt and the steel plates if the bolt is positioned with its centre 15 mm from the edge of each plate.

$$\text{Average shear stress in the bolt} = \frac{F}{\pi \frac{1}{4} D^2} = \frac{40 \times 10^3}{\pi \frac{1}{4} (20 \times 10^{-3})^2} = 127.32 \text{ MN/m}^2$$

$$\text{Average shear stress in plate} = \frac{F}{2st} = \frac{40 \times 10^3}{2 \times (15 \times 10^{-3}) \times (12 \times 10^{-3})}$$

$$= 111.11 \text{ MN/m}^2$$

As the shear stress in the bolt is higher than that in the plate, it follows that, if the load was increased and both bolt and plate had the same limiting failure stress, then the bolt would fail in shear before the plate.

Now try some problems.

11

PROBLEMS

1. A beam, 300 mm × 600 mm, is simply supported over a span of 5 metres and carries a point load of 100 kN at a distance of 1.5 metres from one support. If the unit weight of the material of which the beam is made is 24 kN/m³, determine the largest shearing force in the beam and the average shear stress resulting from this force.

Ans. 80.80 kN, 0.45 MN/m².

2. Solid circular discs are punched out of 3 mm thick steel plates using a 50 mm diameter circular punch. If the ultimate shear strength of steel is 460 MN/m², determine the compressive force that must be developed by the punch.

Ans. 216.86 kN.

3. A hanger bar is fastened to a steel bracket made from 10 mm steel plate with a single 16 mm diameter steel bolt. If the shear stress in both the bracket and the bolt is not to exceed a maximum value of 80 MN/m², calculate the maximum load that can be carried by the hanger based on the strength of the bolt and the bracket.

Ans. 16.09 kN.

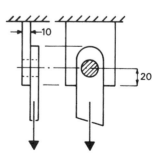

12

Now that we have looked at some simple examples involving shear stress, we can extend our study of shear to cover more complex situations. However, before we do this it is necessary to introduce some new concepts.

Let's reconsider the cantilever beam shown in Frame 2 and look at a small element of the beam between the two sections A–A and B–B as indicated below.

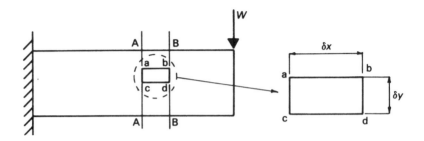

Ignoring the self-weight of the beam, what is the value of the shearing force acting on the vertical sections A–A and B–B?

13

W on both sections.

If you draw the shearing force diagram for this beam, you should realise that the shearing force is in fact W at all sections along the beam. This implies that the shear stresses on the two vertical faces of the small element are equal in magnitude as the equal shearing forces act on equal cross-sectional areas. However, for vertical equilibrium the shear stresses (and forces) must act in opposite directions, as indicated in the figure. Note that we have used the symbol τ to indicate shear stress.

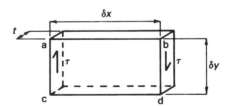

14

Now let's consider the rotational equilibrium of this element. If moments are taken about the corner c of the forces acting on the element, then it is apparent that there is a clockwise moment given by:

$$\text{Moment} = \text{force} \times \delta x$$

$$= \text{stress} \times \text{area on which stress acts} \times \delta x$$

$$= \tau \times (t \times \delta y) \times \delta x$$

where t is the thickness of the beam.

What force provides the anticlockwise moment that for rotational equilibrium must resist this clockwise moment?

15

> A shearing force on the face a–b.

You may have answered that there is no such force, but there has to be if equilibrium of the element is to be maintained—which it has to be! The only possible answer is that there must be a shearing force acting on the horizontal face a–b which provides an anticlockwise moment equal to the moment given by the expression in Frame 14.

The existence of this shearing force implies the existence of shear stress acting on the horizontal face a–b. Such a shear stress is known as a complementary shear stress. In other words, the shear stresses on the vertical faces of the element must be accompanied by a set of shear stresses acting on the horizontal faces.

On a sketch of this element, can you draw the direction of the shear stresses acting on all four faces?

16

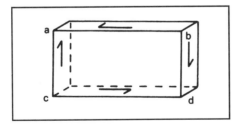

Go on to the next frame.

17

The stresses act in such a way that for horizontal and vertical equilibrium they provide equal and opposite forces on any two parallel faces of the element such that the clockwise moments caused by the shear stresses on the vertical planes are resisted by the anticlockwise moments caused by the shear stresses on the horizontal planes.

Referring back to the diagram in Frame 16, can you think of a simple rule that will enable you to remember the relative directions of the shear stresses acting on any two intersecting perpendicular planes.

18

> The shearing stresses both act either towards or away from the line of intersection of the two planes.

This is a simple observation which is true for any situation in which shear stress and complementary shear stress act at a point within a component.

The diagrams below show the direction of shear stress on one face of a small element of material. Complete each diagram by showing the direction of the stresses acting on the other three faces.

19

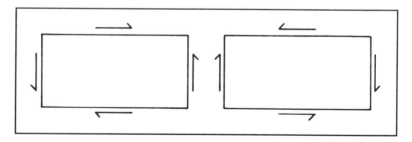

We have shown the existence of the complementary stresses and have identified their direction. What about the magnitude of the complementary stresses? The magnitude of the average stress on the vertical planes can be determined using the methods discussed in previous frames. Now let's see how to calculate the magnitude of the complementary stress.

In Frame 14 we wrote down an expression for the clockwise moment about corner c resulting from the shear stress acting on the vertical face b–d of the element shown in Frame 12.

Can you write down a corresponding expression for the anticlockwise moment about c resulting from the complementary shear stress acting on the horizontal face a–b? In this case, use the symbol τ' to indicate the complementary shear stress.

20

$$\boxed{\text{Moment} = \tau' \times (t \times \delta x) \times \delta y}$$

Your reasoning should have been as follows.

If moments are taken about the corner c, then there must be an anticlockwise moment given by:

$$\text{Moment} = \text{force} \times \delta y$$
$$= \text{stress} \times \text{area on which stress acts} \times \delta y$$
$$= \tau' \times (t \times \delta x) \times \delta y$$

where t is the thickness of the beam.

You know that for equilibrium the clockwise moment and the anticlockwise moment must be equal.

By equating the moment expressions in Frame 14 and this frame, what do you deduce about the relationship between the shear stress τ and the complementary shear stress τ'?

21

$$\boxed{\tau = \tau'}$$

In other words, the magnitude of the complementary shear stress on the horizontal planes is equal to the magnitude of the shear stress on the vertical planes. This is an important conclusion, and should be remembered for use later. If you didn't arrive at this answer, check your solution against the next frame.

22

$$\text{Clockwise moment about c} = \tau \times (t \times \delta y) \times \delta x$$
$$\text{Anticlockwise moment about c} = \tau' \times (t \times \delta x) \times \delta y$$

Equating moments:

$$\tau \times (t \times \delta y) \times \delta x = \tau' \times (t \times \delta x) \times \delta y$$

Cancelling terms:

$$\tau = \tau'$$

So far, we have been looking at a small, finite element of material. If the sides of the element become very small ($\delta x \to 0$ and $\delta y \to 0$) then effectively the element will represent a *point* within the beam, and the proof we have developed will therefore apply to any point. It is important to realise and remember that, if a shearing stress acts on any plane at a point within a component, there must be a *complementary shearing stress* of *equal magnitude* acting on a plane at right angles to the first plane and passing through the same point.

In developing the above proof, we started out by considering the case of a cantilevered beam with a point load at the end, resulting in a constant shearing force and hence constant shear stresses at all sections throughout the structure. In most practical situations, the shear stresses will vary throughout the structure. However, if the element under consideration represents a point, it is reasonable to assume that the shear stress at that point is uniform and constant. The conclusions we have arrived at are therefore still quite valid.

23

SHEAR STRAINS AND MODULUS OF RIGIDITY

In Programme 4 you learnt that direct stresses acting on a material give rise to direct strains. In the same way, *shear stresses* give rise to *shear strains*.

Consider the small element of material shown below, which is subjected to shear stresses and complementary shear stresses on the vertical and horizontal faces.

Assuming that the element is made from an elastic material, can you sketch the distorted shape of the element caused by the application of the applied shear stresses?

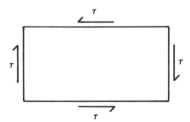

24

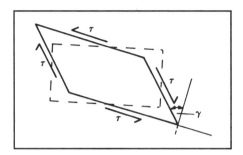

You should have drawn a diagram similar to the one shown above. The initially rectangular element will be distorted into a diamond shape. The corners of the element, which were initially at right angles, will have rotated through a *small* angular distortion shown as γ in the diagram.

γ is known as the *shearing strain*, and as γ is measured in radians it is dimensionless. τ, as we have already shown, is the shear stress, and both shear stress and shear strain are related by a physical property known as the *Shear Modulus (G)* sometimes referred to as the *Modulus of Rigidity*.

In Programme 4 you learnt that direct stress and strains are related by the material property known as Young's Modulus. With this relationship in mind, can you guess the relationship between shearing stress and strain and the Shear Modulus?

25

$$\text{Shear Modulus } (G) = \frac{\text{Shear stress } (\tau)}{\text{Shear strain } (\gamma)} \qquad (6.1)$$

The relationship between shear stress and strain is analogous to that for direct stress and strain, but they are related by the Shear Modulus rather than by Young's Modulus.

What are the units of Shear Modulus?

26

$$N/m^2$$

Shear stress has units of N/m^2; shear strain is an angular measurement and is dimensionless, and therefore the Shear Modulus, which is the ratio of the shear stress and strain, must have units of stress, that is, N/m^2.

27

For most metals, Young's Modulus (E) is approximately 2.5 times as great as the Shear Modulus (G). Typically, steel has a Young's Modulus of 200 GN/m^2 and a Shear Modulus of 80 GN/m^2.

Find out typical Young's Modulus and Shear Modulus values for other materials. (No answers given for this question but, by consulting Materials textbooks, you should be able to determine some typical figures. Try to remember at least the typical orders of magnitude of these figures and the range of values between different materials.)

28

Now try a problem.

An aluminium plate is subjected to a shear stress of 50 MN/m^2 and has a Shear Modulus of 26 GN/m^2. Determine the shear strain and hence calculate the total shear distortion (δ) shown in the figure:

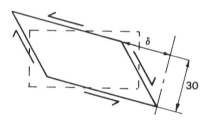

29

$$\boxed{0.0019: 0.058 \text{ mm}}$$

Check your working:

$$\text{Shear strain } (\gamma) = \frac{\text{Shear stress } (\tau)}{\text{Shear modulus } (G)}$$

$$= \frac{50 \times 10^6}{26 \times 10^9}$$

$$= 0.0019$$

$$\text{Shear distortion } (\delta) = \text{shear strain } (\gamma) \times \text{side length of element}$$

$$= 0.0019 \times 30$$

$$= 0.058 \text{ mm}$$

SHEAR STRESSES IN BEAMS

At the beginning of this programme we saw how to calculate the magnitude of average shear stresses in simple mechanical components. The use of the word *average* indicated that we were assuming that the shear stresses were distributed uniformly and evenly across the shear surface. However, this is not always the case and in many practical situations the shear stresses are distributed in a non-uniform manner. Recognition of this non-uniformity can be important in the design of some mechanical elements. We are now going to investigate some typical situations where such non-uniform shear stress distributions occur, and see how to calculate the shape of the stress distributions and the magnitude of such stresses. In doing this we shall be making use of the facts we have learnt about the existence of complementary shear stresses.

Let's look again at the cantilever beam of rectangular cross-section we first considered in Frame 2. In this case, for convenience the beam is viewed with the support on the right:

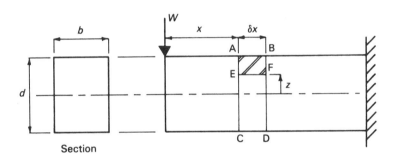

Consider the section AC at a distance x from the free end of the cantilever and the section BD which is at a distance δx from AC.

Can you write down expressions for the bending moments at these two sections?

> Bending moment at AC $= W \times x$
> Bending moment at BD $= W \times (x + \delta x)$

If you didn't get this answer, revise Programme 3 before proceeding.

Now can you remember the general expression you learnt in Programme 5 which will give the variation of bending stress at section AC? Write the expression down.

32

$$\sigma = \frac{My}{I} = \frac{(W \times x)y}{I}$$

This should be a familiar expression. I is the second moment of area of the section about the neutral axis and y is the distance from the neutral axis at which the stress is being calculated. You should also know that the bending stress varies linearly from zero stress at the neutral axis to a maximum value at the outer fibres of the section.

Now let's look at the equilibrium of that segment of the beam that is bounded by the two sections AC and BD, and by the plane EF which is at a distance z from the neutral axis.

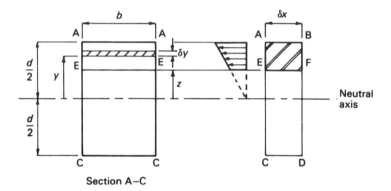

Section A–C

The figure shows the distribution of tensile bending stress acting on the face AE of the section under consideration. The tensile force caused by the tensile stress acting on the small hatched area of thickness δy shown on the cross-section is given by:

$$\text{Force} = \sigma_y \times b \times \delta y$$

where σ_y is the bending stress at a distance y from the neutral axis.

Hence the total tensile force acting on the face AE is given by the summation of the above expression over the whole face:

$$\text{Total force acting on face AE} = \int_z^{d/2} \sigma_y b \, dy$$

and substituting the expression at the top of this frame:

$$\text{Total force acting on face AE} = \int_z^{d/2} \frac{(W \times x)y}{I} b \, dy$$

Complete the integration to give an expression for the total force on AE.

$$\text{Total force on AE} = \frac{Wxb}{2I}\left[\frac{d^2}{4} - z^2\right]$$

Similarly, you should be able to show that the force acting on the opposite face (BF) of this segment of beam is given by a similar expression where the moment is given by the second equation at the top of Frame 31. This expression is given as:

$$\text{Total force on BF} = \frac{W(x + \delta x)b}{2I}\left[\frac{d^2}{4} - z^2\right]$$

$$= \frac{Wxb}{2I}\left[\frac{d^2}{4} - z^2\right] + \frac{W\delta xb}{2I}\left[\frac{d^2}{4} - z^2\right]$$

$$= \text{Total force on AE} + \frac{W\delta xb}{2I}\left[\frac{d^2}{4} - z^2\right]$$

This expression implies that this segment of beam is subject to an out-of-balance tensile force acting to the right and given by:

$$\text{Out of balance force} = \frac{W\delta xb}{2I}\left[\frac{d^2}{4} - z^2\right]$$

For equilibrium of this beam segment, there must be a force resisting this out-of-balance force. Can you deduce where this resisting force comes from, and indicate its position and direction on a sketch of the beam segment?

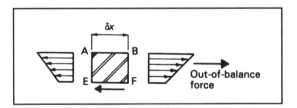

You should have reasoned that there must be a shearing force acting on the horizontal face EF as shown in the figure, and which must equate to the out-of-balance force.

Why is there no shear force acting on the face AB?

35

Because for there to be a shearing force on the face AB there has to be a shear stress. However, AB is a free surface and there can be no shear stress along a free surface as there is no adjacent reactive surface against which shear stresses can develop.

The final equation in Frame 33 gives the out-of-balance force acting on the beam segment, which, as we have deduced, must equal the total shearing force along the face EF. What we are interested in is the magnitude of the shear stress along this face. As the segment is small, it is reasonable to suggest that the shear stress is uniform over the shear surface EF. Knowing the total shear force and the area over which it acts, the shear stress can be calculated:

$$\text{Shear stress} = \frac{\text{Total shear force}}{\text{Area}}$$

$$= \frac{W\delta x b}{2I}\left[\frac{d^2}{4} - z^2\right] \times \frac{1}{(\delta x \times b)}$$

$$= \frac{W}{2I}\left[\frac{d^2}{4} - z^2\right] \tag{6.2}$$

The above expression gives the shear stress on the horizontal face EF, which is at a distance z from the neutral axis.

What is the value of the shear stress on a vertical plane at a distance z from the neutral axis?

36

$$\boxed{\frac{W}{2I}\left[\frac{d^2}{4} - z^2\right]}$$

This should be easy! You should remember that the stress on any horizontal plane must be accompanied by a complementary shear stress on the vertical plane passing through the same point. The expression above therefore gives the shear stress on the vertical cross-section (AE) of the beam at a level at a distance z measured from the neutral axis:

For a rectangular section, the second moment of area (I) about the neutral axis is given by:

$$I = \frac{b \times d^3}{12}$$

Substituting this into Equation (6.2), we therefore obtain the following equation.

$$\text{Shear stress} = \frac{6W}{bd^3}\left[\frac{d^2}{4} - z^2\right]$$

$$= \frac{6W}{bd}\left[\frac{1}{4} - \left(\frac{z}{d}\right)^2\right] \qquad (6.3)$$

What is the value of the shear stress at the level of the neutral axis? (Hint: at the level of the neutral axis, z must be equal to zero.)

37

$$\frac{3}{2}\frac{W}{bd}$$

You should have obtained this solution by substituting $z = 0$ into Equation (6.3). If you think about the work we did at the beginning of this programme, this might seem surprising. You will remember that we started out in this programme by looking at average shear stress, which we defined as the shear force divided by the area of the surface resisting shear.

What do you deduce to be the relationship between the average shear stress and the shear stress at the level of the neutral axis for a rectangular beam section?

38

Shear stress at neutral axis $= 1.5 \times$ average shear stress

The average shear stress is given by W/bd, and hence the shear stress at the level of the neutral axis is 1.5 times this value. This value is, in fact, the *maximum* shear stress that will occur in the cross-section of a rectangular beam. The fact that the *maximum* is 1.5 times the *average* is an important result and is used in the design of beams in materials such as timber, where maximum shear stresses are usually calculated for comparison with allowable or permissible values.

Equation (6.3) defines the distribution of shear stress on the cross-section of a rectangular beam at any position at a distance z from the neutral axis.

Either by inserting suitable values into the equation or by examining the form of the equation, sketch the shape of the distribution of shear stress across the full depth of the beam section.

39

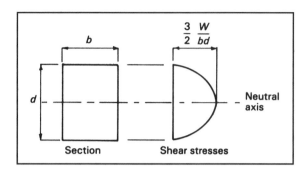

The equation is, in fact, the equation of a parabolic curve and, either by recognising this fact or by simply inserting values into the equation, you should have plotted a stress distribution diagram as shown above. As we have already stated, the maximum shear stress is found to occur at the neutral axis, and in the outer fibres of the section the shear stress is zero.

We have used the simple example of a cantilever with a point load at the end to arrive at the expressions for shear stress distribution. In this case, the shearing forces are constant throughout the beam and the shear stress distribution will be the same at any cross-section. In the more general case of a beam subject to any loading or support conditions, the theory is equally valid provided that the appropriate shear force at the section under consideration is used in the formula for shear stress.

40

PROBLEMS

1. A heavy machine is supported by rubber bearing pads of dimensions as shown in figure Q1. The movement of the machine causes a shearing force on each pad of 8 kN. If the shear modulus (G) of rubber is 1.2 MN/m², determine (a) the average shear stress, (b) the average shear strain and (c) the total horizontal deformation, δ, in the pad.

Ans. (0.267 MN/m^2, 0.222, 5.56 mm)

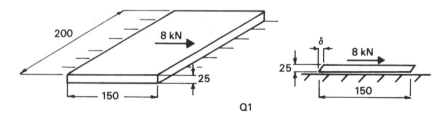

Q1

2. To test the shear strength of an adhesive, a simple test is devised using three wooden blocks glued together and loaded in a test rig as shown. If at some point in the test a load of 5 kN is applied, determine the average shear stress along the surface between the adhesive and the blocks.

Ans. 0.125 MN/m².

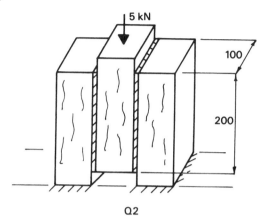

Q2

3. A rectangular beam, 250 mm wide × 400 mm deep, is simply supported over a span of 4 metres and carries a uniformly distributed load (inclusive of its own weight) of 5 kN/m. Determine (a) the maximum shear force in the beam, (b) the average shear stress at the section of largest shear force and (c) the maximum shear stress at this section.

Ans. 10 kN, 0.10 MN/m², 0.15 MN/m².

4. The beam in question 3 now supports an additional point load, W, at a distance of 1 metre from one support. If the maximum shear stress in the beam is limited to a value of 0.8 MN/m², calculate the maximum value of this additional load W. (Note that the answer given is based on considerations of shear only. Other considerations such as bending stresses and deflections would normally have to be considered.)

Ans. 57.78 kN.

5. The beam in question 3 is loaded with the UDL of 5 kN/m and a point load of 40 kN at a distance of 1 metre from the left-hand support. Consider a section at a distance of 1.5 metres from this support. (a) Calculate the maximum bending stress and the maximum shear stress at this section. (b) Sketch the shape of the bending stress diagram and the shear stress diagram. (c) At this section, where does the maximum bending stress occur and where does the maximum shear stress occur?

Ans. 5.16 MN/m², 0.11 MN/m². The maximum bending stress of 5.16 MN/m² occurs at the outer fibres of the section. The maximum shear stress of 0.11 MN/m² occurs at the level of the neutral axis.

41

SHEAR STRESS IN NON-RECTANGULAR BEAMS

So far, we have looked at the distribution of shear stress in beams of rectangular cross-section. The theory developed can now be extended to enable us to determine the distribution of shear stress in non-rectangular sections; for example, in I-section beams which are a common type of mechanical component.

We shall confine our further study of this problem to beam sections having at least one axis of symmetry. In this case, bending of the beam will be taking place about a principal axis. The proof that will follow is merely an extension of the proof for the rectangular section, but the equations we develop can be applied more generally.

Consider the same cantilever beam that we examined in Frame 30, but this time let us assume that it has a more general shape of cross-section as shown below. The vertical Y-axis is taken to be the axis of symmetry.

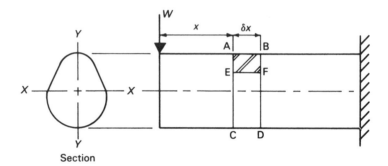

Section

As before, the bending moment at a distance x along the beam is given by:

$$\text{Moment at section AC} = W \times x$$

and the bending stress at a distance y from the neutral axis is given as:

$$\sigma = \frac{My}{I} = \frac{(W \times x)y}{I}$$

where the symbols have the usual meaning.

The second moment of area, I, is taken about the X–X axis which is also the neutral axis of bending.

Now, as before, let's look at the equilibrium of that part of the beam which is bounded by the two section AC and BD, and by the surface, EF, which we will take to be a curved surface to emphasise the generality of the proof that will follow. EF can, of course, represent a flat horizontal plane, which in many problems where this theory is applied will often be taken as the case.

The figure on the next page shows the face AE of the part of the beam under consideration. Let's look at the force developed on the small element of area δA at a distance y from the neutral axis.

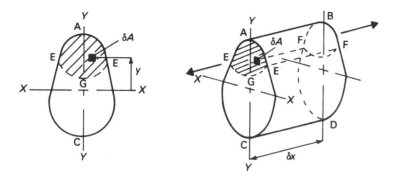

Can you write down an expression for the force developed over this area δA?

42

$$\text{Force} = \sigma_y \times \delta A$$

This is similar to the expression developed in Frame 32, where previously we were taking an elemental area of width b and thickness δy.

The *total* force acting on the face AE (hatched in the above figure) is obtained from the summation of this expression over the whole face. If we assume that the area of this face is A, then this total force can be expressed as:

$$\text{Total force on face AE (hatched in figure)} = \int_A \sigma_y \, dA = \int_A \frac{(W \times x)y}{I} \, dA$$

$$= \frac{(W \times x)}{I} \int_A y \, dA$$

Similarly, the force on the opposite face (BF) is given by a similar expression with the moment given by $W(x + \delta x)$. Hence, as the area of face BF is the same as face AE, the force on the face BF is given by:

$$\text{Total force on face BF} = \int_A \sigma_y \, dy = \int_A \frac{(W \times \{x + \delta x\})y}{I} \, dA$$

$$= \frac{(W \times \{x + \delta x\})}{I} \int_A y \, dA$$

$$= \frac{(W \times x)}{I} \int_A y \, dA + \frac{(W \times \delta x)}{I} \int_A y \, dA$$

$$= \text{Total force on AE} + \frac{(W \times \delta x)}{I} \int_A y \, dA$$

What is the expression for the shear force acting over the curved surface EF?

43

$$\frac{(W \times \delta x)}{I} \int_A y \, dA$$

As in Frame 34, you should have reasoned that this element of beam is subjected to an out-of-balance force caused by the effects of the bending stresses, and this can only be resisted by a shearing force acting along the surface EF. If you are not sure about this, turn back to and revise Frames 32 to 35.

Does the integral expression look familiar? It is in fact the first moment of area of the small elemental area δA about the neutral axis summed over the whole hatched area A of the face of the beam section. Let's assume that the centroid of this area A is at a distance $\bar{y}$ from the neutral axis.

Can you think of another way of writing the above expression for the shear force in terms of the area A and the centroidal distance $\bar{y}$. (Hint: remember how you calculate the centroidal position of an irregular shape.)

44

$$\frac{(W \times \delta x)}{I} A\bar{y}$$

You should know that when calculating the centroidal position of an irregular shape we make use of the general expression:

$$A\bar{y} = \int_A y \, dA$$

Hence the above expression for the shear force. If the length of the side of the curved shear surface (EGE) is b, then the average shear stress acting over the curved shear surface EF is given by:

$$\text{Average shear stress} = \frac{\text{Total shear force}}{\text{Area of surface}}$$

$$= \frac{(W \times \delta x)}{I} A\bar{y} \times \frac{1}{(b \times \delta x)}$$

$$= \frac{WA\bar{y}}{Ib}$$

If the curved surface EF is in fact a horizontal plane, what would be the expression for the shear stress on the vertical face AE at the level of EF?

$$\tau = \frac{WA\bar{y}}{Ib}$$

This expression follows again from considerations of complementary shear stresses. The vertical shear stress at any point on the face AE must be complementary to the horizontal shear stress on the plane EF at the same distance from the neutral axis. Hence the expression derived can be used to determine the shear stress acting on the vertical cross-sections of beams of almost any shape section.

The general form of this expression is:

$$\tau = \frac{QA\bar{y}}{Ib} \tag{6.4}$$

where: $\tau =$ the shear stress;

$Q =$ the shear force acting at the section;

$A =$ the area of the section to the outside of the level where shear stress is being calculated;

$\bar{y} =$ the distance to the centroid of the area A measured from the neutral axis;

$I =$ the second moment of area of the *whole cross-section* about the neutral axis;

$b =$ the width of the cross-section at the level where shear stress is being calculated.

Make use of this general expression to show that, for a rectangular beam section of width b and depth d, the maximum shear stress at the level of the neutral axis is 1.5 times the average shear stress. The solution is in the next frame.

Area above the neutral axis $= b \times 0.5d$

Distance to centroid of this are $= 0.25d$

Second moment of area about neutral axis $= \frac{1}{12}bd^3$

Width of section $= b$

Hence shear stress at level of neutral axis

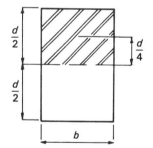

$$= \frac{QA\bar{y}}{Ib}$$

$$= \frac{Q(b \times 0.5d)0.25d}{(b \times d^3/12)b}$$

$$= \frac{3}{2}\frac{Q}{bd}$$

$$= 1.5 \times \text{average shear stress}$$

47

Now let's look at the application of the theory to a very common problem: an I-beam section. I-section beams fabricated using various types of materials are widely used and must be designed to resist the shear stresses resulting from the applied loading system. As an illustration of the theory, we shall look at the I-section shown in the figure and examine the distribution of shear stress under the application of a 50 kN shearing load.

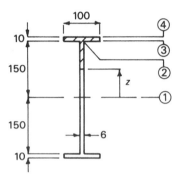

First, let's consider the derivation of the shear stress expression at a level at a distance z from the neutral axis and within the web of the section.

The first moment of area about the centroidal axis ($A\bar{y}$) of that part of the section above the level being considered can be taken as the sum of the first moment of area of the flange plus the first moment of area of that part of the web that lies above the level being considered. Hence:

$$A\bar{y} = \left[(100 \times 10) \times 155 + \{6 \times (150 - z)\} \times \frac{(150 + z)}{2}\right] \times 10^{-9}$$

$$= \left[155\,000 + 3(150^2 - z^2)\right] \times 10^{-9} \text{ m}^3$$

Second moment of area, I (for the whole section)

$$= 2\left[(\tfrac{1}{12} \times 100 \times 10^3) + (100 \times 10 \times 155^2)\right] + \tfrac{1}{12} \times 6 \times 300^3$$

$$= 61.57 \times 10^6 \text{ mm}^4 = 61.57 \times 10^{-6} \text{ m}^4$$

Breadth of section, $b = 6$ mm

Shear force, $Q = 50$ kN

Shear stress, $\tau = \dfrac{QA\bar{y}}{Ib}$

$$= \frac{(50 \times 10^3) \times \left[155\,000 + 3(150^2 - z^2)\right] \times 10^{-9}}{(61.57 \times 10^{-6}) \times (6 \times 10^{-3})}$$

$$= 135.35 \times 10^{-6}[155\,000 + 3(150^2 - z^2)] \text{ MN/m}^2$$

Note that this equation is the equation of a parabola. Hence the shear stress in the web of the beam must vary parabolically.

Use this equation to calculate the shear stress at the level of the neutral axis and the level of the intersection between the web and flange (positions 1 and 2 in the diagram).

48

> 30.12 and 20.98 MN/m²

These stresses are obtained by substituting $z = 0$ and $z = 150$ mm, respectively, into the shear stress expression.

Now determine an expression for the shear stress at any level within the flange of the beam, and use the expression developed to calculate the stresses at the interface of the web and flange and at the top of the section (positions 3 and 4). Use the diagram below and check your solution against the working in the next frame.

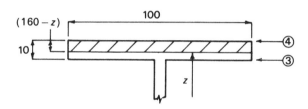

49

> 1.26 and 0.00 MN/m²

$$A\bar{y} = \left[100 \times (160 - z) \times \frac{(160 + z)}{2} \right] \times 10^{-9}$$

$$= 50 \times (160^2 - z^2) \times 10^{-9} \text{ m}^3$$

$$I = 61.57 \times 10^{-6} \text{ m}^4 \text{ (as before)}$$

$$b = 100 \text{ mm}$$

Shear stress, $\tau = \dfrac{QA\bar{y}}{Ib} = \dfrac{50 \times 10^3 \times \left[50 \times (160^2 - z^2) \right] \times 10^{-9}}{61.57 \times 10^{-6} \times (100 \times 10^{-3})}$

$$= 406.04 \times 10^{-6} \times (160^2 - z^2) \text{ MN/m}^2$$

At position 3: $z = 150$: $\tau = 406.04 \times 10^{-6} \times (160^2 - 150^2) = 1.26$ MN/m²

At position 4: $z = 160$: $\tau = 406.04 \times 10^{-6} \times (160^2 - 160^2) = 0.00$ MN/m²

Can you sketch the shear stress distribution throughout the full beam depth?

50

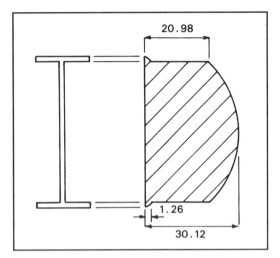

The shape of the stress distribution diagram follows from the general expressions we developed in the preceding frames for the shear stress distribution in both the web and the flange. Both of the expressions were parabolic: hence the parabolic shape of the above diagram. Note that the maximum shear stress occurs at the level of the neutral axis.

Another point of interest is the abrupt change of stress at the level of the intersection of the web and the flange. The underside of the flange is a free surface and therefore the shear stress along this surface must be zero. The above diagram, however, shows a shear stress at this level of 1.26 MN/m^2, not zero. This would indicate that the simple theory we have developed does not give accurate results within the flange. In fact, at the web–flange junction the localised stress distribution is much more complex than we have indicated, resulting in large localised stress gradients which cannot be determined by such a simple analysis. However, the methods we have examined are nevertheless accurate enough for determining the shear stresses within the web of the beam.

You will note from the above diagram that the largest part of the stress diagram is acting on the web of the section. By multiplying the area of this part of the stress diagram by the thickness of the web of the beam, we can calculate what proportion of the shear *force* acting on the section is resisted by shear stresses which are developed in the web. This will lead to an interesting conclusion.

Can you calculate the total shear force carried by the web of the beam and hence determine what percentage of the total applied shearing force is resisted by shearing stresses within the web. The answer and worked solution are in the next frame. (You will need to remember the formula for the area enclosed by a parabola.)

48.73 kN; 97%

Shear force in web

= thickness of web × area of stress diagram

$= 6 \times 10^{-3} \times [(300 \times 10^{-3} \times 20.98) + (300 \times 10^{-3} \times \frac{2}{3}\{30.12 - 20.98\})] \times 10^3$

= 48.73 kN

Note that in the above calculation, in order to work out the area of the stress diagram, we have to split it into a rectangular segment and a parabolic segment. The total shear force acting on the cross-section is 50 kN.

$$\text{Percentage of shear force carried by web} = \frac{48.73}{50.00} \times 100$$
$$= 97\%$$

This figure indicates that the web of this I-beam resists nearly all the applied shear force. In fact, this is the principal structural function of the web. Of course, we have only looked at one example, but the finding is generally true   for most standard section I-beams the web resists between 90% to 98% of the total shear force.

For this reason it is common in the design of I-beams to assume for simplicity that the web of the beam resists *all* the shear force.

If we make this assumption for the beam section we have been considering, what is the **average** *shear stress in the web?*

52

27.78 MN/m^2

$$\text{Average shear stress} = \frac{\text{applied shear force}}{\text{web breadth} \times \text{web depth}}$$
$$= \frac{50 \times 10^3}{(6 \times 10^{-3}) \times (300 \times 10^{-3})}$$
$$= 27.78 \text{ MN/m}^2$$

What is the percentage difference between this average shear stress and the maximum shear stress of 30.12 MN/m^2 which we have previously determined?

53

$$\boxed{7.78\%}$$

Although there is a difference between the average and the maximum shear stress, the difference is small and, again, although this figure only applies to this particular problem, for most I-section beams the average shear stress is within 10 per cent of the maximum shear stress.

For this reason it is common practice in the design of I-section beams not only to assume that all the shear force acting at a section is carried by the web but to base design calculations on the *average* shear stress, which will be compared with an allowable average shear stress value.

For further simplicity in design, it is also common practice to take the depth of the web as equal to the overall depth of the beam section. The error introduced by this assumption is small but leads to much simplification in practical design.

54

$$\boxed{\text{TO REMEMBER}}$$

$$Average \text{ shear stress } = \frac{\text{Shear force}}{\text{Area over which shear force acts}} \text{ (N/m}^2)$$

Shear stresses are always accompanied by *complementary* shear stresses.

$$\text{Shear Modulus } (G) = \frac{\text{Shear stress } (\tau)}{\text{Shear strain } (\gamma)} \text{ (N/m}^2)$$

For a rectangular section: maximum shear stress $= 1.5 \times$ average shear stress

$$\text{Shear stress } \tau = \frac{QA\bar{y}}{Ib}$$

(see Frame 45 for definition of terms)

In commonly occurring sections such as rectangular or I-shaped beams, the maximum shear stress usually occurs at the level of the neutral axis.

The web of an I-beam resists nearly all the applied shear force at any cross-section.

FURTHER PROBLEMS

1. Figure Q1 shows a simple test arrangement to determine the shear strength of timber. The timber specimen is 50 mm wide. At an applied load of 10 kN, calculate the average shear stress along the plane *X–X*.

Ans. 2.0 MN/m².

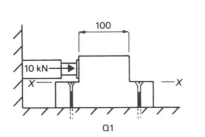

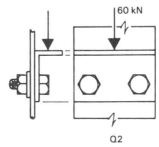

Q1

Q2

2. A steel bracket, as shown in figure Q2, supports a load of 60 kN. if the allowable shear stress in each bolt is 80 MN/m², calculate the minimum diameter of bolt required and select a bolt size from available diameters of 16, 20, 24 and 30 mm.

Ans. 21.84 mm; 24 mm.

3. A crane hook is connected to a shackle by a single bolt as shown in figure Q3. If the hook is to carry a load of 80 kN and the safe shearing stress in the bolt is 80 MN/m², determine the minimum diameter of bolt required. (*Hint*: the bolt is in double shear.)

Ans. 25.23 mm.

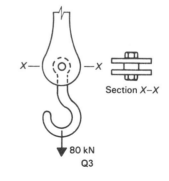

Section *X–X*

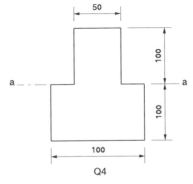

Q3

4. Figure Q4 shows the cross-section of a solid beam which is subject to a vertical shear force of 25 kN. Determine the shear stress (i) just above a–a; (ii) just below a–a; and (iii) at the centroid of the section. Compare the maximum stress with the average shear stress. (*Hint*: first calculate the position of the centroid of the section.)

Ans. (i) 3.63; (ii)1.82; (iii) 1.89 MN/m².
Average = 1.67 MN/m².

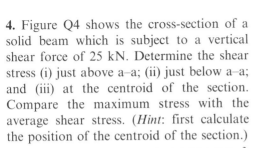

Q4

5. A T shaped beam is fabricated from two sections of timber nailed together, as shown in figure Q5. If the section is subjected to a shearing force of 5 kN, calculate the shear stress at the level of the neutral axis and at the level just below the junction of the two pieces of timber. (*Hint*: first calculate the position of the centroid of the section.)

Ans. 0.58, 0.53 MN/m².

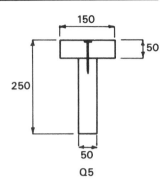

Q5

6. If each nail in the beam in figure Q5 can carry a shear force of 0.95 kN, what is the maximum spacing of the nails along the length of the beam? (*Hint*: you may have to think a little harder about this problem! In Q5 you calculated the shear stress at the level of the junction of the two pieces of timber. This will also be the complementary shear stress along the horizontal interface between the two timbers. What will be the shear *force* along, say, one metre length of the beam? If this shear force is resisted solely by the shearing action of the nails, how many nails are then required?)

Ans. 36.13 mm.

7. A universal beam is strengthened by welding a 200 mm × 20 mm steel plate to the top flange as shown in figure Q7. If the allowable maximum shear stress is 70 MN/m², calculate the maximum shearing force that this section can sustain.

Ans. 119.02 kN.

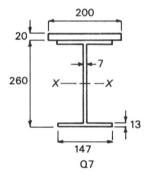

Q7

8. A cantilevered beam carries a point load of W at its free end. If the beam has a circular cross-section of diameter D, what are the average and maximum shear stresses developed in the section? (*Hint*: The centroid of a semi-circle of diameter 'D' is 0.212 D from its base. You will also have to recall the expression for the second moment of area of a circle about a diameter.)

Ans. 1.27W/D²; 1.70W/D².

9. The circular crank shaft of a cycle is 15.8 mm diameter and is subject to a shear force of 0.5kN. Determine the maximum shear stress developed in the shaft.

Ans. 3.40 MN/m².

Programme 7

TORSIONAL STRESS

On completion of this programme you will be able to:

- Define 'Torsional Moment'
- Define and calculate the Polar Second Moment of Area of solid and hollow circular sections
- Recognise the stress variation across a circular section
- State the equations of torsional stress
- Recognise and explain the terms within the torsional stress equations
- Calculate the state of stress within a circular shaft
- Calculate the angular deformation of a circular shaft
- Define the term 'Power'
- State the units of power
- Calculate the power transmitted in a rotating circular shaft
- Carry out simple design procedures for circular shafts in both static and rotational situations
- Calculate the state of stress in non-prismatic circular sections

1

Our study of stress would not be complete without examining the stresses that can occur within a component caused by torsional or twisting effects. In this programme we are going to determine the governing equations that will define the behaviour and response of a component that is subjected to torsion, and see how these equations can be applied to the solution of a number of common problems. A complete treatment of torsional stress for all cross-sectional shapes can be quite complex and is beyond the scope of this text. We shall, however, look at the analysis of circular sections whereby the fundamental analytical expressions can be developed and the basic principles established.

Hollow circular or solid circular sections subject to torsional or twisting effects are quite common in everyday life. Can you think of an example?

2

The drive shaft of a car connecting the engine to the rear axle is a very common example. The rotation of the shaft will cause twisting, resulting in the development of torsional stresses. Other examples could include the propeller shaft of a ship or aircraft. On a simpler level, the application of a spanner to tighten up a steel bolt would result in torsional stresses which, if excessive, could lead to fracture of the bolt, as anybody who has tried to release a rusty bolt well knows.

In order to calculate torsional stress it is necessary first to calculate the magnitude of the torsional moment acting on the component cross-section. Hence it is important to have a sound grasp of the fundamental principles of analysis that were examined in Programmes 1 and 2.

For example, consider the cranked cantilevered beam shown below.

Can you show on a sketch the magnitude and direction of all the reactive forces and moments that occur at the fixed support, A?

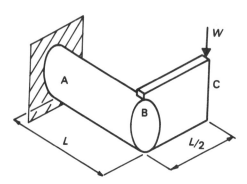

3

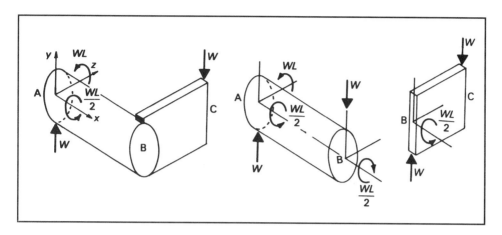

The first figure shows the free body diagram for the beam ABC with a moment about the Z-axis of WL N m (W N $\times$ L metres), a moment about the X-axis of $0.5WL$ N m (W N $\times$ $0.5L$ metres), and a vertical reaction of W N. The moment about the Z-axis is a bending moment giving rise to bending stresses within the section, but the moment about the longitudinal X-axis is a *torsional moment* (or *torque*) which will cause twisting along the length of the beam AB.

The second diagram on the right shows more fully the reactive components acting on each section of the beam, AB and BC, from which it is more apparent that AB is subject to torsion, with twisting taking place along the longitudinal X-axis.

The length of the beam, AB, is in fact subject to a complex stress situation, as within the section there will be shear stresses, bending stresses and torsional stresses. We have already seen how to calculate the shear and bending stresses, so let us concentrate on the torsional stresses by considering the beam AB to be in a state of pure torsion, that is, subject only to a torsional moment which in general terms we shall give the symbol T. We shall also assume that the beam section is a solid circular section and that the end A is fixed.

If under the action of the torque, T, the free end, B, rotates through an angle θ, can you sketch the beam showing the distorted shape of the small surface element, abcd? What do you deduce about the stresses acting on the faces of this element?

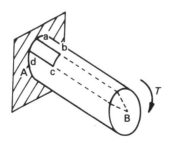

4

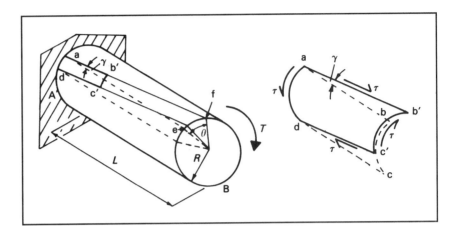

We assume that the deformations are small, and that all cross-sections rotate about the longitudinal axis with radii remaining straight and cross-sections remaining plane and circular.

Hence the small element, abcd, will distort to the shape shown, with the sides remaining straight but the corners rotating through a small angle γ. The shape of this element should lead you to the conclusion that it is in the state of pure shear with shear stresses (τ) and complementary shear stresses acting on the faces of the element as indicated.

What is the significance of the angle γ?

5

γ is the shear strain

Look back at Programme 6, Frame 24, if you don't recall this.

If the beam is made up of a material having a Shear Modulus G, what is the relationship between τ, γ and G?

6

$$G = \frac{\tau}{\gamma}$$

Again, revise Programme 6, Frame 25, if in doubt. Now go on to the next frame, but keep referring to the diagram in Frame 4 above.

Because of the rotation, point e on the circumference of the end section will move to point f through the arc length ef. If the radius of the circular section is R, the arc length ef is given by:

$$ef = R \times \theta$$

and if the geometry of the surface segment is considered, then the arc length ef can also be written as:

$$ef = L \times \gamma$$

Hence combining the above two equations:

$$R \times \theta = L \times \gamma$$

or

$$\gamma = \frac{R \times \theta}{L}$$

But recalling the relationship for shear stress and shear strain at the top of Frame 6, we can rewrite this expression in terms of the shear stress, τ:

$$\frac{\tau}{G} = \frac{R \times \theta}{L}$$

or

$$\frac{\tau}{R} = \frac{G\theta}{L} \qquad (7.1)$$

If this expression is to be used to calculate the shear stress, τ, in units of N/m^2, what are the appropriate units for the other terms in the expression?

8

$$\boxed{R - \text{m}: G - \text{N/m}^2: L - \text{m}: \theta - \text{radians}}$$

Most of these units should be obvious. However, note that θ is expressed in radians (rad) to justify the expression $ef = R \times \theta$ in Frame 7.

Now try an example:

A solid circular aluminium shaft has a diameter of 150 mm and is 1.5 metres long. An applied torque causes an angular twist of 2 degrees. What is the torsional shear stress at (i) the centre of the shaft and (ii) the outside surface? Take $G = 26$ GN/m^2. Check your answer against the solution given in the next frame.

9

$$\boxed{\text{(i) zero; (ii) 45.50 MN/m}^2}$$

Solution to (ii):

Angle of twist $= 2° = \dfrac{\pi}{180°} \times 2 = 0.035$ rad

Shear stress, τ
$$= \frac{RG\theta}{L} \text{ (from equation 7.1)}$$
$$= \frac{(75 \times 10^{-3}) \times (26 \times 10^9) \times 0.035}{1.5}$$
$$= 45.50 \text{ MN/m}^2$$

The solution to (i) should follow from intuition. The central longitudinal axis of a circular shaft is analogous to the neutral axis of bending of a beam. When the shaft is twisted it will rotate about the central longitudinal axis. All points along this axis will remain unstressed.

In fact, inspection of Equation (7.1) shows that the shear stress τ increases linearly with increasing radius. Although we developed the expression by examining a small element on the outer surface of a beam, we could have derived the same expression by considering any small element at any radius, r, measured from the central longitudinal axis. The equation shows that shear stress caused by torsion in a solid circular section increases linearly from zero at the centre to a maximum at the outer surface of the section. Hence, to calculate the stress at any radius r, Equation (7.1) may be written as:

$$\frac{\tau}{r} = \frac{G\theta}{L} \tag{7.2}$$

Now let's look at a small segment of cross-section (bcb'c') which we will assume has a thickness δr, and side length δs. Assume that the centre of the segment is at a radius r from the longitudinal axis.

Cross-section
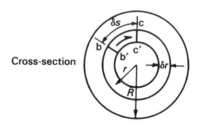

If the shear stress along the face of the segment is τ, what is the total force acting along the face, and hence what is the moment of this force about the longitudinal axis?

$$\text{Force} = \tau \times \delta r \times \delta s; \quad \text{Moment} = (\tau \times \delta r \times \delta s) \times r$$

This moment is in fact the torque exerted by the shear stress acting on the face of the small segment about the longitudinal axis. The torque exerted by all the segments at a radius r is given by the summation of this term over the complete circumference of the circle, that is:

$$\text{Torque exerted} = \Sigma \tau \times \delta r \times \delta s \times r$$
$$= \tau \times \delta r \times r \times \Sigma \delta s$$
$$= \tau \times \delta r \times r \times (2\pi r)$$
$$= \tau 2 \pi r^2 \delta r$$

However, the solid section consists of concentric rings of elements, all of which will exert a torque about the central longitudinal axis. Hence the total torque exerted will be the summation of the above expression over the whole surface area of the cross-section.

Write down the integral expression that will express the total torque over the complete surface of the solid circular section.

$$\int_0^R \tau 2 \pi r^2 \, dr$$

The equation

$$\int_0^R \tau 2 \pi r^2 \, dr$$

gives the torque exerted by the internal stress system about the longitudinal axis. If the externally applied torsional moment is T, this must also be an expression for T, because for equilibrium the external torsional moment must equal the internal torsional resistance.

Hence T may be expressed as:

$$T = \int_0^R \tau 2 \pi r^2 \, dr$$

Previously we derived an expression for τ in terms of the Shear Modulus, G. Use this expression (Frame 9, Equation (7.2)) to eliminate τ from the above equation and write the torsional moment T in terms of G, θ and L.

12

$$T = \frac{G\theta}{L} \int_0^R 2\pi r^3 \, \mathrm{d}r$$

The integral expression is known as the *Polar Second Moment of Area* and in general terms is given the symbol J. Hence, the above expression can be written as:

$$T = \frac{G\theta J}{L}$$

or

$$\frac{T}{J} = \frac{G\theta}{L} \qquad (7.3)$$

If equations (7.3) and (7.2) are combined, a complete set of equations for the torsional analysis of a circular section can be written down:

$$\frac{\tau}{r} = \frac{T}{J} = \frac{G\theta}{L} \qquad (7.4)$$

where τ = shear stress;
r = radius at which shear stress is being calculated;
T = applied Torsional Moment;
J = Polar Second Moment of Area;
G = Shear Modulus;
θ = angle of rotation; and
L = length of the component.

At first sight this might seem a difficult set of equations to remember. However, in Programme 5 we developed a similar-looking set of equations for the analysis of a beam in bending.
Call you recall and write down these equations?

13

$$\frac{\sigma}{y} = \frac{M}{I} = \frac{E}{R}$$

The form of the equations is identical. Hence, if you can recall the equations for the analysis of a beam in bending, you shouldn't have too much trouble in remembering the analogous equations for a section in torsion.

Now move to the next frame to look at some examples of the application of these equations.

14

Many common applications of torsional theory are concerned with the torsion of solid circular sections.

If the radius of a typical solid circular section is R, can you use the integral expression at the top of Frame 12 to derive a general expression for the Polar Second Moment of area of a solid circular section? The solution is in the next frame.

15

$$J = \frac{\pi R^4}{2}$$

The solution to this is simple.

From the expression at the top of Frame 12:

$$J = \int_0^R 2\pi r^3 \, \mathrm{d}r$$

$$= \left[\frac{2\pi r^4}{4} \right]_0^R$$

$$= \frac{\pi R^4}{2}$$

This is a useful expression to commit to memory, to use in the solution of problems involving solid circular sections.

If such a solid circular section has a radius of 10 mm, is 4 metres long and is subject to a torque of 100 N m, can you determine (i) the angle of twist of one end of the shaft relative to the other; and (ii) the maximum shearing stress within the section. Take G = 75 GN/m².

16

$$0.34 \text{ rads}; \quad 63.69 \text{ MN/m}^2$$

If you didn't obtain these answers, check your solution against that given in Frame 17 on the next page.

17

When tackling torsion problems you should first write down the basic expression given in Equation (7.4):

$$\frac{\tau}{r} = \frac{T}{J} = \frac{G\theta}{L}$$

You should then identify which part of the equation should be used to give the answer that is being sought. In this case we know the torque (T), the Shear Modulus (G), the length of the section (L) and the radius, from which we can immediately calculate the Polar Second Moment of Area (J). By inspection, you should be able to see that to calculate the angle of twist (θ) it is necessary to use the middle and third group of terms in the above expresson, in which the only unknown is θ. Similarly, to calculate the shear stress (τ), the first and middle group of terms can be used, as the only unknown in these terms is the shear stress τ.

The polar second moment of area (J) is given by:

$$J = \frac{\pi R^4}{2}$$

$$= \frac{\pi \times (10 \times 10^{-3})^4}{2}$$

$$= 15.71 \times 10^{-9} \text{ m}^4$$

Hence the angle of twist (θ) is given by:

$$\frac{T}{J} = \frac{G\theta}{L}$$

or

$$\theta = \frac{TL}{JG} = \frac{100 \times 4}{(15.71 \times 10^{-9}) \times (75 \times 10^9)}$$

$$= 0.34 \text{ rad}$$

Similarly, the maximum shear stress (τ), which will occur at the outer surface of the section, is given by:

$$\frac{\tau}{r} = \frac{T}{J}$$

or

$$\tau = \frac{Tr}{J} = \frac{100 \times (10 \times 10^{-3})}{15.71 \times 10^{-9}}$$

$$= 63.65 \text{ MN/m}^2$$

Now try some problems.

18

PROBLEMS

1. A hollow circular section has an outer radius of R and an inner radius of r. Determine an expression for the Polar Second Moment of Area of this section.

Ans. $\pi\{R^4 - r^4\}/2.$

2. A hollow circular steel drive shaft has an outer radius of 20 mm and an inner radius of 12 mm. If the maximum allowable shear stress in the shaft is 75 MN/m^2, what is the maximum permitted torsional moment that can be transmitted by the shaft?

Ans. 820 N m.

3. The hollow shaft in question 2 is to be replaced by a solid circular shaft of identical material which is required to transmit the same torsional moment. Calculate the radius of this shaft if the maximum allowable shear stress remains the same.

Ans. 19.1 mm.

4. If the shafts referred to in questions 2 and 3 are 2 metres long and rigidly fixed at one end, calculate the rotation of the free end for both the hollow and solid shafts. (Take $G = 75$ GN/m^2.)

Ans. 0.1, 0.105 rad.

5. If the 'efficiency' of the shafts is measured in terms of the amount of material used in their manufacture, which is the most efficient, the hollow or solid section? What general conclusion do you draw about the advantages of a hollow shaft compared with that of a solid shaft when made from the same material and used to transmit identical torsional moments?

Ans. The solid shaft is 42.5% heavier than the hollow one and hence less efficient. Generally, a hollow section is more efficient than an equivalent solid one.

6. A steel shaft is to be designed as a hollow circular section to carry a torsional moment of 1.5 kN m. If the maximum shear stress is limited to 100 MN/m^2, determine the minimum required dimensions of a hollow section with an outside diameter 1.5 times the inside diameter.

Ans. 15.22 and 22.84 mm.

19

CIRCULAR SECTIONS USED AS DRIVE SHAFTS TO TRANSMIT POWER

A common torsional problem is to be found in the case of a drive shaft used to transmit power from, say, a car engine to the drive wheels, or a ship's engine to the propeller. We can use the theory we have developed so far to look at the design or analysis of drive shafts which are required to rotate at a given constant speed to transmit a given torque. The combination of the torque and speed of revolution is a measure of power transmitted.

Before we proceed further, let's remind ourselves of what we mean by power.
Can you write down the definition of power and state its units?

20

> Power is the rate of doing work.
> Units = Watts = Joule/second

Note that 'power' is usually quoted in kilowatts (kW) or megawatts (MW). Within the above definition we have included the term 'work'. You will no doubt remember that if a force moves through a displacement, the work done is equal to the product of the force and the displacement, that is:

$$\text{Work} = \text{Force} \times \text{Displacement}$$

In the case of problems involving torsion, the definition of work will be different.
Can you write down an expression for the work done by an applied torque (T) acting on a shaft which it rotates through an angle θ? State the units of work.

21

> Work $= T \times \theta$
> Units = Joules = N m

Note that the torque should be expressed in N m and the rotation in radians.

Now try the following problem – answers and solution are given in the next frame:
A drive shaft to an engine transmits a torque of 500 Nm. It rotates at a constant speed of 50 revolutions per minute. Determine (i) the work done during one revolution of the drive shaft; and (ii) the power transmitted.

> 3141.59 Joules   2.62 kW

Check your solution:

$$1 \text{ revolution} = 2\pi \text{ radians}$$

$$\text{Work done per revolution} = \text{Torque} \times \theta$$

$$= 500 \times 2\pi$$

$$= 3141.59 \text{ Joules}$$

$$\text{Number of revs per second} = \frac{\text{revs per minute}}{60}$$

$$= 50/60$$

$$= 0.833$$

$$\text{Power} = \text{Work done per second}$$

$$= \text{Work per rev} \times \text{number revs per second}$$

$$= 3141.59 \times 0.833$$

$$= 2616.95 \text{ Watts} = 2.62 \text{ kW}$$

Note that in the above calculations the torque or torsional moment transmitted by the shaft appears in the calculations of both work and power. In the theory developed previously in this programme, the torsional moment is one of the main parameters in our stress equations. Hence to design or analyse drive shafts we need only combine the general relationship between power and torque with the previous relationships.

From the equations used above, a general relationship between power and torque can be written as:

$$P = T \times 2\pi \times \frac{n}{60}$$

or

$$T = \frac{30P}{\pi n}$$

where:

T = torque (N m);

P = power (Watts); and

n = number of revs per minute.

Try the following problem. If you have understood what we have done above and you have completed the previous set of problems, this shouldn't prove too difficult. The complete solution is given in the next frame.

A solid circular shaft is to transmit 2 MW at 150 revs per minute. What is (i) the torque transmitted; (ii) the minimum required radius of the section if the maximum allowable shear stress is 100 MN/m²?

23

(i) 127 kN m; (ii) 93.14 mm

The torque transmitted is given by:

$$T = \frac{30P}{\pi n}$$

$$= \frac{30 \times (2 \times 10^6)}{\pi \times 150}$$

$$= 0.127 \times 10^6 \text{ N m}$$

$$= 127 \text{ kN m}$$

If the minimum required radius of the section is R, then the polar second moment of area is given by:

$$J = \frac{\pi R^4}{2}$$

and the relationship between the torque and the allowable shear stress is given by:

$$\frac{\tau}{r} = \frac{T}{J}$$

or:

$$\frac{J}{r} = \frac{T}{\tau}$$

Hence:

$$\frac{\pi R^4}{2R} = \frac{(127 \times 10^3)}{(100 \times 10^6)}$$

$$\therefore \quad R^3 = \frac{2 \times (127 \times 10^3)}{\pi \times 100 \times 10^6}$$

Which solves to give:

$$R = 0.09316 \text{ m}$$

$$= 93.16 \text{ mm}$$

Calculate the angular twist (in degrees) over a 5 metre length of this shaft if a radius of 95 mm is provided, Take $G = 80 \text{ GN/m}^2$.

24

3.56 degrees

If you didn't get this solution, look back at the first part of the problem in Frame 17 – it's practically the same.

25

PROBLEMS

1. A solid circular propeller shaft has a radius of 75 mm. If the shearing stress is limited to 100 MN/m^2, what is the maximum power that can be transmitted at a speed of 200 revs per minutes?

Ans. 1.39 MW.

2. If the shaft in question 1 is 3 metres long, and the angular twist must not exceed 2 degrees, what is the maximum power that can be transmitted based on this limiting condition? Take $G = 80$ GN/m^2.

Ans. 969 kW

3. A hollow circular drive shaft is to transmit 100 kW at a constant speed of 150 revs per minute. If the outside diameter of the shaft is to be twice the inside diameter, determine the dimensions of the shaft if the shear stress is not to exceed 50 MN/m^2.

Ans. Outside diameter 88.44 mm.

26

OTHER TORSIONAL PROBLEMS

The problems that we have dealt with so far have been fairly straightforward, but using a combination of the torsion equations and simple statics it is possible to analyse a wide range of problems similar to those we have already considered.

However, there is a range of more complex problems where it is necessary to extend the theory further. It is not possible to examine every single type of problem, but by looking at some typical situations the general principles may be established.

As an example, consider a circular shaft which has both ends rigidly fixed and a torque of 100 kN m applied at its centre point as shown.

Can you say what is the torque resisted by the left-hand segment AB, and what is the torque resisted by the right-hand segment BC?

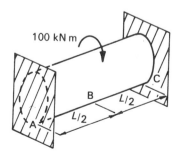

27

| 50 kN m on both segments. |

You should have arrived at this answer by considerations of symmetry. As both halves of the shaft are identical, there is geometrical symmetry and symmetry in loading, and therefore the torque will be resisted equally by both segments.

Now let's consider the same shaft with a torque T applied at some point along the shaft which is not at the centre. Let's also assume, for generality, that the two segments of the shaft on either side of the point of loading are of different radii and therefore have different Polar Second Moments of Area and are made of different material having different shear moduli.

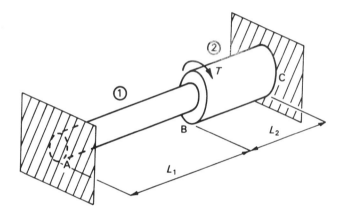

Can you say what proportion of the torque is resisted by the left-hand segment AB and what proportion is resisted by the right-hand segment BC?

28

| The answer should be that you can't! |

The reason you can't is that the problem we are looking at is *statically indeterminate*. This is because there are too many support reactions to permit analysis using only the simple principles of static equilibrium, and it is therefore necessary to supplement the equations of equilibrium by additional relationships that will lead to the complete analysis of the structure.

If we assume that the effect of applied torque, T, is to induce a torque T_1 in the segment AB and a torque T_2 in the segment BC, write down the relationship between T, T_1 and T_2.

29

$$T = T_1 + T_2$$

This is our *equation of equilibrium* for the externally applied and internally induced torsional moments. It can't, of course, be solved as it contains two unknowns: T_1 and T_2. The figure below shows the free body diagram for both segments of shaft, indicating the direction of the torsional moments.

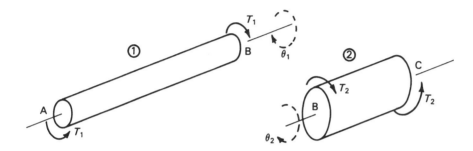

Under the action of the torsional moments, both sections of shaft obviously will rotate. Let's say that AB rotates by an amount θ_1, and BC by an amount θ_2. As both A and C are fixed supports, this rotation will in both cases represent the amount of twisting that takes place at B.

Can you write down a relationship between θ_1 and θ_2?

$$\theta_1 = \theta_2$$

This is common sense. As both segments of shaft are connected rigidly at B, it follows that they must rotate by the same amount. This is, in fact, an expression of *compatibility of displacements* and provides the additional equation that is necessary to solve for T_1 and T_2. The concept of displacement compatibility is common and is widely used in the analysis of solid components.

Now move to the next frame to see how the equation of equilibrium and the equation of displacement compatibility can be combined to solve for the unknown Torsional Moments, T_1 and T_2.

31

So far, we have produced two equations:

Equilibrium: $\qquad\qquad\qquad\qquad T = T_1 + T_2$

Displacement compatibility: $\qquad \theta_1 = \theta_2$

We are attempting to find a solution for T_1 and T_2 but the second equation is expressed in terms of θ_1 and θ_2. It is therefore necessary to eliminate θ_1 and θ_2 from this second equation, replacing both terms by expressions in T_1 and T_2 and hence leading to two equations which can be solved directly for the torsional moments in each segment of the shaft.

   Can you write down a relationship between θ_1 and T_1, and a corresponding relationship between θ_2 and T_2? (Hint: think back over the work we have been dealing with in this programme.)

32

$$\theta_1 = \frac{T_1 L_1}{G_1 J_1}; \quad \theta_2 = \frac{T_2 L_2}{G_2 J_2}$$

These relationships follow directly from the general torsion equations (see Frame 12, Equation (7.4) if in doubt). It follows, therefore, that the two fundamental equations describing the behaviour of this shaft can be written as:

Equilibrium: $\qquad\qquad\qquad\qquad T = T_1 + T_2$

Displacement compatibility: $\quad \dfrac{T_1 L_1}{G_1 J_1} = \dfrac{T_2 L_2}{G_2 J_2}$

   Rearrange the above two equations to give the expressions for T_1 and T_2.

33

$$T_1 = \frac{T(G_1 J_1 L_2)}{(G_1 J_1 L_2 + G_2 J_2 L_1)}; \quad T_2 = \frac{T(G_2 J_2 L_1)}{(G_1 J_1 L_2 + G_2 J_2 L_1)}$$

34

These final two equations give the torsional moments in each segment of the shaft. If the stress in each segment is required, or the angular rotation is to be determined, the general torsional stress equations (Equation (7.4)) can be applied to either segment using the appropriate torsional moment calculated from the equations in Frame 33.

The equations in Frame 33 need not necessarily be remembered. If you understand the principles behind their derivation, you should be able to tackle any similar problem working from first principles of *equilibrium* and *displacement compatibility*.

Now try a problem.

A solid circular shaft, AC, has a total length of 1.5 metres and is 50 mm in diameter. A gear wheel positioned at B, 0.5 metres from the left-hand end of the shaft ,A, exerts a torque of 450 N m. If the ends A and C are instantaneously locked in position by brakes just before the torque is applied, determine the torsional moment induced in both segments of the shaft.

35

$$T_1(\text{AB}) = 300 \text{ N m}; \quad T_2(\text{BC}) = 150 \text{ N m}$$

The solution follows directly from the equations in Frame 33, although for practice you should develop the answers from first principles. However, if the equations are used, they can be simplified considerably, as both segments of the shaft are identical and therefore the Shear Modulus terms (G) and the Polar Second Moment of Area terms (J) cancel.

Hence:

For the length AB: $\qquad T_1 = \dfrac{T \times L_2}{(L_1 + L_2)} = \dfrac{450 \times 1.0}{(0.5 + 1.0)} = 300 \text{ N m}$

For the length BC: $\qquad T_2 = \dfrac{T \times L_1}{(L_1 + L_2)} = \dfrac{450 \times 0.5}{(0.5 + 1.0)} = 150 \text{ N m}$

Note that for a continuous uniform shaft, the distribution of a torque applied at some point along its length is merely proportional to the lengths into which the shaft is divided by the point of application of the torque.

Using the result you have just obtained, calculate the maximum shearing stresses in both segments of the shaft and the angular twist of the shaft after the torque is applied. Take G = 80 GN/m².

36

> (AB) 12.22 MN/m^2;   (BC) 6.11 MN/m^2;   0.0031 rad

Check your solution:

The polar second moment of area (J) is given by:

$$J = \frac{\pi R^4}{2}$$

$$= \frac{\pi \times (25 \times 10^{-3})^4}{2}$$

$$= 613.59 \times 10^{-9} \text{ m}^4$$

Hence the maximum shear stress (τ) in the length AB, which will occur at the outer surface of the section is given by:

$$\tau = \frac{TR}{J}$$

$$= \frac{300 \times (25 \times 10^{-3})}{613.59 \times 10^{-9}}$$

$$= 12.22 \text{ MN/m}^2$$

The torsional moment in the length BC is half that in the length AB and hence the maximum shear stress in this length will be half as great, that is, 6.11 MN/m^2.

To calculate the angular twist in the shaft, either AB or BC can be considered, as the result must be the same in both cases. Hence, considering the length AB:

The angle of twist (θ) is given by:

$$\theta = \frac{TL}{JG}$$

$$= \frac{300 \times 0.5}{(613.59 \times 10^{-9}) \times (80 \times 10^9)}$$

$$= 0.0031 \text{ rad}$$

You should also calculate the angle of twist for the length BC to convince yourself that either calculation will give the same answer.

This is just one example of this type of problem. There are more examples of a similar nature for you to practice on at the end of this programme.

Now on to the next frame.

37

NON-PRISMATIC SECTIONS

So far we have looked mainly at problems involving prismatic sections; that is, those having constant cross-sectional area. To complete our study of torsional stresses we shall look briefly in some more detail at the case of non-prismatic sections where the cross-sectional area varies along the length of the member. The figure below illustrates a simple example of a non-prismatic shaft, in this case manufactured from two separate prismatic sections. For simplicity, we shall assume that the torsional moment is constant along the length of the shaft.

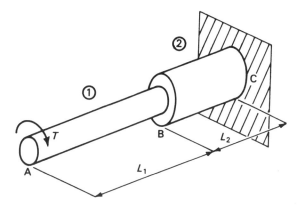

Generally, there are two sets of calculations associated with the design or analysis of such a shaft:

(i) Calculation of sectional stress.
The general formula to use is the one that by now you should be quite familiar with:

$$\frac{\tau}{r} = \frac{T}{J}$$

In order to calculate the stress at any particular cross-section it is only necessary to calculate and use the polar second moment of area based on the radius appropriate to the section under consideration.

(ii) Calculation of the total angle of twist along the shaft.
The formula we would use for prismatic sections is given by:

$$\frac{T}{J} = \frac{G\theta}{L}$$

or

$$\theta = \frac{TL}{GJ}$$

In the case of the shaft shown in the diagram above, can you write down an expression for the total angular rotation along the shaft?

38

$$\boxed{\theta = \theta_1 + \theta_2 = \frac{TL_1}{GJ_1} + \frac{TL_2}{GJ_2}}$$

You should have reasoned that the total angular rotation along the length of the shaft is the rotation of the length AB plus that of the length BC.

If the shaft consists of several lengths of differing sectional properties, the total angular rotation can be expressed in general terms as:

$$\theta = \sum \frac{TL_i}{GJ_i}$$

The shaft shown in the figure in Frame 37 consists of two lengths each 500 mm long, but the polar second moments of area of AB and BC are 1×10^{-6} m^4 and 2×10^{-6} m^4 respectively. If a clockwise torque of 400 N m is applied to the free end, A, what is the total angular rotation of the shaft? Take $G = 80$ GN/m^2.

39

$$\boxed{0.00375 \text{ rad}}$$

The solution is as follows:

$$\theta = \frac{TL_1}{GJ_1} + \frac{TL_2}{GJ_2}$$

$$= \frac{400 \times 0.5}{(80 \times 10^9) \times (1 \times 10^{-6})} + \frac{400 \times 0.5}{(80 \times 10^9) \times (2 \times 10^{-6})}$$

$$= \frac{400 \times 0.5}{80 \times 10^9} \left[\frac{1}{1 \times 10^{-6}} + \frac{1}{2 \times 10^{-6}} \right]$$

$$= 0.00375 \text{ rad}$$

We have, of course, assumed that the torsional moment is constant along the shaft. This may not always be the case.

If the shaft in Frame 37 now has a clockwise torque of 400 N m applied at A and an additional clockwise torque of 300 N m acting at B, what is the torsional moment acting on the lengths AB and BC?

400 N m;   700 N m

The figure below shows the free body diagrams for the two segments of the shaft.

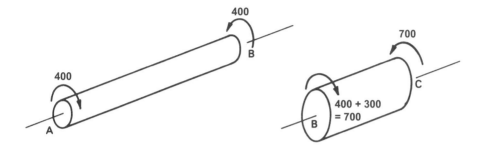

What would the total torsional rotation of the shaft be under the action of these two applied torques? (Hint: this is practically the same as the last problem, only the values of the moments have changed.)

41

0.00469 rad

The solution is as follows:

$$\theta = \frac{T_1 L_1}{GJ_1} + \frac{T_2 L_2}{GJ_2}$$

$$= \frac{400 \times 0.5}{(80 \times 10^9) \times (1 \times 10^{-6})} + \frac{700 \times 0.5}{(80 \times 10^9) \times (2 \times 10^{-6})}$$

$$= \frac{0.5}{80 \times 10^9} \left[\frac{400}{1 \times 10^{-6}} + \frac{700}{2 \times 10^{-6}} \right]$$

$$= 0.00469 \text{ rad}$$

Now let's look at a more complex case of torsion in non-prismatic sections.

42

Consider the case of a circular shaft with a continuously varying cross-section, as shown below. As the radius varies, so does the polar second moment of area, and because the torsion equations have been derived for a shaft of constant sectional profile they can no longer be used directly to determine the rotation of this shaft.

However, let's approximate the profile to a series of short prismatic sections, as shown in the second figure, the length of each section being very small and equal to δx.

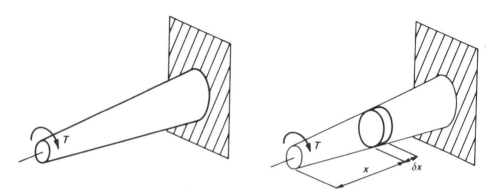

If each segment is assumed to be prismatic, the small rotation $\delta\theta$ of a typical segment at a distance x from the free end can be calculated using the usual formula with the length of the segment taken as δx:

$$\delta\theta = \frac{T\delta x}{GJ_x}$$

where J_x is the polar second moment of area of the segment which will vary with the distance x along the shaft.

Using this formula, can you write down an expression for the total angular rotation along the shaft?

43

$$\theta = \int_0^L \frac{T\mathrm{d}x}{GJ_x}$$

This expression follows from the application of the normal principles of calculus and can be used to determine the rotation of any non-prismatic section. However, as the polar second moment of area varies with distance x, the integration of this expression can be quite complex and may necessitate the use of numerical integration methods.

Try the following problem – you may need to revise your integral calculus first!

A shaft of circular cross-section has a polar second moment of area that varies according to the formula $J_x = J_0(1 + \{x/L\})^4$, where x is measured from the end where the polar second moment of area is J_0. If the length of the shaft is L and it is subject to a torsional moment T, determine an expression for the total rotation of the shaft.

44

$$\boxed{\frac{7}{24}\frac{TL}{GJ_0}}$$

Using the formula in Frame 43, the rotation of the shaft is given by:

$$\theta = \int_0^L \frac{T\,\mathrm{d}x}{GJ_x}$$

$$= \frac{T}{GJ_0} \int_0^L \frac{\mathrm{d}x}{(1 + \{x/L\})^4}$$

$$= \frac{T}{GJ_0} \left[-\frac{L}{3(1 + \{x/L\})^3} \right]_0^L$$

$$= \frac{TL}{3GJ_0} \left[-\frac{1}{8} + 1 \right]$$

$$= \frac{7}{24}\frac{TL}{GJ_0}$$

We have looked only at shafts where the cross-sectional geometry varies, and shown how to calculate the rotation caused by a constant applied torque. In more complex problems, both the torque, T, and the shear modulus, G, could vary along the length of the shaft. Such problems can be tackled using the methods employed above, provided that the variation of all the parameters can be defined in terms of a variable distance x measured along the shaft, enabling appropriate integration methods to be employed.

45

TORSION OF NON-CIRCULAR SECTIONS

In this programme we have confined our studies to the torsion of circular sections and have derived the relationship that:

$$\frac{T}{J} = \frac{G\theta}{L}$$

or

$$T = \frac{GJ\theta}{L}$$

For circular sections, J is the polar second moment of area. For sections that are not circular, the above equation can still be used provided that J is taken as the *torsional constant* for the section, which in general will not be equal to the polar second moment of area. The calculation of the torsional constant and the treatment of non-circular sections is outside the scope of this book.

46

$$\boxed{\text{TO REMEMBER}}$$

$$\frac{\tau}{r} = \frac{T}{J} = \frac{G\theta}{L} \quad \text{(See Frame 12 for a definition of terms.)}$$

For a solid circular section:

$$J = \frac{\pi R^4}{2}$$

For a non-prismatic section:

$$\theta = \int_0^L \frac{T \, dx}{G J_x}$$

47

$$\boxed{\text{FURTHER PROBLEMS}}$$

Note: In all these problems, take the Shear Modulus, G, to be 80 GN/m^2.

1. A solid circular drive shaft has a diameter of 50 mm. If it is subjected to a torque of 2 kN m, calculate (i) the maximum shear stress developed; and (ii) the angular twist per unit length of shaft.

Ans. 81.49 MN/m^2, 0.041 rad/metre.

2. The shear stresses in a solid circular shaft are limited to a maximum value of 75 MN/m^2 and the angular twist permitted is no greater than 0.5 degrees over a length of 1 metre. If both of these limiting conditions are to be satisfied simultaneously, determine the least radius of the section and the maximum permissible torque.

Ans. 107.43 mm; 146.07 kNm.

3. A hollow circular shaft has an external radius of 50 mm and an internal radius of 25 mm. If the allowable maximum shear stress is 80 MN/m^2, what is the allowable torque and the twist of the shaft per metre length when this torque is applied?

Ans. 14.73 kN m; 0.02 rad/metre.

4. The shear stresses in a hollow circular shaft are limited to a maximum value of 50 MN/m^2 and the angular twist permitted is no greater than 0.5 degrees over a length of 1 metre. If both of these limiting conditions are to be met simultaneously when a torque of 25 kNm is applied, determine the required internal and external diameters of the shaft.

Ans. 143.24 mm; 86.58mm.

5. A solid circular shaft rotates at 100 revs per minute and is to be designed to transmit 200 kW. If the maximum shear stress is not to exceed 50 MN/m^2, what is the least radius of the shaft?

Ans. 62.42 mm.

6. A propeller shaft of a ship is fabricated from a hollow circular section with external and internal diameters of 500 mm and 300 mm, respectively. If it rotates at a constant speed of 100 revs per minute, what power can be transmitted if the maximum shear stress is not to exceed 40 MN/m^2?

Ans. 8.95 MW.

7. Determine the maximum torque that can be applied at the junction of the two solid circular shafts shown in figure Q7. Both shafts are firmly restrained at their ends as shown and the maximum shear stress is limited to 75 MN/m^2.

Ans. 1.04 kN m.

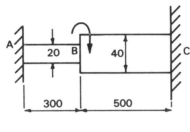

Q7

8. The shaft in question 7 is to be redesigned to carry a 10% increase in the calculated torque. Determine the necessary diameters of both sections of the shaft if the ratio of the shaft diameters remains constant.

Ans. 41.28 and 20.64 mm.

9. An alternative design for the shaft in question 7 is for the length BC to be fabricated from a hollow tubular section as shown in figure Q9. Calculate the torque that can be applied to this shaft if the maximum shear stress is still limited to 75 MN/m².

Ans. 981.75 N m.

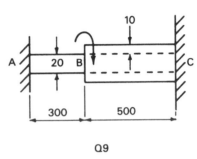

Q9

10. The shaft in figure Q10 is fabricated from solid circular section and is stepped as shown. If torques are applied as shown, determine (i) the total angular twist of the section and (ii) the maximum shear stress in each length of the shaft.

Ans. 0.0763 rad; 244.46, 71.30 and 39.23 MN/m².

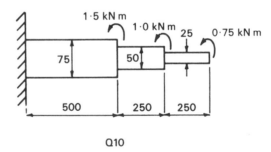

Q10

11. A solid circular shaft has a diameter of d at one end and a diameter of $1.2d$ at the other end with a uniform taper between. The length of the shaft is L and it is subject to a torque T. Determine an expression for the total angular twist over the length of the shaft. *(Hint: look at the equation in Frame 43 and the example in Frame 44.)*

Ans. $22.47TL/\pi Gd^4$.

12. The shaft in question 11 is 2 metres long, the diameter $d = 100$ mm and it rotates at 100 revs per minute. If the total angular twist over the length of the shaft is limited to 1 degree, what is the maximum power that can be transmitted based on this limiting condition?

Ans. 102 kW.

Programme 8

STRESS
TRANSFORMATIONS
AND MOHR'S CIRCLE
OF STRESS

On completion of this programme you will be able to:

- Define 'Principal Stress'
- Define 'Principal Plane'
- Draw a Mohr's Circle of Stress for a range of complex stress situations
- Interpret a Mohr's Circle of Stress
- Determine the magnitude of the principal stresses
- Identify the orientation of the principal planes
- Determine the magnitude and orientation of the planes of maximum shear stress
- Identify the orientation of a plane of given stress condition
- Determine the state of stress on a plane of given orientation

1

In Programmes 4 to 7 we learnt how to calculate the stress within a mechanical component when it is subjected to direct axial loading, bending, shear and torsion. The theories we have developed are applicable to a wide range of problems and the formulae we have used are widely utilised in the design of many types of component using different materials.

However, in practice, many components have to withstand a combination of loading. A connecting rod in a reciprocating engine is subject to an axial load when the piston is top dead-centre. Away from this position, the rod is subject to both axial and bending loads. Hence many components are subject to much more complex stress situations than those we have already considered. For example, we have seen that the cranked cantilever beam in Frame 2 of Programme 7 is stressed from a combination of bending, shear and torsion, and indeed there are many practical situations where such complex stress combinations occur. In Programme 13 we shall look at the development of stresses in cylinders: another example of a complex stress situation.

One of the most important combinations of stress that can occur in practical design is that of direct stress acting on a body in combination with shearing stress. A typical example is a propellor shaft in which the thrust causes axial loading on the shaft while the transmission of power causes torsional shear stress. If such a shaft is also subjected to bending the stress combination can be quite complex and in this programme we are going to look at both numerical and graphical techniques through which detailed stress analysis may be performed.

Before you go on you will need to have a supply of graph paper, a compass and a protractor. When you have these, move on to the next frame.

2

Let's start by looking at a simple problem. The bar shown in the figure (at the top of the next page) is stressed by the application of an axial load F. Let's assume that the bar has a uniform rectangular cross-sectional area A and we are interested in the stress condition at the cross-section B–B.

State what sort of stress condition exists at this cross-section and write down the equation for this stress in terms of F and A.

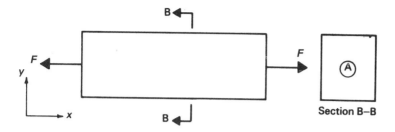

3

> Uniform direct stress normal to the section: $\sigma_x = \dfrac{F}{A}$

Now let's look at the same bar but this time take a section B–B which is inclined at an angle θ to the vertical. If we look at the free body diagram of that part of the bar to the right of section B–B it is obvious that, to ensure horizontal equilibrium, there must be a horizontal force F acting at the section. This force will have components acting normal to the section (N) and along the section (S). We shall assume that the directions of these components are as shown. We shall say more about sign conventions later.

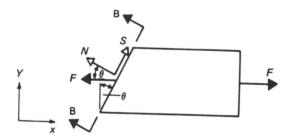

Can you write down two equation relating N and S to F and θ?

4

$$N = F\cos\theta; \quad S = -F\sin\theta$$

This follows from a straightforward resolution of the force F acting at the section into its components along and perpendicular to the section.
What do you deduce about the stresses acting on the face B–B?

5

> There are both normal and shear stresses acting on this face.

As the face B–B has a normal force N acting on it, it follows that there must be normal *stresses* acting on this face. Similarly, if there is a force S acting along the face B–B, there must be shearing stresses acting along this face.

This is an important conclusion. So far we have looked at components in tension or compression and determined the stresses in these components based on a simple calculation of axial force divided by the cross-sectional area of the member. The cross-sectional area was in fact the area *normal* to the direction of the force.

What we have now concluded is that if we take a section that is not normal to the direction of the force, the state of stress on this section is more complex and consists of a combination of normal and shear stresses. This is an important observation – make sure that you fully appreciate it.

Remembering that the basic definition of stress is force divided by the area on which the force acts, derive equations for the normal (σ) and shear (τ) stresses acting on the inclined face B–B expressed in terms of the stress σ_x ($= F/A$).

6

> $$\sigma = \sigma_x \cos^2 \theta \qquad \tau = -\sigma_x \sin \theta \cos \theta$$

These equations follow directly from the general definition of stress, and from the geometry of the section we are considering:

The area (A') of the face B–B is given by:

$$A' = \frac{A}{\cos \theta} \quad \text{(simple geometry)}$$

Hence the normal stress is given by:

$$\sigma = \frac{N}{A'} = \frac{F \cos \theta}{A / \cos \theta} = \frac{F}{A} \cos^2 \theta = \sigma_x \cos^2 \theta$$

and the shear stress is given by:

$$\tau = \frac{S}{A'} = \frac{F \sin \theta}{A / \cos \theta} = -\frac{F}{A} \sin \theta \cos \theta = -\sigma_x \sin \theta \cos \theta$$

These stress equations can be written more conveniently as:

$$\sigma = \frac{\sigma_x}{2}(1 + \cos(2\theta)) \tag{8.1}$$

and

$$\tau = -\frac{\sigma_x}{2}\sin(2\theta) \tag{8.2}$$

which follow from the double angle relationships that:

$$\cos^2\theta = \frac{(1 + \cos(2\theta))}{2} \quad \text{and} \quad \sin\theta\cos\theta = \frac{\sin(2\theta)}{2}$$

Now try the following exercise.

A horizontal bar of rectangular cross-sectional area 100 mm² is subject to an axial tensile force of 10 kN. Prepare a table of values of normal and shearing stresses on planes inclined at θ to the vertical where θ varies from 0° to 180° in steps of 15°. Plot a graph of shearing stress (τ as y-coordinate) against normal stress (σ as x-coordinate), and answer the following question:
(i) What is the shape of the graph?
(ii) What is
 (a) the maximum normal stress;
 (b) the minimum normal stress;
 (c) the maximum shear stress; and
 (d) the angle to the vertical of the planes on which these stresses occur?

7

(i) Circular
(ii) (a) 100 MN/m²; (b) 0 MN/m²; (c) ± 50 MN/m²; (d) 0°, 90°, 45° and 135°

Check your solution:

$\theta°$	$\sigma\,(\text{MN/m}^2)$	$\tau\,(\text{MN/m}^2)$
0	100	0
15	93.3	−25
30	75	−43.3
45	50	−50
60	25	−43.3
75	6.7	−25
90	0	0
105	6.7	25
120	25	43.3
135	50	50
150	75	43.3
165	93.3	25
180	100	0

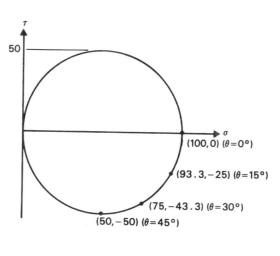

8

The diagram you have just drawn is known as a *Mohr's Circle of Stress*. We shall look more closely at Mohr's circles later in this programme, but essentially this form of construction enables us to describe in graphical form the variation of stresses acting on any inclined plane.

We drew this circle by calculating and plotting a number of points. However, once it is recognised that the plot is circular and the properties of the circle are identified, then it is possible to draw and use such a circle to carry out a stress analysis of any such similar problem without the necessity of calculating and plotting every point.

Let's look again at the circle we have just plotted. You have already deduced that the maximum normal stress was 100 MN/m^2 and occurred on the plane inclined at 0°. This is in fact the stress σ_x and corresponds to the point marked C in the diagram. The minimum normal stress was 0 MN/m^2 acting on a plane at 90° to the vertical, which corresponds to the point A on the diagram.

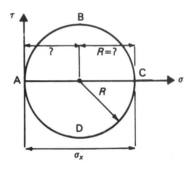

If σ_x is a known stress, what would be the radius of the circle, and which point defines its centre?

9

$$\boxed{\text{Radius} = \frac{\sigma_x}{2}; \quad \text{Centre at } \sigma = \frac{\sigma_x}{2}, \tau = 0}$$

Hence for any component subject to a direct tensile (or compressive) stress, σ_x, acting on a vertical section then the Mohr's Circle of Stress can be drawn simply by locating the centre at coordinates of $\sigma_x/2$ and zero, and drawing a circle of radius $\sigma_x/2$. This will now define fully the state of stress (σ and τ) on all inclined planes. How then do we use the circle to determine the stresses on any given plane?

Can you recall the expressions for σ and τ in terms of $\cos(2\theta)$ and $\sin(2\theta)$?

$$\sigma = \frac{\sigma_x}{2}(1 + \cos(2\theta)); \quad \tau = -\frac{\sigma_x}{2}\sin(2\theta)$$

It follows from these two equations that if a point (E) is taken on the circle which is at an angular distance of 2θ from C, then this point must represent the stresses σ and τ on the plane inclined at an angle θ to the vertical. The angle 2θ is the angle subtended at the centre of the circle by the arc CE and is measured in a *clockwise* direction from C. The construction below shows that E must represent the two equations above.

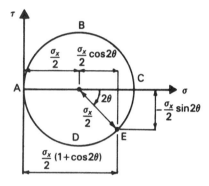

Refer to the Mohr's Circle of Stress that you drew in response to the problem in Frame 6 and use the circle to determine the stress on two perpendicular planes inclined at 20° and 110° to the vertical.

11

$$\begin{array}{lll} \theta = 20° & \sigma = 88.3 \text{ MN/m}^2 & \tau = -32.1 \text{ MN/m}^2 \\ \theta = 110° & \sigma = 11.7 \text{ MN/m}^2 & \tau = +32.1 \text{ MN/m}^2 \end{array}$$

You should obtain these answers by turning off angles of 40° and 220° in a clockwise direction from C and reading off the appropriate stresses. You could have calculated these values using the equations, and it is probably a good idea to check your answers using the equations to convince yourself that the circle is merely a graphical interpretation of the equations.

The two planes you have just considered are at right angles. What do you notice about the shear stress on these two planes and the corresponding points you have drawn on the diagram?

12

> The shear stresses have the same numerical value and
> the two points are on opposite ends of a diameter.

The fact that the shear stresses are of the same magnitude on two perpendicular planes should not surprise you – remember the concept of *complementary shear stresses*? The fact that the two points representing these two planes are on the opposite ends of a diameter is a useful result to remember, as the form of construction is such that any pair of points at the opposite ends of the diameter *always* represent the stresses on a pair of mutually perpendicular planes.

Now let's look at some other features of the Mohr's Circle of Stress that will be useful in our further studies of this subject.

Refer to the diagram in Frame 10 and write down what you think is significant about the stresses and the inclination of the planes represented by the points marked C, A, B and D.

13

Did you draw the following conclusions?

Point C.   Point C represents a plane on which the shear stress is zero. It also represents the plane on which the normal stress is at a maximum. A plane subject to zero shear stress is in fact called a *principal plane*, and the normal stress on this plane is a principal stress – in this case a *maximum* principal stress.

Point A.   Point A also represents a plane on which the shear stress is zero and on which the normal stress is at a minimum. By the above definition it is also a principal plane and the normal stress (which in this instance happens to be zero) is a *minimum* principal stress.

Points A and C are also on the opposite ends of the diameter, thus indicating that the principal planes are at right angles to each other.

Points B and D.   These two points represent the planes on which the shear stress is at a maximum. Note that the magnitude of the maximum shear stress is equal to the radius of the circle which in this instance is one half of the maximum principal stress. The angular distance of D from C is 90° ($2\theta = 90°$). C represents a principal plane and hence the plane of maximum shear represented by D is inclined at 45° to the principal plane ($\theta = 45°$). As the other plane of maximum shear represented by B is on the opposite end of the diameter to D, it also follows that both planes of maximum shear are at right angles to each other and at 45° to the principal planes.

Make sure that you fully understand these conclusions as they are generally applicable to the work we shall do later in this programme. Now try some problems.

PROBLEMS

1. Define the terms *principal stress* and *principal planes*.
Ans. See Frame 13.

2. A bar of circular cross-section of radius 20 mm carries an axial tensile load of 100 kN. Draw the Mohr's Circle of Stress and determine the values of the principal stresses and the maximum shear stresses.
Ans. 79.6; 0; ± 39.8 MN/m².

3. What is the inclination to the longitudinal axis of the bar of the planes on which the normal stress is 50 MN/m²?
Ans. 52.5°; 127.5°.

4. If the bar in question 2 has a shear strength of 50 MN/m², to what value can the axial load be safely increased?
Ans. 125.66 kN.

5. If the load on the bar is increased to the value calculated in question 4, what will be the values of the maximum and minimum principal stresses?
Ans. 100 MN/m²; 0 MN/m².

15

The theory we have developed so far has been based on an examination of the state of stress in a uniformly loaded bar where the stresses acting on the face of any inclined section are uniform throughout the section under consideration. In many other types of problem this is often not the case, and it is more usual to describe the state of stress at a *point* in a component. In the case of the bar we originally considered in Frame 2, this point can be represented by the small rectangular element indicated in the figure below.

Although this element is infinitesimally small, in practice we draw it with a finite size so that we can show clearly the stresses acting at the point. The sides of this element represent the faces of the plane inclined at an angle θ and the plane which is perpendicular to this first plane. The stresses acting *at this point* on the two perpendicular planes can be indicated in magnitude and direction on this element.

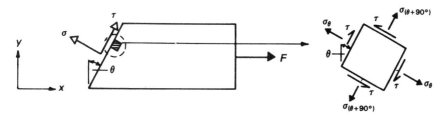

16

At this stage we shall now define more clearly the sign convention we have been using and will continue to use:

(i) The angle θ which defines the inclination of the face of an element is measured in a clockwise direction from the positive direction of the y-axis.

(ii) A normal stress is positive if it causes tension in the element.

(iii) Shear stresses are positive if the stresses on the two opposite faces of an element form a couple that would cause a *clockwise* rotation of the element.

Because shear stresses on two parallel faces must be accompanied by equal complementary shear stresses on the two perpendicular faces, it follows that one pair of faces will always be acted on by positive shear stresses and the other by negative shear stresses.

The figure below shows the stresses acting on a typical element according to this convention. In the derivation of our original stress equations we in fact took the shear stresses on the face inclined at θ to the positive direction of the y-axis as being positive. We shall continue to do this.

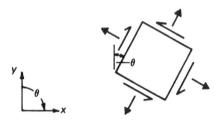

In the problem in Frame 11 you calculated that the stresses on a plane inclined at 20°
were $\sigma = 88.3$ MN/m^2 and $\tau = -32.1$ MN/m^2. The corresponding stresses on the
perpendicular plane were $\sigma = 11.7$ MN/m^2 and $\tau = +32.1$ MN/m^2. Show this set of
stresses on a sketch of a small element.

17

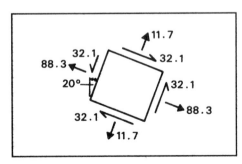

Now go on to the next frame.

18

We have looked at a relatively simple case of stress analysis and developed some important concepts by examining the case of a bar in uniaxial tension. Let's extend these concepts by examining the state of stress at a point in a component which is subject to *biaxial* stress; that is, subject to direct stresses in the direction of both the *x*- and *y*-axes, as shown in the figure below. There are many practical situations where such a state of stress can exist including, for example, shell structures with thin walls used as pressure vessels to contain gas or liquids.

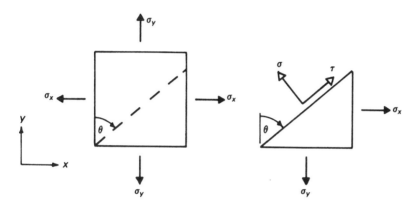

If we are interested in the state of stress on a plane inclined at an angle θ to the positive direction of the *y*-axis, we can take a section through our small element as shown in the second diagram above. We will assume that the stresses on the inclined face of the element consist of both normal stresses, σ, and shear stresses, τ.

By considering the equilibrium of this wedge-shaped element, can you derive expressions for σ and τ in terms of σ_x, σ_y and θ? (Hint: take the area of the inclined face as A and remember that force = stress × area.)

$$\sigma = \sigma_x \cos^2 \theta + \sigma_y \sin^2 \theta; \quad \tau = -(\sigma_x - \sigma_y) \sin \theta \cos \theta$$

If you got this answer, can you express the equations in terms of 2θ by using the double angle relationship:

$$\sin(2\theta) = 2 \sin \theta \cos \theta$$

and
$$\cos(2\theta) = 2 \cos^2 \theta - 1 = 1 - 2 \sin^2 \theta$$

The complete solution is in the next frame.

20

$$\sigma = \frac{(\sigma_x + \sigma_y)}{2} + \frac{(\sigma_x - \sigma_y)}{2}\cos(2\theta); \quad \tau = \frac{-(\sigma_x - \sigma_y)}{2}\sin(2\theta)$$

The proof of these equations follows directly from considerations of the equilibrium of the small, wedge-shaped element which, for clarity, is reproduced below:

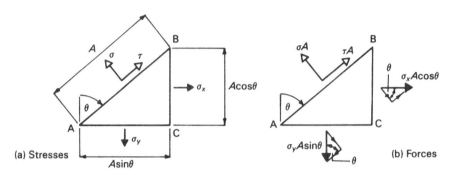

(a) Stresses   (b) Forces

The area of face AB $= A$

Hence: the area of face BC $= A\cos\theta$

the area of face AC $= A\sin\theta$

The normal force on the face AB $= \sigma \times A$

The shear force on the face AB $= \tau \times A$

The force on the face BC $= \sigma_x \times (A\cos\theta)$

The force on the face AC $= \sigma_y \times (A\sin\theta)$

Resolving forces perpendicular to the plane AB (see figure (b)):

$$\sigma \times A = (\sigma_x \times A\cos\theta) \times \cos\theta + (\sigma_y \times A\sin\theta) \times \sin\theta$$

Hence: $\sigma = \sigma_x \cos^2\theta + \sigma_y \sin^2\theta$

$$= \sigma_x \frac{(\cos(2\theta) + 1)}{2} + \sigma_y \frac{(1 - \cos(2\theta))}{2}$$

that is $\sigma = \dfrac{(\sigma_x + \sigma_y)}{2} + \dfrac{(\sigma_x - \sigma_y)}{2}\cos(2\theta)$ (8.3)

Similarly, resolving along the face AB:

$$\tau \times A = -(\sigma_x \times A\cos\theta) \times \sin\theta + (\sigma_y \times A\sin\theta) \times \cos\theta$$

hence: $\tau = -(\sigma_x - \sigma_y)\sin\theta\cos\theta$

$$= -\frac{(\sigma_x - \sigma_y)}{2}\sin(2\theta)$$ (8.4)

If Equations (8.3) and (8.4) are used to plot the variation of σ and τ for different values of θ, what shape of graph would you expect?

21

> A circle – a *Mohr's Circle*

If Equations (8.3) and (8.4) are compared with Equations (8.1) and (8.2), you will see that they are almost identical. In fact if we put $\sigma_y = 0$ in both Equations (8.3) and (8.4), we would obtain Equations (8.1) and (8.2). We saw that Equations (8.1) and (8.2) were in fact the equations of a circle, and indeed this second pair of equations also describes a circle.

If the equations are plotted as shown below, with tensile normal stresses taken as positive to the right of the origin, it can be seen that the circle is practically the same as the one we considered for uniaxial stress. However, it no longer passes through the origin but is displaced so that its centre is at $(\sigma_x + \sigma_y)/2$ and its radius is equal to $(\sigma_x - \sigma_y)/2$. In all other respects the interpretation of the stresses from the circle is the same as before.

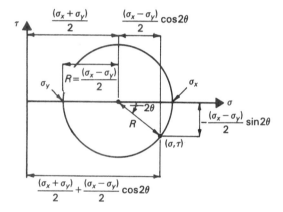

Note that as both σ_x and σ_y occur on planes on which the shear stress is zero, by our previous definitions σ_x and σ_y are principal stresses and the planes on which they occur are principal planes.

Sketch the Mohr's Circle of Stress for a point in a component where the principal stresses (σ_x and σ_y) are given by (i) 60 & 30 MN/m² (ii) 60 & −30 MN/m²; and (iii) −60 & −30 MN/m². In all cases, indicate the value of the maximum shear stress. Remember that tensile stresses are plotted as positive.

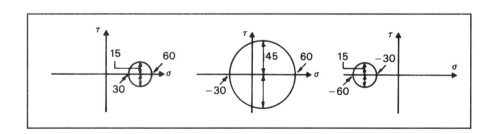

22

23

Now let's look at another stress situation: in this case a small element of a material which is subjected to shear stresses only. Note that in the diagram the shear stresses on the vertical faces (τ') have been drawn in a direction that would cause clockwise rotation of the element (positive shear according to our sign convention). Similarly, the complementary shear stresses have been drawn as negative shear stresses according to our sign convention.

Again, if we are interested in the stress situation on a plane inclined at an angle θ to the positive direction of the y-axis, we can take a section through the small element and consider the equilibrium of the small wedge-shaped element shown in the second figure.

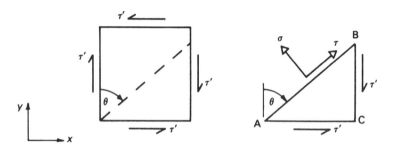

Can you derive expressions for σ and τ in terms of τ' and θ. Express your answers in terms of 2θ, making use of the double-angle relationships.

24

$$\sigma = \tau' \sin(2\theta) \qquad \tau = \tau' \cos(2\theta)$$

This derivation is very similar to that given in Frame 20. Check your working:

The area of face $AB = A$

Hence:
the area of face $BC = A \cos\theta$

the area of face $AC = A \sin\theta$

The normal force on the face $AB = \sigma \times A$

The shear force on the face $AB = \tau \times A$

The force on the face $BC = \tau' \times (A \cos\theta)$

The force on the face $AC = \tau'(A \sin\theta)$

Resolving forces perpendicular to the plane AB:

$$\sigma \times A = (\tau' \times A \cos\theta) \times \sin\theta + (\tau' \times A \sin\theta) \times \cos\theta$$

Hence:
$$\sigma = \tau' 2\sin\theta\cos\theta$$

∴
$$\sigma = \tau' \sin(2\theta) \tag{8.5}$$

Similarly, resolving along the face AB:

$$\tau \times A = (\tau' \times A \cos\theta)\cos\theta - (\tau' \times A \sin\theta)\sin\theta$$

Hence
$$\tau = \tau'(\cos^2\theta - \sin^2\theta)$$

∴
$$\tau = \tau' \cos(2\theta) \tag{8.6}$$

These equations define the variation of σ and τ for different values of θ. By now you should be anticipating that a plot of these equations will be circular.

Can you sketch the Mohr's Circle given by these two equations, indicating the direction of the angle 2θ which would give the stresses on any plane inclined at an angle θ?

25

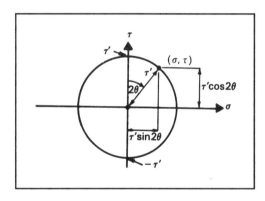

You will note that in the case of an element subjected to pure shear, the Mohr's Circle is centred on the origin and has a radius equal to the value of the shear stress, τ'.

Expressed in terms of τ', what are the values of the principal stresses and the inclination of the planes on which they occur?

26

+τ' on a plane at 45° ($2\theta = 90°$) and $-\tau$ on a plane at 135° ($2\theta = 270°$)

Now try some further problems to give you more practice at transforming stresses and drawing and interpreting Mohr's Circles of Stress.

27

$$\boxed{\text{PROBLEMS}}$$

1. Figure Q1 shows an element in a state of biaxial stress. If $\sigma_x = 70$ MN/m² and $\sigma_y = 30$ MN/m² determine, by working from first principles (a) the stresses acting on planes inclines at 20° and 110° to the positive direction of the y-axis; and (b) the magnitude of the maximum shear stress.

Ans. (a) 65.32, −12.86 and 34.68, 12.86 MN/m²; (b) 20 MN/m².

2. Repeat question 1(a), but this time plot a Mohr's Circle of Stress and obtain the answers from the diagram. Show the magnitude and direction of the stresses on a sketch of a small rectangular element orientated at the correct angle.

Ans. See diagrams at the bottom of the page.

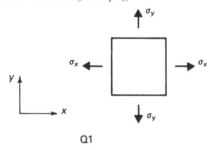

Q1

3. Repeat questions 1 and 2 for stresses of $\sigma_x = 70$ MN/m² and $\sigma_y = -20$ MN/m²

Ans. (a) 59.47, −28.92 and −9.47, 28.92 MN/m²; (b) 45 MN/m².

4. Using the Mohr's Circle drawn in question 3, determine the inclinations of the planes that are subjected only to shear stresses. What is the value of shear stress on these planes?

Ans. 61.9° and 118.1° measured from the positive direction of the y-axis, ±37.5 MN/m².

5. Use your Mohr's Circle diagram from question 3 to determine the inclinations of the planes on which the normal stresses are 35 MN/m²?

Ans. 38.6° and 141.4° measured from the positive direction of the y-axis.

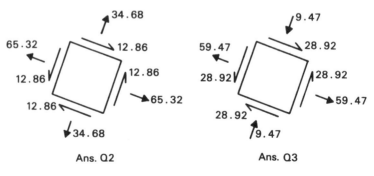

Ans. Q2   Ans. Q3

So far we have considered particular cases of stress analysis: either uniaxial stress, biaxial stress or pure shear. The more general application of stress analysis is to the case of problems where a combination of direct and shear stresses acting on two perpendicular planes at a point in a component are known. Typically, the principal stresses and maximum shear stresses and the orientation of the planes on which these stresses act are to be determined. Often the failure of a stressed component will be governed by a limiting maximum principal stress or maximum shear stress being reached and it is these stresses which must be calculated from known stress components acting in known directions.

Let's now develop the theory further so that we can produce a general theory applicable to all types of problems. Consider the element shown which is now subjected to direct stresses combined with shear stresses. The problem again is to determine equations for the normal and shear stresses on a plane inclined at an angle θ to the positive directions of the y-axis.

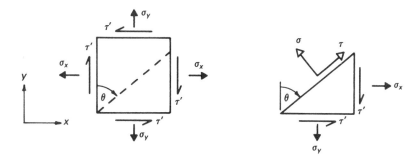

Based on the work we have already done, can you write down the equations for the normal stress σ and the shear stress τ?

$$\sigma = \frac{(\sigma_x + \sigma_y)}{2} + \frac{(\sigma_x - \sigma_y)}{2}\cos(2\theta) + \tau'\sin(2\theta) \qquad (8.7)$$

$$\tau = -\frac{(\sigma_x - \sigma_y)}{2}\sin(2\theta) + \tau'\cos(2\theta) \qquad (8.8)$$

The figure above is merely a combination of the cases we have already considered. The equations here are obtained by simply combining Equations (8.3) with (8.5), and (8.4) with (8.6). In other words we have made use, yet again, of the principle of superposition. Let's look at the **Mohr's Circle** for this case.

30

It is not obvious that the equations given for σ and τ describe a circle. However they have been obtained by combining other equations which we have already seen to be the equations of a circle, and you should therefore anticipate that the two equations will describe a circle. The figure below gives the Mohr's Circle interpretation of these equations. As an exercise to show that this circle is in fact a correct interpretation, you should assign some numerical values to σ_x, σ_y and τ'. For differing values of θ, calculate and plot pairs of values of θ and τ using Equations (8.7) and (8.8). (You did a similar exercise in Frame 7.)

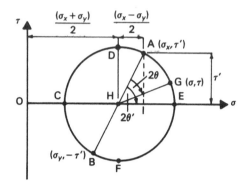

Note that, provided σ_x, σ_y and τ' are known, the points A and B can be plotted and joined together. This describes a diameter of the circle, the intersection of which with the σ-axis will give the centre of the circle. Once the centre is found, the circle can be drawn. An angle 2θ turned in a *clockwise* direction from the line HA will define a point G which will give the stresses σ and τ acting on a plane inclined at an angle θ to the positive direction of the y-axis.

As in all the previous cases, the values of the principal stresses will be given by the points marked C and E, and the maximum shear stresses by the points marked D and F. The inclination of the planes on which these stresses act is given by the angle 2θ when G in coincident with whichever of these points is being considered.

For the element shown below, plot the Mohr's Circle and determine (i) the maximum and minimum principal stresses; and (ii) the maximum shear stresses.

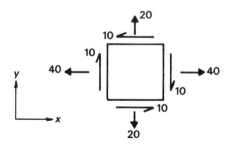

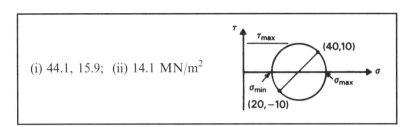

(i) 44.1, 15.9; (ii) 14.1 MN/m^2

Referring back to the Mohr's Circle diagram in Frame 30, some useful and important relationships can be derived:

(i) The centre is at $(\sigma_x + \sigma_y)/2$. As the centre is in a fixed position it follows that for any given stress system at a point in a component, the sum of the normal stresses on any two perpendicular planes must be a constant no matter to what angle the planes are rotated.

(ii) From the geometry of the triangle HAI and using Pythagoras's Theorem, the radius of the circle is given by:

$$\text{Radius} = [\{0.5(\sigma_x - \sigma_y)\}^2 + \tau'^2]^{\frac{1}{2}}$$

(iii) The maximum shear stresses equal the radius of the circle. Therefore:

$$\tau_{max} = \pm[\{0.5(\sigma_x - \sigma_y)\}^2 + \tau'^2]^{\frac{1}{2}} \tag{8.9}$$

(iv) The maximum principal stress is represented by the point E, such that:

$$\sigma_{max} = \text{OH} + \text{HE}$$
$$= \text{OH} + \text{radius of circle}$$
$$= 0.5(\sigma_x + \sigma_y) + [\{0.5(\sigma_x - \sigma_y)\}^2 + \tau'^2]^{\frac{1}{2}} \tag{8.10}$$

(v) Similarly, the minimum principal stress is represented by point C such that:

$$\sigma_{min} = \text{OH} - \text{HC}$$
$$= \text{OH} - \text{Radius of circle}$$
$$= 0.5(\sigma_x + \sigma_y) - [\{0.5(\sigma_x - \sigma_y)\}^2 + \tau'^2]^{\frac{1}{2}} \tag{8.11}$$

(vi) The angle of inclination of the plane on which the maximum principal stress acts is given in the diagram by the angle $2\theta'$ where, from the geometry of the triangle HAI:

$$\tan(2\theta') = \frac{\tau'}{(\sigma_x - \sigma_y)/2} = \frac{2\tau'}{(\sigma_x - \sigma_y)} \tag{8.12}$$

The minimum principal stress acts on a plane at $90°$ to the plane of maximum principal stress and follows directly once θ' is known.

Use these equations to check your answers to the problem at the end of Frame 30 which you have already solved graphically.

32

You have already got the answers to this problem but you may wish to check your working:

$$\text{Radius} = [\{0.5(\sigma_x - \sigma_y)\}^2 + \tau'^2]^{\frac{1}{2}}$$
$$= [\{0.5(40 - 20)\}^2 + 10^2]^{\frac{1}{2}}$$
$$= 14.1 \text{ MN/m}^2$$

$$\sigma_{\max} = 0.5(\sigma_x + \sigma_y) + \text{Radius}$$
$$= 0.5(40 + 20) + 14.1$$
$$= 44.1 \text{ MN/m}^2$$

$$\sigma_{\min} = 0.5(\sigma_x + \sigma_y) - \text{Radius}$$
$$= 0.5(40 + 20) - 14.1$$
$$= 15.9 \text{ MN}_{\ldots}$$

$$\tau_{\max} = \text{Radius of circle}$$
$$= 14.1 \text{ MN/m}^2$$

Now use the circle that you plotted for the last problem in Frame 30 to read off the stresses on planes inclined at $\theta = 30°$ and $60°$. Check your answers by calculation using the equations for σ and τ (Equations 8.7 and 10.8 in Frame 29).

33

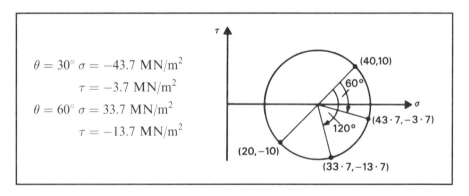

$\theta = 30° \ \sigma = -43.7 \text{ MN/m}^2$
$\tau = -3.7 \text{ MN/m}^2$
$\theta = 60° \ \sigma = 33.7 \text{ MN/m}^2$
$\tau = -13.7 \text{ MN/m}^2$

The problem you have been working on was for a particular set of stresses. Both the normal stresses σ_x and σ_y were positive (tensile), the shear stresses on the side faces of the element were positive (clockwise), and those on the top and bottom faces were negative (anticlockwise). The circle was drawn by plotting the two points $(\sigma_x, +\tau')$ and $(\sigma_y, -\tau')$ resulting in the construction we have already examined.

If the signs of the stresses are different, the circle can still be drawn provided that, when plotting the two points, the signs of the stresses are taken into account.

For the elements shown, sketch the Mohr's Circles of Stress, indicating the two points that are used to construct the circles.

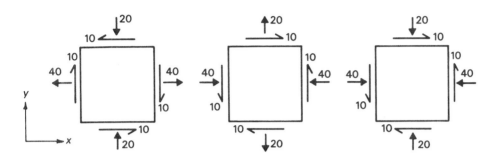

34

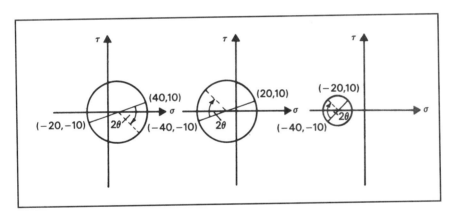

The most important points on all these Mohr's Circle diagrams are the points representing the principal stresses and the points representing the maximum shear stresses. As we have seen, these stresses can be calculated using equations but the use of the Mohr's Circle gives a complete visual picture of the state of stress at a point in a component and is often easier to use and interpret than a set of equations.

Reading the values of stresses from a Mohr's Circle is relatively easy, provided that the circles are drawn correctly, taking account of the signs of the known stresses. What can be a little more difficult is the determination of the inclination of the planes on which these stresses act, particularly when the circle relates to stresses that are not positive according to our chosen sign convention.

Let's look at a further geometrical construction that will enable us to determine the orientation of planes of stress using a previously constructed Mohr's Circle.

35

This geometric construction is known as the *Pole Method* and will enable us to determine the inclination of the principal planes (and indeed the planes for any other set of stresses) which can be plotted on the Mohr's Circle. This construction makes use of the fact that the angle subtended at the centre of a circle by a chord is twice that subtended by the same chord at the circumference.

The figure below reproduces the Mohr's Circle first introduced in Frame 30. Assuming, as we have done so far, that the element for which the stresses are known is orientated with its side faces vertical and its top and bottom faces horizontal, then the following geometric construction is shown and can be used in all cases:

(i) From A which represents the stresses σ_x, τ' on the *vertical* faces of the element, draw a vertical line to meet the circle at P. P is known as the *pole point*.

(ii) The pole point P could alternatively have been located by drawing a *horizontal* line through B which represents the stresses σ_y, $-\tau'$ on the *horizontal* faces of the element.

(iii) From P draw a line to connect P to G which represents the stresses σ_θ, τ on a plane inclined at an angle θ to the positive direction of the y-axis.

(iv) The angle APG is equal to θ as this is the angle subtended by the chord AG on the circumference which is half the angle AHG (equal to 2θ) subtended at the centre. Hence the line PG is inclined at the same angle as the face of the element on which the stresses σ_θ and τ act. The line PG' is the inclination of the perpendicular plane on which stresses represented by the point G' act.

(v) If the pole point P is connected to E and C, this gives the inclinations of the principal planes.

(vi) If P is connected to D and F, this will give the inclination of the planes of maximum shear stress.

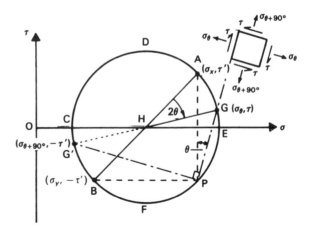

This form of construction can be used to either:

(a) determine the inclination of the planes on which known stresses act; or

(b) determine the stresses acting on planes of known inclination.

Use this method of construction to determine the orientation of the principal planes and the planes of maximum shear stress for the problem we considered in Frames 30 and 31. The graphical solution is given in the next frame.

36

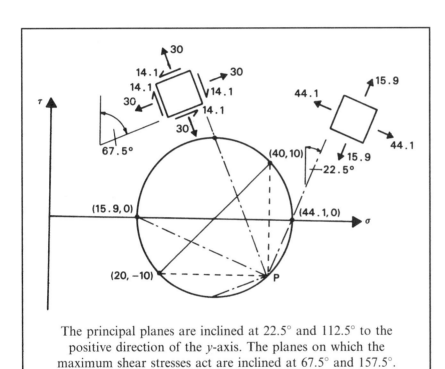

The principal planes are inclined at 22.5° and 112.5° to the positive direction of the *y*-axis. The planes on which the maximum shear stresses act are inclined at 67.5° and 157.5°.

Now use the same methods to determine the magnitude of the principal stresses and the orientation of the planes on which they occur for the stress system indicated in the diagram below.

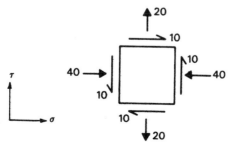

37

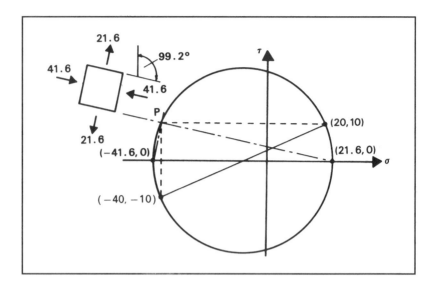

It is worth noting that, if the stresses shown in the figure at the end of Frame 36 represent a set of applied stresses at a point in a component, then the principal stresses at the point are numerically greater than the applied direct stresses and the maximum shear stress at the point is greater than the applied shear stress. For example, the applied direct compressive stress is 40.0 MN/m² but the principal compressive stress is 41.6 MN/m². Similarly the applied shear stress is 10 MN/m² while the maximum shear stress is 31.6 MN/m² (the radius of the circle). You will find that this observation is true for most of the problems we have looked at in this programme, and is in fact generally true. It is important to recognise that this is the case as, under the action of complex stress systems, material failure of a component may occur at apparently much lower applied stresses than if a single stress was applied.

*Now look at the element of material subjected to the direct **compressive** stresses and shear stresses shown. If the material will fail at a **tensile** stress of 5 MN/m², do you think that material failure is likely? Sketch the Mohr's Circle of Stress to help you answer this question.*

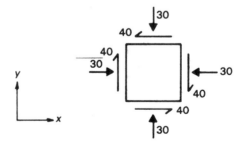

38

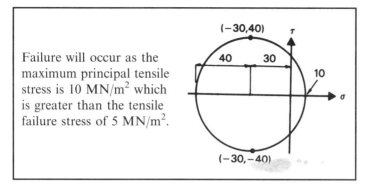

Failure will occur as the maximum principal tensile stress is 10 MN/m^2 which is greater than the tensile failure stress of 5 MN/m^2.

This example illustrates that, although a point in a component may be subjected to shear stresses together with direct applied stresses of one type (in this case compressive stresses), one of the principal stresses induced at the point may be of the opposite sign to the applied direct stresses. It is important to recognise the fact that, although a point in a component may be subjected to one type of stress system, stresses of an opposite sense may be induced at the point on planes inclined at different angles to those on which the applied stresses act.

Finally, it should be pointed out that, in all the problems in this programme, we have drawn Mohr's Circle of Stress for known stresses acting on small elements which for convenience were orientated with the side faces vertical and the top and bottom faces horizontal. The known stresses acting at a point in a component may not necessarily be acting on horizontal and vertical planes and may in fact be acting on planes which are inclined. In this case all that is required is to orientate the x and y reference axis parallel to the side faces of the inclined element. The Mohr's Circle can then be drawn and interpreted in the usual way with the angle θ still taken as positive when measured clockwise from the positive direction of the y-axis.

39

$\boxed{\text{TO REMEMBER}}$

This programme is more concerned with techniques rather than specific formulae to remember. However, you should know how to construct and interpret a Mohr's Circle and should know that:

The principal stresses are the maximum and minimum normal stresses that occur at a point within a component and they act on the principal planes, which are orientated at 90° to each other.

There are no shear stresses acting on the principal planes.

The planes on which the maximum shear stresses act are at 45° to the direction of the principal planes.

40

(Note: The Mohr's Circle of Stress for the problems below are given together at the end of the frame.)

1. A short bar is loaded in axial compression to give uniform uniaxial stress of $80 \, MN/m^2$. Working from first principles, determine the normal and tangential stresses on planes inclined to the longitudinal axis of the bar at (i) 35°; (ii) 45°; and (iii) 60°.

   Ans. (i) −26.32, 37.58   (ii) −40, 40   (iii) −60.0, 34.64 MN/m².

2. Repeat question 1 but use Equations (8.7) and (8.8) in Frame 29.

3. Check your answers to question 1 by drawing the Mohr's Circle of Stress and reading the appropriate stresses from the circle.

4. A drive shaft of circular cross-section is designed to carry a uniform tensile stress of $15 \, MN/m^2$ and a shearing stress of $20 \, MN/m^2$ at a point on the outer surface of the shaft. Taking the shear stresses as positive, determine by calculation (i) the principal stresses at the point and the angle of the planes on which these occur; and (ii) the maximum shear stresses at the point and the angles of the planes on which these occur.

   Ans. (i) 28.86, −13.86 MN/m² at 34.72° and 124.72°; (ii) ±21.36 MN/m² at 79.72° and 169.72° – angles measured relative to an axis perpendicular to the longitudinal axis of the shaft.

5. Repeat question 4 but solve it graphically using a Mohr's Circle of Stress.

6. Draw the Mohr's Circle of Stress for the element shown in figure Q6 and use the circle to determine the principal stresses and the orientation of the planes on which they act. Show the principal stresses on a drawing of a correctly orientated element as in the example in Frame 36.

   Ans. 20.0, 95.0 MN/m² at 63.4° and 153.4° – angles measured relative to the given y-axis.

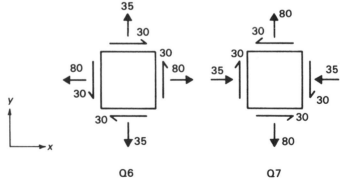

Q6   Q7

---

7. Draw the Mohr's Circle of Stress for the element shown in figure Q7 and use the circle to determine the principal stresses and the orientation of the planes on which they act. Show the principal stresses on a drawing of a correctly orientated element as in the example in Frame 36.

Ans. 87.4, −42.4 MN/m² at 76.2° and 166.2° – angles measured relative to the given y-axis.

8. Figure Q8 shows a point in a test specimen which is stressed with a constant stress of 50 MN/m² in the x direction and with an increasing stress σ_y in the y direction. If the specimen fails at a shearing stress of 35 MN/m², what is the value of σ_y at failure?

Ans. 20 MN/m².

9. A glued joint between two lengths of material is shown in figure Q9. The glue used is one of a range of modern adhesives which have extremely high shear strength. The joint is therefore best orientated in a plane that has shear stresses only acting on it. Determine by drawing a Mohr's Circle the optimum value of the angle θ, and the magnitude of the corresponding shear stresses.

Ans. 57.7° or 122.3°, 9.5 MN/m².

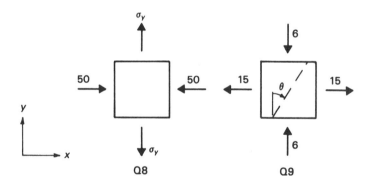

Q8   Q9

10. Figure Q10 (see overleaf) shows a cantilevered beam which carries a point load of 20 kN. Calculate the bending stresses and shear stresses at A, B and C and use these stresses to calculate for each of these points (i) the magnitude of the principal stresses; and (ii) the values of the maximum shear stresses. In each case determine the orientation of the planes on which these stresses act.

(Hint: you may need to refer to Programme 6 to remind yourself how to calculate shear stresses at a cross-section.)

Ans. (i) A: 4.5, 0 MN/m² at 0° and 90°; B: 2.72, −0.47 MN/m² at 157.5° and 67.5°; C: 1.5, −1.5 MN/m² at 135° and 45°; (ii) A: ±2.25 MN/m² at 135° and 45°; B: ±1.59 MN/m² at 112.5° and 22.5°; C: ±1.5 MN/m² at 90° and 0° – all angles measured relative to an axis at right angles to the longitudinal axis of the beam.

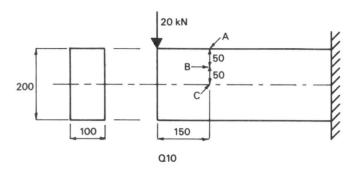

Q10

11. (a) A drive shaft is to be designed as a solid circular section to transmit a torsional moment of 2 kN m. If the maximum shear stresses are limited to 60 MN/m², what is the least diameter of section necessary?

(b) To allow for the possible existence of an axial force in the shaft which could give rise to the development of axial tensile stresses, the drive shaft is slightly overdesigned and is fabricated out of a solid 60 mm diameter circular section. If the allowable shear stresses are still 60 MN/m², what is the largest axial thrust that can be tolerated together with the torque of 2 kN m?

Ans. 55.37 mm; 209.69 kN.

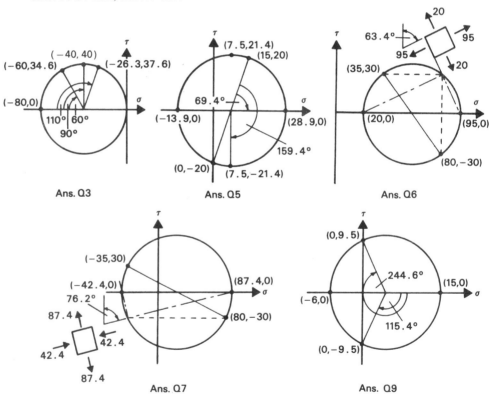

Programme 9

STRAIN
TRANSFORMATIONS
AND MOHR'S CIRCLE
OF STRAIN

On completion of this programme you will be able to:

- Draw a Mohr's Circle of Strain for a range of complex strain situations
- Interpret a Mohr's Circle of Strain
- Determine the magnitude of the principal strains
- Identify the orientation of the principal planes
- Determine the magnitude and orientation of the planes of maximum angular shear strain
- Identify the orientation of a plane of given strain condition
- Determine the state of strain on a plane of given orientation
- Explain the use of strain gauge rosettes
- Determine the magnitude and direction of the principal strains from a set of 45° strain gauge rosette readings
- Determine the magnitude and direction of the principal strains from a set of 120° strain gauge rosette readings
- Calculate the principal stresses from the principal strains

1

In Programme 8 we showed that the state of stress within a mechanical component can be much more complex than our original study of stress systems might have led us to believe. We also showed that in a two dimensional stress system the use of Mohr's Circle of Stress allows us to determine stress variations and to find the magnitude of the principal stresses, the maximum shear stresses and the orientation of the planes on which they act.

You will know from Programme 4 that the application of direct stress will give rise to deformation, which is measured as direct strain. Similarly, shear stress will be accompanied by angular shear strain (see Programme 6, Frame 24). The relationship between stress and strain depends on the properties of the material from which the component is fabricated.

Can you write down the relationship between (i) direct stress and strain and (ii) shear stress and strain?

2

$$\boxed{\text{(i)}\ \sigma = E \times \varepsilon;\ \ \text{(ii)}\ \tau = G \times \gamma}$$

The symbols for stress and strain have their usual meaning. E is Young's Modulus of Elasticity, and G is the Shear Modulus of the material. It is apparent therefore that, as the stress changes throughout a component, the resulting strains must vary in a way that is dependent on the material properties.

In this programme we are going to investigate the variation of strain within a component and show how strain variations can be determined using a Mohr's Circle approach that is very similar to the approach we have already used in the analysis of complex stress systems. We will also investigate the use and application of *strain gauge rosettes*, which are simple items of electronic equipment used to measure, and hence interpret, the strains developed in a component when loaded either in the laboratory or when in actual use. The results of strain rosette measurements can lead to the calculation of the stresses arising within a loaded component to determine, for example, whether or not the component is over-stressed in use.

Now let's consider the simple case of an axially loaded bar that we first saw in Frames 2 and 3 of Programme 8

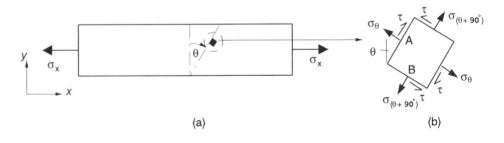

(a)   (b)

Figure (a) shows the bar subject to a longitudinal stress σ_x acting in the direction of the x-axis; and figure (b), a small element of material with one face (face A) inclined at a *clockwise* angle θ to the y-axis, and the other (face B) inclined at $\theta + 90°$. The direct stresses acting on these faces are σ_θ and $\sigma_{(\theta+90°)}$, respectively.

If we first consider the direct stresses, then Equation (8.1) of Programme 8 tells us that the direct stress on the face inclined at θ is given by:

$$\sigma_\theta = \frac{\sigma_x}{2}(1 + \cos 2\theta) \tag{9.1}$$

and the corresponding direct stress on the face inclined at $(\theta + 90°)$ is given by:

$$\begin{aligned}\sigma_{(\theta+90°)} &= \frac{\sigma_x}{2}(1 + \cos 2(\theta + 90°)) \\ &= \frac{\sigma_x}{2}(1 - \cos 2\theta)\end{aligned} \tag{9.2}$$

Now we know from Programme 4 that when an element of material is subject to a direct stress it strains in the direction of the applied stress. We also know that because of Poisson's Ratio effects there will be a lateral strain equal to $-Poissons\ Ratio \times longitudinal\ strain$.

Referring to figure (b), what is the strain in the direction of the stress σ_θ caused by (i) the stress σ_θ and (ii) the stress $\sigma_{(\theta+90°)}$ acting on face B. What is the total strain in the direction of the stress σ_θ?

3

> (i) $\dfrac{\sigma_\theta}{E}$; (ii) $-\dfrac{\nu\sigma_{(\theta+90°)}}{E}$; (iii) $\dfrac{\sigma_\theta}{E} - \dfrac{\nu\sigma_{(\theta+90°)}}{E}$

Equation (i) comes directly from our usual stress–strain relationship for an elastic material. Equation (ii) is derived by considering the strain in the direction of the stress $\sigma_{(\theta+90°)}$, given by $\sigma_{(\theta+90°)}/E$, then multiplying this strain by Poisson's Ratio to give the strain in the lateral direction. Note the negative sign to account for the fact that if one strain is an extension, then the lateral one is a contraction and vice versa. Equation (iii) is merely the superposition of these two effects to give the total strain in the direction of the stress σ_θ.

Hence we can write the expression which represents the strain at right-angles to face A as:

$$\varepsilon_\theta = \frac{\sigma_\theta}{E} - \frac{\nu\sigma_{(\theta+90°)}}{E} \tag{9.3}$$

Can you combine Equations (9.1), (9.2) and (9.3) to express ε_θ in terms of σ_x?

4

$$\varepsilon_\theta = \frac{\sigma_x}{2E}((1-v) + (1+v)\cos 2\theta)$$

This equation comes from the substitution of Equations (9.1) and (9.2) directly into Equation (9.3). But we know that:

$$\varepsilon_x = \frac{\sigma_x}{E} \quad \text{and} \quad \varepsilon_y = -v\frac{\sigma_x}{E}$$

Hence the above equation can be written as:

$$\varepsilon_\theta = \frac{\sigma_x}{2E}((1-v) + (1+v)\cos 2\theta)$$

$$= \frac{1}{2}\left[\left(\frac{\sigma_x}{E} - v\frac{\sigma_x}{E}\right) + \left(\frac{\sigma_x}{E} + v\frac{\sigma_x}{E}\right)\cos 2\theta\right]$$

$$= \frac{(\varepsilon_x + \varepsilon_y)}{2} + \frac{(\varepsilon_x - \varepsilon_y)}{2}\cos 2\theta \qquad (9.4)$$

This equation describes the variation of direct strain at right-angles to a plane inclined at θ to the y-axis expressed in terms of the direct strain in the x direction and the lateral strain in the y direction. Before we develop this equation further let's look at how we can develop a similar equation for the corresponding angular shear strain.

Can you recall from Programme 8 the expression for the shear stress on the inclined plane?

5

$$\tau = -\frac{\sigma_x}{2}\sin 2\theta$$

This is Equation (8.2) of Programme 8. From complementary shear considerations this is also the shear strain on the plane inclined at $(\theta + 90°)$. Now, recalling that shear stress (τ) and angular shear strain (γ) are related by the Shear Modulus (G) we can write the shear strain as:

$$\gamma = \frac{\tau}{G} = -\frac{\sigma_x}{2G}\sin 2\theta \qquad (9.5)$$

But the Shear Modulus (G), Young's Modulus (E), and Poisson's ratio (v) for an elastic material are related by the expression:

$$E = 2G(1+v)$$

This is a standard relationship that we are not going to prove but simply state and use. Hence substituting for G in Equation (9.5) we can write the expression for shear strain as:

$$\gamma = \frac{\tau}{G} = -\frac{\sigma_x}{2G}\sin 2\theta = -\frac{\sigma_x}{E}(1+v)\sin 2\theta$$

$$= -\left(\frac{\sigma_x}{E} + v\frac{\sigma_x}{E}\right)\sin 2\theta$$

$$= -(\varepsilon_x + v\varepsilon_x)\sin 2\theta$$

$$= -(\varepsilon_x - \varepsilon_y)\sin 2\theta$$

And, to express the right-hand side of the equation in a similar form to Equation (9.4) we can divide both sides by a factor of 2 to give:

$$\frac{\gamma}{2} = -\frac{(\varepsilon_x - \varepsilon_y)}{2}\sin 2\theta \qquad (9.6)$$

Equations (9.4) and (9.6) describe the state of direct strain on the inclined plane and the corresponding angular shear strain, respectively, in terms of the strains in the x and y directions. Let's look at a simple example to see what these equations tell us.

A horizontal bar of rectangular cross-sectional area 100 mm² is subject to an axial tensile force, in the x direction, of 10 kN. Calculate the longitudinal strain in the x direction and the corresponding lateral strain if E = 200 GN/m² and v = 0.3.

6

$$\boxed{\varepsilon_x = 500 \times 10^{-6}; \quad \varepsilon_y = -150 \times 10^{-6}}$$

This should have been easy and follows directly from the work we did in Programme 4:

Stress in bar $= \sigma_x =$ force/area $= (10 \times 10^{-3})/(100 \times 10^{-6}) = 100\text{MN/m}^2$

Longitudinal strain in bar $= \varepsilon_x = \sigma/E = (100 \times 10^6)/(200 \times 10^9) = 500 \times 10^{-6}$

Lateral strain $= \varepsilon_y = -v \times \varepsilon = -0.3 \times 500 \times 10^{-6} = -150 \times 10^{-6}$

Now, using Equations (9.4) and (9.6) prepare a table of values of normal and shearing strain for planes inclined at θ to the vertical where θ varies from 0° to 180° in steps of 15°. Plot a graph of one-half shearing strain ($\gamma_\theta/2$ – as y-coordinate) against normal strain (ε_θ – as x-coordinate) and answer the following questions:
(i) What is the shape of the graph?
(ii) What is
    (a) the maximum normal strain;
    (b) the minimum normal strain;
    (c) the maximum shear strain; and
    (d) the angle to the vertical of the planes on which these strains occur?

7

> (i) Circular
>
> (ii) (a) 500×10^{-6}; (b) -150×10^{-6}; (c) $\pm 650 \times 10^{-6}$; (d) $0°$, $90°$, $45°$ and $135°$

Check your solution. Note that we have calculated $\gamma/2$ and therefore to give the correct value of shear strain we must double our answer.

θ	$\varepsilon_\theta \times 10^{-6}$	$\gamma/2 \times 10^{-6}$
0	500.00	0.00
15	456.46	−162.50
30	337.50	−281.46
45	175.00	−325.00
60	12.50	−281.46
75	−106.46	−162.50
90	−150.00	0.00
105	−106.46	162.50
120	12.50	281.46
135	175.00	325.00
150	337.50	281.46
165	456.46	162.50
180	500.00	0.00

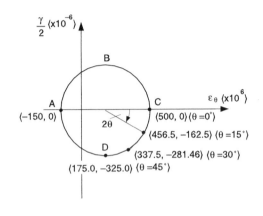

The diagram that you have just drawn is a *Mohr's Circle of Strain*. You should compare it with the Mohr's Circle of Stress drawn in Frame 7 of Programme 8. You will see that the circles are very similar although the strain circle does not pass through the origin of the graph.

We can conclude that the strain circle can be drawn and interpreted in a similar way to the stress circle provided that we plot $\gamma/2$ as the vertical axis. Hence, although we have drawn the circle by calculating and plotting a number of points it is only necessary to plot two key points on the circle. You have already deduced that the maximum normal strain was 500×10^{-6} and occurs normal to the plane inclined at $0°$. This is the strain ε_x and is marked as point C on the diagram above. The minimum normal strain was -150×10^{-6} acting normal to the plane at $90°$ to the vertical. This is the strain ε_y and is marked as point A on the diagram. Both A and C represent *principal planes* on which the *principal strains* act. On these planes we have normal strain combined with zero angular shear strain.

The centre of the circle is located mid-way between these two points. Hence, as with the stress circle, this circle can be plotted by simply plotting A and C, finding the point mid-way between them and drawing a circle centred on this point and passing through both A and C.

As with the Mohr's Circle of Stress the strains *normal* to any plane inclined at an angle θ to the *y*-axis, together with the corresponding angular shear strain, can be determined by turning off an angle 2θ in a *clockwise* direction from C.

Refer to the Mohr's Circle of Strain you plotted in response to the problem in Frame 6 and use the circle to determine the strains normal to two perpendicular planes inclined at 20° and 110° to the vertical. What are the corresponding shear strains?

8

$\theta = 20°$	$\varepsilon_\theta = 424 \times 10^{-6}$	$\gamma/2 = -209 \times 10^{-6}$:	$\gamma = -418 \times 10^{-6}$
$\theta = 100°$	$\varepsilon_\theta = -74 \times 10^{-6}$	$\gamma/2 = +209 \times 10^{-6}$:	$\gamma = +418 \times 10^{-6}$

You should obtain these answers by turning off angles of 40° and 220° in a clockwise direction from C and reading off the appropriate strains. Remember that you must double the strains read from the vertical axis as we have plotted $\gamma/2$. These values could be calculated alternatively using Equations (9.4) and (9.6) directly.

9

PROBLEMS

Answer questions 1 and 2 by (i) plotting a Mohr's Circle of Strain and (ii) making direct use of Equations (9.4) and (9.6).

1. A horizontal bar of circular cross-section and of radius 20 mm carries an axial tensile load of 100 kN. If $E = 200 \text{ GN/m}^2$ and $v = 0.3$, determine the values of maximum and minimum normal strain and the maximum shear strain.

Ans. 398×10^{-6}; -119×10^{-6}; $\pm 517 \times 10^{-6}$.

2. What is the inclination to the vertical of the planes normal to which there is a strain of 250×10^{-6}? What is the corresponding angular shear strain?

Ans. 32.3° and 147.7°; $\pm 467 \times 10^{-6}$.

3. At a point in a material the principal strains are given by ε_x and ε_y. Sketch the Mohr's Circle of Strain for

(i) $\varepsilon_x = 500 \times 10^{-6}$, $\varepsilon_y = 200 \times 10^{-6}$;
(ii) $\varepsilon_x = 500 \times 10^{-6}$, $\varepsilon_y = -200 \times 10^{-6}$; and
(iii) $\varepsilon_x = -500 \times 10^{-6}$, $\varepsilon_y = +200 \times 10^{-6}$.

Hint: think about how you plotted Mohr's Circle of Stress, given similar information.

Ans. See the next page.

10

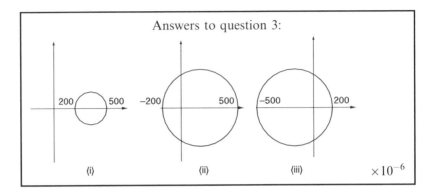

Did you get the correct answers to question 3? The work we have done so far has been based on an axially loaded component subjected to longitudinal strain, ε_x, and lateral strain, ε_y, caused by the Poisson's Ratio effect. We saw that both ε_x and ε_y are principal strains. Question 3 was asking you to make the connection between the case of an axially loaded component, or element of material, and one that is stressed directly in both the x and y directions, giving rise to strains in both of these directions. As they were stated to be principal strains, the assumption was that there is no angular shear strain associated with these principal planes. Drawing the Mohr's Circle is simply a matter of plotting the two points that represent each pair of principal planes and then drawing the corresponding circle, as shown.

It should be obvious by now that there is a close similarity between the construction of the Mohr's Circle of Stress and the Mohr's Circle of Strain – the only fundamental difference being that, in the strain circle, we plot one-half of the shear strain as the ordinate of the circle. Hence, with this difference in mind, we can take the more general case of an element of material subject to a combination of direct and shear stress which give rise to a more complex state of normal and shear strain. We can plot the strain circle using the stress circle as a direct analogy.

The figure below shows a small element of material subject to a general set of stresses and the corresponding set of direct and shear strains. Both the direct and shear stresses are shown as being positive according to the sign convention we adopted regarding the Mohr's Stress Circle in Programme 8.

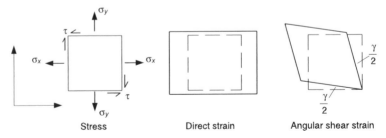

| Stress | Direct strain | Angular shear strain |

If $\sigma_x = 30$, $\sigma_y = 20$ and $\tau = 10$ MN/mm^2 what are the coordinates of the two points that you would plot to draw the Mohr's Circle of Stress?

11

> $(30, +10); \quad (20, -10)$

If in doubt about this revise Programme 8, Frame 33 before proceeding.
    Now let's assume that this set of stresses gives rise to a set of strains given by:

$$\varepsilon_x = 120 \times 10^{-6} \quad \varepsilon_y = 55 \times 10^{-6} \quad \gamma' = 125 \times 10^{-6}$$

where the sign convention used is given by:

(i)   a normal strain is taken as positive if it is an *elongational* strain, that is, the result of a tensile stress; and
(ii) if the shear stresses acting on the faces of the element on which the normal strain ε_x acts tend to rotate the element in a *clockwise* direction (that is, positive shear stress) the angular shear strain for this face will be taken as positive.

With the analogy of Mohr's Circle of Stress in mind what are the coordinates of the two points you would plot to draw the Mohr's Circle of Strain?

12

> $(120, +62.5) \quad (55, -62.5) \qquad \times 10^{-6}$

Did you remember that we are plotting $\gamma/2$ on the vertical axis and not γ?
    Now draw the Mohr's Circle of Strain for these strain values and determine the principal strains.

13

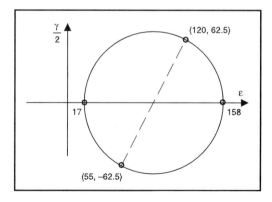

Now move on to the next frame.

14

The strain circle we have just plotted can be interpreted in a similar way to Mohr's Circle of Stress to give principal strains, the strains associated with a given plane, the planes associated with a particular set of strains and so on.

In Programme 8 we introduced a powerful way of interpreting the Mohr's Circle of Stress using the Pole Method which required the identification of the pole point. This pole point construction can be used equally to interpret the strain circle with only a minor modification to the interpretation of the information required.

The figure below shows a general Mohr's Circle of Strain which would be constructed from a known set of strains $\left[(\varepsilon_x, \gamma'/2)\,(\varepsilon_y, -\gamma'/2)\right]$. Assuming, as we have done so far, that the element for which the strains are known is orientated with its side faces vertical and its top and bottom faces horizontal, the pole point can be located in an identical way to that used for the stress circle (see Programme 8, Frame 35):

(i) From A, which represents the strains $(\varepsilon_x, \gamma'/2)$, where ε_x is normal to the *vertical* faces of the element, draw a *vertical* line to meet the circle at P; P is the pole point.

(ii) The pole point P could have been located alternatively by drawing a *horizontal* line through B which represents the strains $(\varepsilon_y, -\gamma'/2)$ associated with the *horizontal* faces of the element.

(iii) From P draw a line to connect P to G, which represents the strains $(\varepsilon_\theta, \gamma/2)$ associated with the plane inclined at an angle θ. The line PG is automatically inclined at the same angle as the face of the element normal to which the strain ε_θ acts.

(iv) If the pole point is connected to E and C this gives the inclination of the principal planes. The *direction* of the maximum and minimum principal strains is normal to the inclination of the maximum and minimum principal planes, respectively.

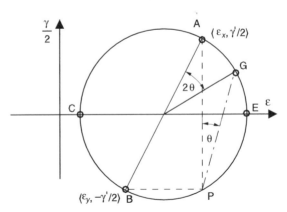

Use the above method of construction to determine the direction of the principal planes for the problem we considered in Frames 12 and 13.

15

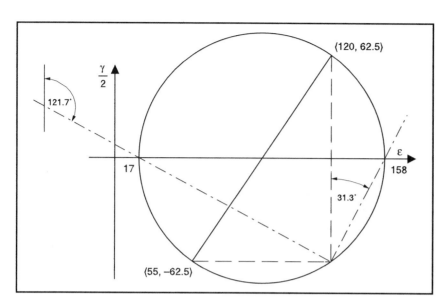

Now use the same method to determine the magnitude of the principal strains and the direction of the principal planes for $\varepsilon_x = 420 \times 10^{-6}$; $\varepsilon_y = 180 \times 10^{-6}$; $\gamma = 350 \times 10^{-6}$.

16

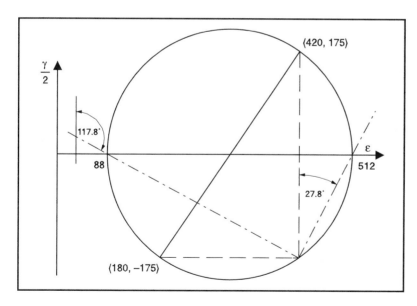

What is the magnitude of the normal strain on a plane inclined at 45° in a clockwise direction from the y-axis?

17

$$475 \times 10^{-6}$$

Now try some problems.

18

PROBLEMS

Use a Mohr's Circle approach to determine the magnitude of the principal strains and the inclination of the principal planes for the following combinations of strain:

(i) $\varepsilon_x = 200 \times 10^{-6}$; $\varepsilon_y = 56 \times 10^{-6}$; $\gamma = 230 \times 10^{-6}$

(ii) $\varepsilon_x = 200 \times 10^{-6}$; $\varepsilon_y = -56 \times 10^{-6}$; $\gamma = 230 \times 10^{-6}$

(iii) $\varepsilon_x = -200 \times 10^{-6}$; $\varepsilon_y = 56 \times 10^{-6}$; $\gamma = 230 \times 10^{-6}$

Take the angular shear strain associated with the strain in the x direction as being positive in all cases

     Ans. (i) 264×10^{-6}, -8×10^{-6}, $29°$, $119°$; (ii) 244×10^{-6}, -100×10^{-6}, $21°$, $111°$; (iii) 100×10^{-6}, -244×10^{-6}, $-21°$, $79°$.

19

EQUATIONS OF THE MOHR'S CIRCLE OF STRAIN

In Frame 31 of Programme 8 we saw that Mohr's Circle of Stress can be defined in terms of a series of equations for known values of stress acting on any two mutually perpendicular planes. These planes are normally assumed for convenience to be orientated in the x and y directions of our chosen x/y axis system. We have shown that the Mohr's Circle of Strain is practically identical to the circle of stress provided that we remember that *the vertical axis of the circle represents one-half of the angular shear strain.*

     With this in mind, and referring back to Frame 31 of Programme 8, Equations (8.9) to (8.12) for the circle of stress can be written as follows for the circle of strain:

(i)   The centre of the strain circle is at $(\varepsilon_x + \varepsilon_y)/2$ (9.7)

(ii)   The radius of the circle is given by:

$$\text{Radius} = \left[\{0.5(\varepsilon_x - \varepsilon_y)\}^2 + \left(\frac{1}{2}\gamma\right)^2 \right]^{\frac{1}{2}} \tag{9.8}$$

(iii)   The maximum angular shear strain is given by the radius of the circle multiplied by 2 where the radius is given by Equation (9.8) above

(iv) The maximum principal strain is given by the point on the circle that is represented by the centre of the circle *plus* the radius, that is:

$$\varepsilon_{max} = 0.5(\varepsilon_x + \varepsilon_y) + \left[\left\{ 0.5(\varepsilon_x - \varepsilon_y) \right\}^2 + \left(\frac{1}{2}\gamma \right)^2 \right]^{\frac{1}{2}} \qquad (9.9)$$

(v) Similarly, the minimum principal strain is given by:

$$\varepsilon_{min} = 0.5(\varepsilon_x + \varepsilon_y) - \left[\left\{ 0.5(\varepsilon_x - \varepsilon_y) \right\}^2 + \left(\frac{1}{2}\gamma \right)^2 \right]^{\frac{1}{2}} \qquad (9.10)$$

(vi) The inclination of the principal plane, normal to which is the direction of the maximum principal strain, is given by:

$$\tan(2\theta') = \frac{(\gamma/2)}{(\varepsilon_x - \varepsilon_y)/2} = \frac{\gamma}{(\varepsilon_x - \varepsilon_y)} \qquad (9.11)$$

20

$$\boxed{\text{PROBLEMS}}$$

Use Equations (9.7) to (9.11) to determine the magnitude of the principal strains and the orientation of the principal planes for the following combinations of strain:

(i) $\varepsilon_x = 200 \times 10^{-6}$; $\varepsilon_y = 56 \times 10^{-6}$; $\gamma = 230 \times 10^{-6}$

(ii) $\varepsilon_x = 200 \times 10^{-6}$; $\varepsilon_y = -56 \times 10^{-6}$; $\gamma = 230 \times 10^{-6}$

(iii) $\varepsilon_x = -200 \times 10^{-6}$; $\varepsilon_y = 56 \times 10^{-6}$; $\gamma = 230 \times 10^{-6}$

Take the angular shear strain associated with the strain in the x direction as being positive in all cases

    Ans. *(i)* 264×10^{-6}, -8×10^{-6}, $29°$, $119°$; *(ii)* 244×10^{-6}, -100×10^{-6}, $21°$, $111°$; *(iii)* 100×10^{-6}, -244×10^{-6}, $-21°$, $79°$.

21

ELECTRICAL STRAIN GAUGE ROSETTES

In many practical engineering situations it may be desirable, or indeed necessary, to determine the state of stress within a component either in a laboratory situation or in actual use. Other than in simple cases it is not possible to measure stress directly. It is possible, however, to measure strains and hence to determine stress variations using our knowledge of stress–strain relationships.

There are a number of devices available for measuring strain, one of the most common of which is the electrical strain gauge. Move on to the next frame where we shall look at the theory and practice of electrical strain gauges.

22

Electrical strain gauges consist of lengths of fine wire, sandwiched between a plastic film as shown below. A typical gauge will be 10–20 mm in length, although sizes vary according to the nature of the application.

The gauge is stuck firmly to the component at the location where strains are to be measured. As the component strains, the gauge will also strain and the lengths of wire will change in length. This will be accompanied by a change in the cross-sectional area of the wires and a resulting proportional small change in the electrical resistance of the gauge. This change can be measured using a Wheatstone Bridge system, and through a process of calibration a measured change in resistance can give a direct reading of strain in the direction of the gauge.

For complex stress/strain systems measuring strains in a single direction may not be sufficient, and *strain gauge rosettes* may be used. Typical rosette configurations are shown below. These rosettes are attached firmly to the test component at the location where strains are to be determined.

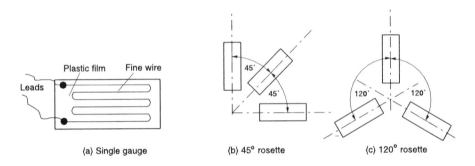

(a) Single gauge   (b) 45° rosette   (c) 120° rosette

Let's look at the 45° rosette to develop the theory of strain gauge application. The figure below shows a small element of material orientated such that the principal planes are parallel to our chosen x/y axis system. We shall denote the principal strains as ε_{p1} and ε_{p2}. An inclined plane at a clockwise angle θ is shown with a 45° strain gauge rosette located such that gauge 1 measures strains normal to this plane with gauges 2 and 3 orientated at 45° and 90°, respectively, to gauge 1.

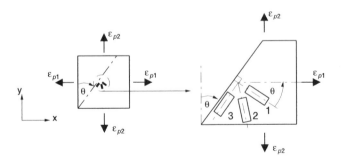

What is the expression that relates ε_θ to ε_{p1} and ε_{p2}?

$$\varepsilon_\theta = \frac{(\varepsilon_{p1} + \varepsilon_{p2})}{2} + \frac{(\varepsilon_{p1} - \varepsilon_{p2})}{2} \cos 2\theta$$

This expression follows from Equation (9.4), which we can apply directly as the principal planes have only direct stress acting on them with no associated angular shear strain. As this strain is that measured by strain gauge 1, we can therefore express the strain measured by gauge 1 as:

$$\varepsilon_1 = \frac{(\varepsilon_{p1} + \varepsilon_{p2})}{2} + \frac{(\varepsilon_{p1} - \varepsilon_{p2})}{2} \cos 2\theta \tag{9.12}$$

Similarly, the strain measured by gauge 2, which will measure the strain normal to a plane at $(\theta + 45°)$, will be given by:

$$\varepsilon_2 = \frac{(\varepsilon_{p1} + \varepsilon_{p2})}{2} + \frac{(\varepsilon_{p1} - \varepsilon_{p2})}{2} \cos 2(\theta + 45°)$$

$$= \frac{(\varepsilon_{p1} + \varepsilon_{p2})}{2} - \frac{(\varepsilon_{p1} - \varepsilon_{p2})}{2} \sin 2\theta \tag{9.13}$$

and for gauge 3:

$$\varepsilon_3 = \frac{(\varepsilon_{p1} + \varepsilon_{p2})}{2} + \frac{(\varepsilon_{p1} - \varepsilon_{p2})}{2} \cos 2(\theta + 90°)$$

$$= \frac{(\varepsilon_{p1} + \varepsilon_{p2})}{2} - \frac{(\varepsilon_{p1} - \varepsilon_{p2})}{2} \cos 2\theta \tag{9.14}$$

If ε_1, ε_2 and ε_3 are known, measured strains, then these three simultaneous equations can be solved for the magnitude of the two principal strains and the inclination θ. As the first principal plane is orientated at an anticlockwise angle θ from gauge 1, the inclination of the principal planes can be determined directly from the solution of the equations.

The solution of these equations is best done by computer but they can be solved algebraically to give expressions for the principal strains as follows:

$$\varepsilon_{p1} = \frac{1}{2}(\varepsilon_1 + \varepsilon_3) + \frac{1}{\sqrt{2}} \sqrt{\left[(\varepsilon_1 - \varepsilon_2)^2 + (\varepsilon_3 - \varepsilon_2)^2\right]} \tag{9.15}$$

and

$$\varepsilon_{p2} = \frac{1}{2}(\varepsilon_1 + \varepsilon_3) - \frac{1}{\sqrt{2}} \sqrt{\left[(\varepsilon_1 - \varepsilon_2)^2 + (\varepsilon_3 - \varepsilon_2)^2\right]} \tag{9.16}$$

A strain gauge rosette records strains of $\varepsilon_1 = 350 \times 10^{-6}$; $\varepsilon_2 = 213 \times 10^{-6}$; $\varepsilon_3 = 250 \times 10^{-6}$. Calculate the magnitude of the principal strains.

24

$$400 \times 10^{-6}; \quad 200 \times 10^{-6}$$

This follows from a direct substitution of the gauge readings into Equations (9.15) and (9.16), that is:

$$\varepsilon_{p1,p2} = \frac{1}{2}(\varepsilon_1 + \varepsilon_3) \pm \frac{1}{\sqrt{2}}\sqrt{\left[(\varepsilon_1 - \varepsilon_2)^2 + (\varepsilon_3 - \varepsilon_2)^2\right]}$$

$$= \frac{1}{2}(350 + 250) \pm \frac{1}{\sqrt{2}}\sqrt{\left[(350 - 213)^2 + (250 - 213)^2\right]}$$

$$= 300 \pm 100$$

$$= 400, \, 200$$

Note that to keep the arithmetic simple, it is best to work in microstrain, where one microstrain represents 10^{-6} units of strain. The three measured strains and the principal strains are all represented by points on a single Mohr's Circle. If the Mohr's Circle is sketched for the 45° rosette we are considering, then the physical interpretation of the readings is more apparent.

Can you sketch the Mohr's Circle for the above problem, indicating the magnitude and position of the three measured strain readings and the principal strains?

25

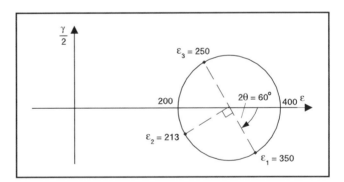

You should have drawn the above sketch where the clockwise angle 2θ shown defines the inclination θ of the plane normal to which is the measured strain ε_1. Note that the point representing ε_3 is located at the opposite end of the diameter to ε_1, which must be the case as these strains are measured in mutually perpendicular directions. The point representing ε_2 lies halfway around the circle between ε_1 and ε_3. Note also that, for convenience, you should take gauge 1 to be whichever of the two mutually perpendicular gauges gives the greatest tensile strain reading.

Use Equation (9.12) to calculate the angle θ and compare this with the value obtained from your Mohr's Circle

$$\boxed{30°}$$

You should have calculated:

$$\varepsilon_1 = \frac{(\varepsilon_{p1} + \varepsilon_{p2})}{2} + \frac{(\varepsilon_{p1} - \varepsilon_{p2})}{2}\cos 2\theta$$
$$\therefore \quad 350 = \frac{(400 + 200)}{2} + \frac{(400 - 200)}{2}\cos 2\theta$$

which, when rearranged, gives $\cos 2\theta = 0.5$. So $2\theta = 60°$ or $300°$. Hence $\theta = 30°$ or $150°$. It may not be clear from this calculation which of the two solutions is correct. However, if, as we have done, the Mohr's Circle is sketched, it is apparent that the correct answer must be $2\theta = 60°$ or $\theta = 30°$.

If the circle had been drawn to scale, then the double-angle could have been measured directly from the diagram. If reference is made back to the diagram at the foot of Frame 22 it is apparent that the direction of maximum principal strain is located at an *anticlockwise* angle of 30° from gauge 1, with the direction of the other principal strain at right angles to this one. The figure below shows the relative positions of the three gauges and the principal strains:

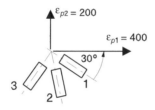

Repeat the above problem for a strain gauge rosette which records strains of $\varepsilon_1 = 145 \times 10^{-6}$; $\varepsilon_2 = 40 \times 10^{-6}$; $\varepsilon_3 = 145 \times 10^{-6}$.

$$\boxed{\varepsilon_{p1} = 250 \times 10^{-6}; \quad \varepsilon_{p2} = 40 \times 10^{-6}; \quad \theta = 45°}$$

The solution to this question is practically identical to that of the previous problem. In order to identify the correct angle between gauge 1 and the principal planes did you sketch the Mohr's Circle indicating the correct relative locations of the three gauges?

The above examples were based on the use of a 45° rosette. The figure in Frame 22 showed an alternative type of rosette, with the gauges positioned at equal angles of 120°. Other configurations are available. The interpretation of the readings from other rosette types follows a similar procedure to that demonstrated for the 45° rosette. Move on to the next frame to see the equations that apply to the 120° rosette.

28

120° rosettes

Although we are not going to work through the proof, which is similar to that demonstrated for the 45° gauge, the following equation can be used to determine the principal strains for a 120° rosette:

$$\varepsilon_{p1} = \frac{1}{3}(\varepsilon_1 + \varepsilon_2 + \varepsilon_3) + \frac{\sqrt{2}}{3}\sqrt{\left[(\varepsilon_1 - \varepsilon_2)^2 + (\varepsilon_2 - \varepsilon_3)^2 + (\varepsilon_1 - \varepsilon_3)^2\right]} \qquad (9.17)$$

and

$$\varepsilon_{p2} = \frac{1}{3}(\varepsilon_1 + \varepsilon_2 + \varepsilon_3) - \frac{\sqrt{2}}{3}\sqrt{\left[(\varepsilon_1 - \varepsilon_2)^2 + (\varepsilon_2 - \varepsilon_3)^2 + (\varepsilon_1 - \varepsilon_3)^2\right]} \qquad (9.18)$$

It is important, when using the equations, that gauge 2 is identified as the gauge located at 120° clockwise from gauge 1, and that gauge 3 is at 240° in the same direction. For convenience, gauge 1 should be taken as the gauge reading the highest value of strain. Equation (9.12) can again be used to determine the correct orientation of the principal planes.

A 120° strain gauge rosette records strains of $\varepsilon_1 = 557 \times 10^{-6}$; $\varepsilon_2 = 437 \times 10^{-6}$; $\varepsilon_3 = -94 \times 10^{-6}$. Calculate the magnitude and direction of the principal strains.

29

$$\boxed{\varepsilon_{p1} = 700 \times 10^{-6}; \quad \varepsilon_{p2} = -100 \times 10^{-6}; \quad \theta = 25°}$$

The solution follows directly from Equations (9.17) and (9.18) above:

$$\varepsilon_{p1}, \varepsilon_{p2} = \frac{1}{3}(\varepsilon_1 + \varepsilon_2 + \varepsilon_3) \pm \frac{\sqrt{2}}{3}\sqrt{\left[(\varepsilon_1 - \varepsilon_2)^2 + (\varepsilon_2 - \varepsilon_3)^2 + (\varepsilon_1 - \varepsilon_3)^2\right]}$$

$$= \frac{1}{3}(557 + 437 - 94) \pm \frac{\sqrt{2}}{3}\sqrt{\left[(557 - 437)^2 + (437 + 94)^2 + (557 + 94)^2\right]}$$

$$= 300.0 \pm 400.0$$

$$= 700, -100 \text{ microstrain}$$

Equation (9.12) can be used again to determine the angle θ:

$$\varepsilon_1 = \frac{(\varepsilon_{p1} + \varepsilon_{p2})}{2} + \frac{(\varepsilon_{p1} - \varepsilon_{p2})}{2}\cos 2\theta$$

$$\therefore \quad 557 = \frac{(700 - 100)}{2} + \frac{(700 + 100)}{2}\cos 2\theta$$

which, when rearranged, gives $\cos 2\theta = 0.643$. So $2\theta = 50°$ or $310°$. Hence $\theta = 25°$ or $155°$. To determine which of these two solutions is correct, the Mohr's Circle should be sketched as shown on the next page.

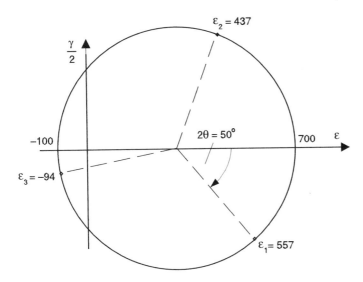

It can be seen from the circle that the solution of $\theta = 25°$ must be the correct solution. Hence the maximum principal strain will act in a direction which is at $25°$ measured *anticlockwise* from gauge 1.

Repeat the above problem for a 120° strain gauge rosette which records strains of $\varepsilon_1 = 382 \times 10^{-6}$; $\varepsilon_2 = 48 \times 10^{-6}$; $\varepsilon_3 = -129 \times 10^{-6}$.

30

$$\varepsilon_{p1} = 400 \times 10^{-6}; \quad \varepsilon_{p2} = -200 \times 10^{-6}$$
$$\theta = 10° \text{ (anti-clockwise from gauge 1)}$$

The solution to this question is practically identical to that for the previous problem. In order to identify the correct angle between gauge 1 and the principal planes did you sketch the Mohr's Circle indicating the correct relative locations of the three gauges?

PRINCIPAL STRESSES

The results of a strain gauge analysis will give us the principal strains and their orientation. What is usually required, and indeed necessary, to decide whether a component is over-stressed, is to determine the magnitude of the principal stresses. Once the principal strains have been established this is a relatively easy calculation to perform. Move on to the next frame to see how to do this.

31

If we refer back to Equation (9.3) we defined the strain at right angles to a plane at an angle θ as:

$$\varepsilon_\theta = \frac{\sigma_\theta}{E} - \frac{v\sigma_{(\theta+90°)}}{E}$$

and if we apply this expression in the direction of the maximum principal strain this can be expressed as:

$$\varepsilon_{p1} = \frac{\sigma_{p1}}{E} - \frac{v\sigma_{p2}}{E}$$

where σ_{p1} and σ_{p2} are the maximum and minimum principal stresses respectively, v is Poisson's Ratio and E is Young's Modulus.

What is the corresponding expression that defines the minimum principal strain, ε_{p2}?

32

$$\boxed{\varepsilon_{p2} = \frac{\sigma_{p2}}{E} - \frac{v\sigma_{p1}}{E}}$$

These two equations define strain in terms of stress.

Can you re-arrange the equations to express stress in terms of strain?

33

$$\boxed{\begin{aligned} \sigma_{p1} &= \frac{E}{1-v^2}(\varepsilon_{p1} + v\varepsilon_{p2}) \qquad (9.19) \\ \sigma_{p2} &= \frac{E}{1-v^2}(\varepsilon_{p2} + v\varepsilon_{p1}) \qquad (9.20) \end{aligned}}$$

These two equations can hence be used to determine the principal stresses from the principal strains, which will have been determined from the analysis of a set of measured strains.

The analysis of the results of a set of strain gauge measurements gives the maximum and minimum principal strains at a point in a component as 400 and −200 microstrain respectively. If $E = 200$ GN/m² and $v = 0.3$ determine the principal stresses.

34

$$74.73 \text{ MN/m}^2; \quad -17.58 \text{ MN/m}^2$$

The solution follows from a direct substitution of the given information into Equations (9.19) and (9.20):

$$\sigma_{p1} = \frac{E}{1 - v^2}(\varepsilon_{p1} + v\varepsilon_{p2})$$

$$= \frac{200 \times 10^9}{1 - 0.3^2}\left((400 \times 10^{-6}) + 0.3(-200 \times 10^{-6})\right)$$

$$= 74.73 \text{ MN/m}^2$$

$$\sigma_{p2} = \frac{E}{1 - v^2}(\varepsilon_{p2} + v\varepsilon_{p1})$$

$$= \frac{200 \times 10^9}{1 - 0.3^2}\left((-200 \times 10^{-6}) + 0.3(400 \times 10^{-6})\right)$$

$$= -17.58 \text{ MN/m}^2$$

where the negative sign for the minimum principal stress indicates a compressive stress. Once the principal stresses have been determined, the Mohr's Circle of Stress could be drawn and interpreted using the techniques we established in Programme 8.

What is the magnitude of the maximum shear stress at the point in the component where the above principal stresses have been determined?

$$46.16 \text{ MN/m}^2$$

If you recalled the Mohr's Stress Circle theory this should have been easy! The maximum shear stress is given by the radius of the stress circle which is simply calculated as $0.5(74.73 - (-17.58)) = 46.16 \text{ MN/m}^2$.

TO REMEMBER

As with the previous programme, this programme is concerned with techniques rather than specific formulae to remember. You should, however, be able:

(i) to draw and interpret a Mohr's Strain Circle;
(ii) to interpret the results of a set of strain gauge readings in order to determine the principal strains and their orientation; and
(iii) to calculate the principal stresses from a calculated set of principal strains.

37

1. At a point in a component the strains are known to be $\varepsilon_x = 200$, $\varepsilon_y = 200$, $\gamma = \pm100$ microstrain. Calculate the magnitude of the principal strains and the inclination of the principal planes.

  Ans. 250×10^{-6}, 150×10^{-6}, $45°$, $135°$ – angles measured in relation to the vertical y-axis.

2. Repeat Q1 for $\varepsilon_x = 300$, $\varepsilon_y = -100$, $\gamma = \pm100$ microstrain.

  Ans. 306.2×10^{-6}, -106.2×10^{-6}, $7°$, $97°$ – angles measured in relation to the vertical y-axis)

3. For the problem given in Q2, determine the strain normal to a plane inclined at $30°$ to the y-axis

  Ans. 243.3×10^{-6}.

4. At a point in a component, the strains are known to be $\varepsilon_x = -200$, $\varepsilon_y = 100$, $\gamma = \pm50$ microstrain. Calculate the magnitude of the principal strains and the inclination of the principal planes.

  Ans. 102.1×10^{-6}, -202.1×10^{-6}, $-4.7°$, $85.3°$ – angles measured in relation to the vertical y-axis)

5. For the problem given in Q4, what is the angular shear strain associated with the plane(s) for which there is zero normal strain?

  Ans. $\pm287.2 \times 10^{-6}$.

6. A $45°$ strain gauge rosette records strains of $\varepsilon_1 = 50 \times 10^{-6}$, $\varepsilon_2 = -86.6 \times 10^{-6}$, $\varepsilon_3 = -50 \times 10^{-6}$. Calculate the magnitude of the principal strains and the orientation of the principal planes relative to gauge 1.

  Ans. 100×10^{-6}, -100×10^{-6}, $30°$ measured anti-clockwise from gauge 1.

7. If, for the problem in Q6, $E = 200$ GN/m^2 and $v = 0.3$, what are the values of the principal stresses?

  Ans. 15.4, -15.4 MN/m^2.

8. Repeat questions 6 and 7 for $\varepsilon_1 = -73 \times 10^{-6}$, $\varepsilon_2 = -214 \times 10^{-6}$, $\varepsilon_3 = -226 \times 10^{-6}$.

  Ans. -50×10^{-6}, -250×10^{-6}, $20°$ measured anticlockwise from gauge 1, -27.5, -58.2 MN/m^2.

9. A $120°$ strain gauge rosette records strains of $\varepsilon_1 = 294 \times 10^{-6}$, $\varepsilon_2 = 183 \times 10^{-6}$, $\varepsilon_3 = 123 \times 10^{-6}$. Calculate the magnitude of the principal strains and the orientation of the principal planes relative to gauge 1.

  Ans. 300×10^{-6}, 100×10^{-6}, $10°$ measured anticlockwise from gauge 1.

Programme 10

BEAM
DEFLECTIONS

On completion of this programme you will be able to:

- Explain why it is important to know the magnitude of beam deflections
- Define 'flexural stiffness'
- Calculate the magnitude of deflection and slope at a point along a simply supported beam subject to different combinations of loading
- Calculate the magnitude of deflection and slope at a point along a cantilevered beam subject to different combinations of loading
- State the formula for mid-span deflection of a simply supported beam subject to a centrally applied point load
- State the formula for mid-span deflection of a simply supported beam subject to a continuous uniformly distributed load

1

Programmes 4 to 8 were concerned with the analysis of different forms of stress and the application of the theories we have developed to the analysis and design of mechanical components.

In mechanical design, the primary requirement is to ensure that the component can resist adequately the loading to which it is subjected. Usually this means that under normal loading conditions the stresses set up within the component must be less than some permissible value, that value being the failure stress of the material divided by some appropriate factor of safety. This aspect of design is concerned with designing for strength.

However, there are other important aspects of design, and in the case of the design of beams, another consideration is the value of the vertical deflections that will occur when the beam is loaded. This programme is intended as an introduction to the analytical techniques used for calculating deflections in beams and also for calculating the slope at critical locations along the length of a beam.

Can you think why it is necessary to calculate the vertical deflections that take place when a beam is loaded?

2

> (a) To check that visual appearance is acceptable; and
> (b) To ensure that the component can perform its design function adequately.

A bookshelf acts as a simply supported beam and will deflect under the weight of the books it is supporting. Excessive sagging of the shelf will spoil its visual appearance and also raise doubts about its structural integrity.

Similarly, the wing of an aircraft behaves as a cantilever beam. Excessive deflection of the wing tip would not only cause passenger distress but would also affect the aerodynamic behaviour of the wing. If we look at a typical mechanical engineering application: the shaft within a gear box will deflect under load. The deflection has to be limited otherwise the gears will not mesh properly, resulting in excessive wear, noise and vibration.

In Mechanical Engineering, allowable deflections are determined according to the specific application, whereas, in Civil Engineering, Codes of Practice specify a limit on the ratio of maximum deflection to the overall span of the beam – typically limits are of the order of 1:360. Generally, this means that the designer must be able to assess deflections and compare them with allowable values, or values determined by experience, to be acceptable for the particular design situation. This may mean using standard formulae for standard loading cases, or using analytical techniques if the loading case is non-standard.

A wooden bridge with a span of 4 metres crosses a stream. If the deflection is limited to 0.003× the span length, what is the maximum allowable deflection?

3

$$\boxed{12 \text{ mm}}$$

That was fairly straightforward ($4000 \times 0.003 = 12$ mm). But where in practice does the maximum deflection that we are calculating take place? If you are to calculate the deflections to compare with allowable values, it is necessary to identify the critical location(s) where the maximum deflection may occur. The ability to sketch the deflected shape of the structure (see Programme 3) is therefore important because, unless you can envisage the deformations that are taking place in the structure, you may not identify correctly the critical position for calculating deflections.

Consider the beams shown below. Sketch the deflected shapes and mark the critical position where the maximum deflection will occur.

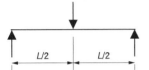  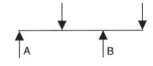

4

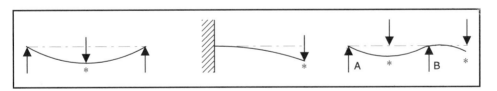

In the case of the simply supported beam, the maximum deflection must occur at mid-span. For the simple cantilever, the maximum deflection will occur at the end of the cantilever. However, in the third diagram there are two locations where the deflection may be at a maximum: at the end of the cantilever and at some position along the span AB. The maximum deflection within the span AB will not necessarily be at mid-span and its position must be identified. Both deflections may have to be calculated. Now go on to the next frame.

5

In Programme 5 we examined the structural efficiency of several shapes of beam cross-section and came to some conclusions about the relative efficiency of the sections when considering their ability to resist the same value of bending moment. Let's consider the same cross-sections, which, you may remember, have identical cross-sectional areas.

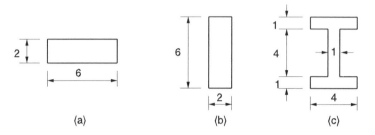

(a)   (b)   (c)

Three beams span identical distances, carry identical loads and are made of identical material. If they are made from three different sections as shown in the figures above, which beam would deflect the least?

6

> The beam made from section (c).

You should have reasoned that section (b) is much *stiffer* then section (a) and will therefore deflect less. If in doubt about this, take your ruler and rotate both ends to cause it to bend. Now turn the ruler through 90° and repeat the exercise. Which direction offers greatest resistance to deformation?

Section (c) will deflect less than section (b). This may not be quite so obvious. If you guessed that this is the case, did you reason that section (c) deflects less because it has the greater second moment of area about the axis of bending (the neutral axis) and is therefore *stiffer*? The geometric property we have identified as the second moment of area of a cross-section not only affects the strength of a beam but also the deformation under load.

If we now have two identical beams each having a cross-section as shown in figure (a) above and carrying the same load over identical spans but one being made of aluminium and the other of steel, which beam would deflect least?

7

> The steel beam.

You probably guessed this, but do you know why? As the beams are identical in every respect except their material of construction, the stresses within the beams must be identical. However the *strains* will be different, as the two materials will have different values of Young's Modulus of Elasticity. The amounts of straining in both tension and compression will be related to the beam deformations, and as steel has a modulus of elasticity approximately 3 times that of aluminium, the steel beam will deflect proportionately less.

What we have deduced is that the deflection of a beam is related to (a) the second moment of area of the beam section; and (b) the modulus of elasticity of the material of which the beam is made. We shall prove that these are important relevant properties later in this programme. The product of the modulus of elasticity (E) and the second moment of area (I) is known as the *flexural stiffness* (EI) of the beam. Note that, in using a modulus of elasticity, we are again assuming *linear elastic behaviour*, as we have done in all previous programmes.

Can you think of any factors other than the flexural stiffness which will affect the deflection of a beam?

8

> (a) The magnitude and distribution of the load;
> (b) The length of the span.

Item (a) should be obvious: double the load should give double the deflection, and so on (the principle of superposition again!).

The fact that the length of the span will affect the deflection should again be intuitively obvious: if there are two identical beams made from identical materials and sections, and carrying the same total loading over different spans, the longer span must deflect the most. But in what way will the span length affect the deflections: does twice the span mean twice the deflections? That might seem a reasonable supposition but is in fact incorrect. We shall see why and how later.

Let's now get down to the theory. There are in fact quite a number of methods for calculating beam deflections. Some are appropriate to manual calculation, some are more applicable to the use of modern computer methods. We shall develop one manual method to introduce the basic concepts.

9

Consider the short length of beam shown in the figure which is subjected to loading, causing sagging bending moment M which results in downward deflection (v) of the beam. The bending moment along this short length is assumed to be constant even though the bending moments in the beam, of which this is part, may vary. This short length of beam is assumed to be bent into a circular arc of radius R and is defined in terms of an x/y axis system where the y-axis is taken as being positive downwards. Thus the direction of the loading that causes deflection and the vertical deflection (v) are both positive according to our chosen axis system.

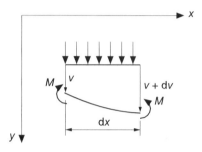

From the work you did previously on the bending of beams, can you write down a relationship between the beam curvature ($1/R$) and the moment M?

10

$$\boxed{\frac{1}{R} = \frac{M}{EI}}$$

In Programme 5 we developed the general theory of bending equalities:

$$\frac{\sigma}{y} = \frac{M}{I} = \frac{E}{R}$$

The equation at the top of this frame is merely a rearrangement of the second two terms in this expression. Note that the term EI is, as previously stated, the flexural stiffness of the beam.

However, there is a mathematical expression that defines the curvature ($1/R$) at any point on a curve in terms of differential functions of v and x. The proof of this expression can be found in many mathematics textbooks and should be familiar to you from your studies of mathematics.

The expression is given as:

$$\frac{1}{R} = \frac{\pm\dfrac{d^2v}{dx^2}}{[1 + (dv/dx)^2]^{1.5}}$$

In most methods of analysis we are concerned with *small* deflections on the assumption that the deflections of a component are small when compared with the overall system geometry. This implies that the slope at any point on the beam (dv/dx) is small, and is even smaller when squared and hence can be neglected in the above equation, which can then be written as:

$$\frac{1}{R} = \pm\frac{d^2v}{dx^2}$$

Our moment–curvature relationship can then be written as:

$$\frac{1}{R} = \frac{M}{EI} = \pm\frac{d^2v}{dx^2}$$

or

$$EI\frac{d^2v}{dx^2} = \pm M \tag{10.1}$$

Equation (10.1) is the fundamental expression that describes the vertical deflection (v) at any point distance x along the beam in terms of the applied bending moment (M) and the flexural stiffness (EI) of the beam. The intention of the analysis is to evaluate the vertical deflection, v, assuming that all the other parameters in the equation are known.

Can you write Equation (10.1) in a way in which it can be used to evaluate the vertical deflection (v) at any distance (x) along the beam?

11

$$\boxed{v = \pm\iint\frac{M}{EI}\,dx\,dx} \tag{10.2}$$

Mathematically, Equation (10.1) can be solved in terms of v by rearranging the terms in the expression and carrying out a double integration of the resulting expression. You are probably wondering whether the sign in front of the integral should be positive or negative. This depends on the choice of sign convention, which we shall clarify a little later. However, before we consider sign conventions, move to the next frame to try a simple problem to illustrate the application of Equation (10.2).

12

The beam in the figure is subjected to end couples of moment M causing sagging, as shown. For convenience, the origin of the axis system is taken through the left-hand end of the span. The problem is to find the maximum deflection which by symmetry must occur at mid-span.

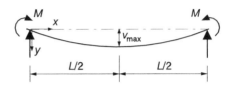

For the given loading configuration, the bending moment along the beam is constant and at any point distance x from the origin must equal M. If you are not sure about this, sketch the bending moment diagram and refer to Programme 3 if in doubt.

Hence from Equation (10.1) the general equation to describe the deformation of the beam is:

$$EI\frac{d^2v}{dx^2} = M$$

where M is constant. For the time being, we won't worry about the sign of the moment M.

Can you now carry out a double integration of this expression?

13

$$\boxed{v = (0.5Mx^2 + Ax + B)/EI}$$

This standard integral equation gives the deflection v at any distance x along the span. However, it contains two constants of integration (A and B) which must be evaluated before the equation can be used. To determine these two constants it is usual to apply the equation at *two known* locations (two values of x) where the deformations (v) are known, and hence A and B can be solved in terms of known deformations and distances. These are often referred to as the *boundary conditions*.

Can you identify appropriate boundary conditions for this problem?

14

$$x = 0: v = 0$$
$$x = L: v = 0$$

Both ends of the beam are supports where the deflections must be zero. The origin is located at the left-hand support, hence at $x = 0$, $v = 0$; and at the right-hand support, $x = L$ and $v = 0$. Substituting these boundary conditions into the equation in Frame 13, both A and B can be derived:

when $x = 0$: $v = 0 = (0.5M0^2 + A0 + B)/EI$:   Hence $B = 0$
when $x = L$: $v = 0 = (0.5ML^2 + AL + 0)/EI$: Hence $A = -0.5ML$

The complete solution to describe the deflection at any point along the span is therefore given by:

$$v = 0.5(Mx^2 - MLx)/EI$$

Now use this equation to calculate the deflection at mid-span.

15

$$v = -\frac{ML^2}{8EI}$$

The equation gives the deflection at any point, distance x, along the span. To obtain the mid span deflection, simply substitute $x = L/2$ into the equation:

$$v = 0.5(Mx^2 - MLx)/EI$$
$$= 0.5(M \times [L/2]^2 - ML \times [L/2])/EI$$
$$= -\frac{ML^2}{8EI}$$

To obtain the deflection at any other location along the beam, simply substitute the appropriate value of x into the equation. The slope at any point can also be obtained from the first differential (dv/dx) of the equation.

The above equation describes the deflection of a simply supported beam for a standard loading case of two equal but opposite end moments.

16

In solving the previous problem we did not consider whether the sign of the moment M should be positive or negative, and as a result the answer for the mid-span deflection came out as a negative quantity. However, it is obvious that when the beam is subjected to end sagging moments it must deflect downwards in the direction of the positive y-axis. The mid-span deflections should therefore have been a positive quantity to be consistent with our chosen axis system, and to achieve this the moment should have been preceded by a negative sign in our original integral expression.

Let's reconsider the diagram we originally drew in Frame 9, which defined the positive direction of beam deformation:

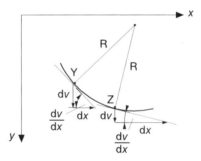

The curvature at any point distance x along the span can be written as:

$$\frac{1}{R} = \frac{d^2v}{dx^2} = \frac{d}{dx}\left(\frac{dv}{dx}\right)$$

But as (dv/dx) is the slope of the beam, then the curvature is the change of slope as x increases in the positive x direction. Hence as we move in the positive x direction from, say, point Y to point Z, the slope *decreases* and therefore the *change of slope* must be *negative*. To account for the negative curvature, the general expression that we originally developed should be written as:

$$\frac{1}{R} = \frac{M}{EI} = -\frac{d^2v}{dx^2}$$

or

$$EI\frac{d^2v}{dx^2} = -M$$

or

$$v = \int\int -\frac{M}{EI}\, dx\, dx$$

where *sagging* moments are taken as being positive and *downward* deflections are also taken as being positive. Now move on to the next frame.

Equations (10.1) and (10.2) were developed by considering a small length of beam curved to a circular shape as a result of the application of a constant sagging bending moment. The problem we have just considered was of a beam subjected to constant moments and therefore also deformed to a circular shape.

In most practical situations the bending moments along a beam will vary, and hence the curvature at different locations will also vary. However, the equations we have developed for deflection calculations can still be used, provided that the variation of bending moment can be described mathematically at all positions along the beam span.

Let's look at another example and develop an expression for the maximum deflection which by symmetry must occur at mid-span.

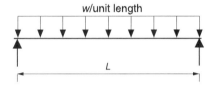

What is the correct expression for the sagging moment at the section distance x along the span?

$$M = \frac{wLx}{2} - \frac{wx^2}{2}$$

This follows from straightforward analysis of the beam. The end reaction R is given by:

$$R = wL/2$$

and the moment at the section being considered is obtained by taking moments of all forces to the left:

$$M = Rx - (wx)(x/2)$$
$$= \frac{wLx}{2} - \frac{wx^2}{2}$$

The general expression for the beam deformation is therefore:

$$v = \int\int -\frac{M}{EI}\,\mathrm{d}x\,\mathrm{d}x = \int\int -\frac{1}{EI}\left(\frac{wLx}{2} - \frac{wx^2}{2}\right)\mathrm{d}x\,\mathrm{d}x$$

Carry out the double integration of this expression.

19

$$v = \frac{1}{EI}\left(-\frac{wLx^3}{12} + \frac{wx^4}{24} + Ax + B\right)$$

Check your working:

$$\frac{d^2v}{dx^2} = \frac{1}{EI}\left(-\frac{wLx}{2} + \frac{wx^2}{2}\right) \qquad (a)$$

Integrate once:

$$\frac{dv}{dx} = \frac{1}{EI}\left(-\frac{wLx^2}{4} + \frac{wx^3}{6} + A\right) \qquad (b)$$

Integrate again:

$$v = \frac{1}{EI}\left(-\frac{wLx^3}{12} + \frac{wx^4}{24} + Ax + B\right) \qquad (c)$$

Look at the diagram of the problem. Can you identify the boundary conditions that would enable you to solve for the constants A and B in the above expressions?

20

$$x = 0: v = 0 \text{ and } x = L: v = 0 \text{ also } x = L/2 \quad dv/dx = 0$$

To solve for the two constants of integration, we need only two boundary conditions. However, in addition to the two end conditions of zero displacement, in this case there is a further boundary condition which could be used more readily. By symmetry the slope at mid-span must be zero, and as the slope is the differential expression dv/dx we can say that when $x = L/2$, $dv/dx = 0$.

Substituting $x = 0$ and $v = 0$ in to Equation (c) above will give the constant $B = 0$. To determine the constant A, either substitute $x = L$ and $v = 0$ in to Equation (c) or $x = L/2$ and $dv/dx = 0$ into Equation (b). In either case, the solution is:

$$A = wL^3/24$$

and the complete expression to describe the deformation of this beam is given by:

$$v = \frac{1}{EI}\left(-\frac{wLx^3}{12} + \frac{wx^4}{24} + \frac{wL^3x}{24}\right)$$

Use this expression to determine the mid-span deflection.

$$v = \frac{5wL^4}{384EI}$$

This follows from a straightforward substitution of $x = L/2$ into the final equation in Frame 20 and simplifying the answer. Make sure that you arrive at this solution before proceeding: it is only a matter of simple algebra.

This is a standard formula for a very common case of a uniformly distributed load on a simply supported span. It is worth remembering as it is widely used in the design of beams. Now try working through the next problem for yourself. The solution is in the next frame.

Determine the maximum end deflection and the slope of the free end of the cantilevered beam shown. (Hint: take the origin at the left-hand end.)

$$\frac{WL^3}{3EI} \qquad -\frac{WL^2}{2EI}$$

Moment at distance x from origin $= -Wx$ (hogging moment; hence negative)

General equation given by:

$$\frac{d^2v}{dx^2} = -\frac{1}{EI}(-Wx)$$

Integrate once:

$$dv/dx = (Wx^2/2 + A)EI$$

Integrate again:

$$v = (Wx^3/6 + Ax + B)/EI$$

Boundary conditions: $x = L$: $v = 0$ and $x = L$: $dv/dx = 0$ (zero rotation at support)

Hence: $\qquad A = -WL^2/2$ and $B = WL^3/3$

The complete expression is given by:

$$v = (Wx^3/6 - WL^2x/2 + WL^3/3)/EI$$

Maximum deflection when $x = 0$: $\qquad v = WL^3/3EI$

Slope dv/dx given by $\qquad dv/dx = (Wx^2/2 + A)/EI = (Wx^2/2 - WL^2/2)/EI$

Slope when $x = 0$ given by $\qquad dv/dx = -WL^2/2EI$

23

PROBLEMS

1. For the cantilevered beam in figure Q1, calculate the deflection and slope at the free end.

Ans. $wL^4/8EI$; $-wL^3/6EI$.

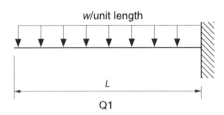

2. The cantilevered beam in figure Q2 is subjected to a couple of magnitude M at the free end. Determine an expression for the deflection and slope at the free end.

Ans. $ML^2/2EI$; $-ML/EI$.

3. A cantilevered beam shown in figure Q3 carries a triangular load of maximum intensity w per unit length. Determine expressions for the deflection and slope at the free end. (*Hint*: the load intensity at a distance x from the free end of the cantilever is wx/L. Remember, also, where the centroid of a triangular load acts when calculating the bending moment expression.)

Ans. $wL^4/30EI$; $-wL^3/24EI$.

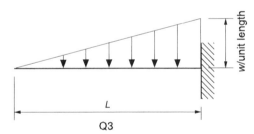

4. The simply supported beam in figure Q4 supports a triangular load of maximum intensity w per unit length. What is the mid-span deflection?

Ans. $5wL^4/768EI$.

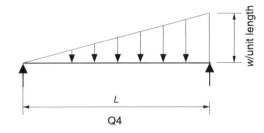

So far we have looked at problems where the bending moment at any location along the beam span can be defined in terms of a single expression containing the variable x. This is not always the case, and in fact often will not be as beam loading is usually more complicated than indicated in the previous problems.

Consider the simply supported beam carrying a central point load:

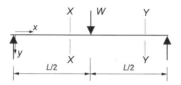

Taking the origin at the left-hand support, write down the expression for the bending moment at sections X and Y.

25

$$x \leq 0.5L: M_X = (W/2)x$$
$$x \geq 0.5L: M_Y = (W/2)x - W(x - L/2)$$
$$= W(L/2 - x/2)$$

Both of these equations are obtained by taking moments of forces to the left of the relevant points. What is important here is that we now have two equations describing the variation of bending moments in different regions of the beam, and hence it is necessary to apply Equations (10.1) and (10.2) simultaneously to both regions of the beam.

Hence we can write:

$$\frac{d^2v}{dx^2} = -\frac{1}{EI}\frac{Wx}{2} \qquad \text{for } x \leq 0.5L$$

and:

$$\frac{d^2v}{dx^2} = -\frac{1}{EI}W\left(\frac{L}{2} - \frac{x}{2}\right) \qquad \text{for } x \geq 0.5L$$

Both of these equations can be integrated twice with respect to x.

Hence in the region $x \leq 0.5L$:

$$\frac{dv}{dx} = \frac{1}{EI}\left(-\frac{Wx^2}{4} + A\right) \tag{a}$$

and

$$v = \frac{1}{EI}\left(-\frac{Wx^3}{12} + Ax + B\right) \tag{b}$$

Complete the integration for the region $x \geq 0.5L$.

26

$$\frac{\mathrm{d}v}{\mathrm{d}x} = \frac{1}{EI}\left(\frac{Wx^2}{4} - \frac{WLx}{2} + C\right) \quad \text{(c)} \qquad v = \frac{1}{EI}\left(\frac{Wx^3}{12} - \frac{WLx^2}{4} + Cx + D\right) \quad \text{(d)}$$

The integration should present no problem, but what is important is that now there are four constants of integration: two for each of the two separate equations.

How many boundary conditions must we find in order to eliminate the constants of integration?

27

Four

To eliminate four unknowns, we must effectively set up four equations making use of four known boundary conditions.

Look back at the original diagram of the beam in Frame 24. Can you identify four boundary conditions: two for each of the two sections of the beam?

28

For $x \leq 0.5L$: $x = 0$; $v = 0$ and $x = 0.5L$; $\mathrm{d}v/\mathrm{d}x = 0$
For $x \geq 0.5L$: $x = L$; $v = 0$ and $x = 0.5L$; $\mathrm{d}v/\mathrm{d}x = 0$

The two supports are obvious boundary conditions, and because the beam is symmetrical the slope at mid-span must be zero. The zero slope condition applies to both equations, because the centre of the span is a point common to both equations.

Hence, substituting the boundary conditions for $x \leq 0.5L$ into Equations (b) and (a) of Frame 25:

$$v = \frac{1}{EI}\left(-\frac{Wx^3}{12} + Ax + B\right) \tag{b}$$

when $x = 0$; $v = 0$ gives $B = 0$.

$$\frac{\mathrm{d}v}{\mathrm{d}x} = \frac{1}{EI}\left(-\frac{Wx^2}{4} + A\right) \tag{a}$$

when $x = L/2$; $\mathrm{d}v/\mathrm{d}x = 0$ gives $A = WL^2/16$.

Hence substituting the constants of integration, A and B, back into Equation (b):

$$v = \frac{1}{EI}\left(-\frac{Wx^3}{12} + \frac{WL^2x}{16}\right) \tag{e}$$

which defines the deformation of the beam in the region of the left-hand half of the span.

Can you complete this calculation by forming the equation which defines the deformations for the right-hand side of the span?

29

$$\boxed{v = \frac{1}{EI}\left(\frac{Wx^3}{12} - \frac{Wx^2L}{4} + \frac{3WL^2x}{16} - \frac{WL^3}{48}\right)}$$

Check your solution:

The equations for slope and deflection to the right of mid-span were given in Frame 26 as:

$$\frac{dv}{dx} = \frac{1}{EI}\left(\frac{Wx^2}{4} - \frac{WLx}{2} + C\right) \tag{c}$$

and

$$v = \frac{1}{EI}\left(\frac{Wx^3}{12} - \frac{WLx^2}{4} + Cx + D\right) \tag{d}$$

Boundary condition: $x = L/2$; $dv/dx = 0$ substituted into Equation (c) gives:

$$C = \frac{3WL^2}{16}$$

Boundary condition: $x = L$; $v = 0$ substituted into Equation (d) together with the known expression for C gives:

$$D = -\frac{WL^3}{48EI}$$

Hence substituting for C and D into Equation (d) gives:

$$v = \frac{1}{EI}\left(\frac{Wx^3}{12} - \frac{WLx^2}{4} + \frac{3WL^2x}{16} - \frac{WL^3}{48}\right) \tag{f}$$

We therefore have two equations defining the deflection of this beam. Equation (e) gives the deflections for $x \le 0.5L$ and Equation (f) for $x \ge 0.5L$.

Determine the expression for the mid-span deflection of this beam.

30

$$v = \frac{WL^3}{48EI}$$

This expression can be determined by substituting $x = L/2$ into either of the two equations we have developed.

For example, from Equation (e) in Frame 28:

$$v = \frac{1}{EI}\left(-\frac{Wx^3}{12} + \frac{WL^2x}{16}\right) \qquad (e)$$

Substitute $x = L/2$:

$$v = \frac{1}{EI}\left(-\frac{W(L/2)^3}{12} + \frac{WL^2(L/2)}{16}\right)$$

$$= \frac{WL^3}{EI}\left(-\frac{1}{96} + \frac{1}{32}\right)$$

$$= \frac{WL^3}{48EI}$$

Make the same substitution into Equation (f) to convince yourself that the same result can be obtained.

Now use both equations to determine the slopes of the beam at either end.

31

$$\text{Left-hand end: } \mathrm{d}v/\mathrm{d}x = +\frac{WL^2}{16}; \quad \text{Right-hand end: } \mathrm{d}v/\mathrm{d}x = -\frac{WL^2}{16}$$

These results are obtained by substituting $x = 0$ into Equation (a) (Frame 25) with the constant A being known, and by substituting $x = L$ into Equation (c) (Frame 26) with the constant C being known. As you would expect from the symmetry of the problem, the slopes are of the same magnitude but the opposite sign. This is a straightforward substitution and simplification of results, so no solution has been given; but do not proceed until you get these answers.

The formula for the mid-span deflection of the beam under a central point load is for another standard loading case and is worth remembering for use in your further studies of engineering design.

32

Earlier in this programme we reasoned that the amount of deflection of a beam must depend upon (a) the magnitude of the load; (b) the flexural stiffness, EI; and (c) the span of the beam. We also reasoned that, as a consequence of the principle of superposition, the deflection must be related linearly to the magnitude of the load, but posed the question whether such a linear relationship existed between the deflection and the span of the beam.

Examination of any of the formulae we have derived shows that this is obviously not the case. For a beam supporting a central point load, the deflection formula was given by $WL^3/48EI$. In other words, the deflection is related to the third power of the span. A doubling of the span will result in eight times (2^3) the central deflection for the same load! This seemingly minor observation is of considerable importance when deflection control is considered in practical design.

Another simple observation is that the *form* of all the deflection equations we have developed for all cases considered so far is practically the same. The only difference is the multiplying constant: 1/48 for a point load at mid-span of a simply supported beam; 5/384 for a uniformly distributed load over the full span of a simply supported beam, and so on. Therefore memorising a few of the formulae for the more common loading cases is not difficult, as only the constant needs to be committed to memory. Even if such constants cannot be remembered, however, they are readily available in commonly available design manuals and reference books.

Not all load cases are so simple that they can be considered to be standard cases, so let's develop the theory even further to see how to deal with more complex problems.

33

In the previous problem of a simply supported beam with a central point load, we derived two equations defining the beam's deflection and containing four constants of integration that had to be determined. Let's look now at a more realistic example.

If similar methods were used to analyse the beam shown above, how many deflection equations would you have to develop, and how many integration constants would you have to determine?

34

5 equations and 10 integration constants

If you sketch the bending moment diagram for this beam you will see that there are five separate straight lines which form the diagram, hence five separate moment equations must be written down and integrated within the five separate lengths of the beam. Each integration will result in two constants of integration, hence ten (2×5) constants.

It should be obvious that, even for a fairly simple problem, the amount of arithmetic will soon become unwieldy. The method can, however, be refined and simplified into a more powerful variation attributable to a mathematician called W. H. Macaulay. Hence you will often see the theory we shall now develop referred to as 'Macaulay's Method'.

To develop this variation, let's consider the case of a simply supported beam with a point load which on this occasion we shall locate at some position other than the centre of the span. The support reactions, which are obtained in the usual way by taking moments, are shown on the diagram below.

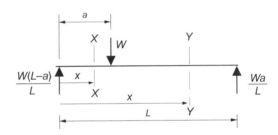

Write down the equation for the sagging moment at X and Y.

35

$$M_X = \frac{W(L - a)}{L} x \quad (x \leq a): \qquad M_Y = \frac{W(L - a)}{L} x - W(x - a) \quad (x \geq a)$$

These equations are obtained by taking moments of the forces to the left of the respective points.

The second equation gives the bending moment to the right of the load for all values of $x \geq a$. If this second equation is compared with the first, you will see that the first term in the second equation also appears in the first equation.

The second equation can be written as:

$$M = \frac{W(L-a)}{L}x - W\{x-a\}$$

where the term in the curled brackets {} is ignored (or put equal to zero) if its value is negative (that is, for all values of $x \leq a$) but included if its value is positive (that is, for all values of $x \geq a$). Hence this single expression can be used to describe the moments at any location along the span. For example:

$$M = \frac{W(L-a)}{L}x - W\{x-a\}$$

if $x = a/2 (< a)$
$$M = \frac{W(L-a)}{L}a/2 - W\{a/2 - a\}^0$$

Since the second term within brackets is negative, we can ignore it, and M is given by:

$$M = \frac{W(L-a)a}{2L}$$

but if $x = L (> a)$

$$M = \frac{W(L-a)}{L}x - W\{x-a\}$$

$$M = \frac{W(L-a)}{L}L - W\{L-a\}$$

$$= WL - Wa - WL + Wa = 0$$

This technique of neglecting or including a term in brackets depending on which section of beam is being considered is an application of a mathematical technique known as step functions or discontinuity functions.

The general expression to describe the deformation of the beam can then be written as a single expression:

$$\frac{d^2v}{dx^2} = -\frac{1}{EI}\left[\frac{W(L-a)}{L}x - W\{x-a\}\right]$$

This expression can now be integrated and boundary conditions substituted in the usual way to solve the constants of integration. However the integration *must* be performed *without expanding the terms contained within the curled brackets*. These terms must only be expanded when, after integration, appropriate values of x are substituted, and the terms are then expanded only *if positive*, but *ignored if negative*.

Integrate this expression and substitute the boundary conditions to obtain the deflection v. The complete solution is given in the next frame.

36

$$v = \frac{1}{EI}\left[-\frac{W(L-a)}{6L}x^3 + \frac{W\{x-a\}^3}{6} + \frac{Wa}{6L}(2L^2 - 3aL + a^2)x\right]$$

If you didn't get this answer, you probably made an error in integrating the general expression without expanding the curled brackets. Check your solution against the main steps given below.

The general equation is given by:

$$\frac{d^2v}{dx^2} = -\frac{1}{EI}\left[\frac{W(L-a)}{L}x - W\{x-a\}\right]$$

Integrate once

$$\frac{dv}{dx} = -\frac{1}{EI}\left[\frac{W(L-a)}{2L}x^2 - \frac{W\{x-a\}^2}{2} + A\right] \tag{a}$$

Integrate again

$$v = -\frac{1}{EI}\left[\frac{W(L-a)}{6L}x^3 - \frac{W\{x-a\}^3}{6} + Ax + B\right] \tag{b}$$

Boundary condition: $x = 0$; $v = 0$ gives:

$$0 = -\frac{1}{EI}\left[\frac{W(L-a)}{6L}0^3 - \frac{W\{0-a\}^3}{6} + A0 + B\right]$$

Hence:

$B = 0$ (note the term in curled brackets is negative and hence ignored)

Boundary condition: $x = L$; $v = 0$ gives:

$$0 = -\frac{1}{EI}\left[\frac{W(L-a)}{6L}L^3 - \frac{W\{L-a\}^3}{6} + AL + 0\right]$$

Hence:

$$A = -\left[\frac{W(L-a)}{6}L - \frac{W\{L-a\}^3}{6L}\right]$$

which simplifies to

$$A = -\frac{Wa}{6L}(2L^2 - 3aL + a^2)$$

Substituting for A and B in Equation (b) gives:

$$v = \frac{1}{EI}\left[-\frac{W(L-a)}{6L}x^3 + \frac{W\{x-a\}^3}{6} + \frac{Wa}{6L}(2L^2 - 3aL + a^2)x\right]$$

This equation describes the deflection at all locations along the span provided that, whenever a substitution is made for x, the term contained within the curled brackets is ignored (or put equal to zero) if it is negative.

A simply supported beam spans 6 metres and carries a point load of 10 kN at a point 2 metres from the left-hand support. Use the above equation to calculate the deflection (a) at one metre from the left-hand end; and (b) at mid span. Take $EI = 20 \times 10^3$ kN m².

$$\boxed{1.06 \text{ mm} \quad 1.92 \text{ mm}}$$

Check your working if you didn't get the correct answer:
The equation for the beam deflection is given by:

$$v = \frac{1}{EI}\left[-\frac{W(L-a)}{6L}x^3 + \frac{W\{x-a\}^3}{6} + \frac{Wa}{6L}(2L^2 - 3aL + a^2)x\right]$$

where $L = 6$ metres, $a = 2$ metres and $W = 10$ kN. Hence:

$$v = \frac{1}{EI}\left[-\frac{10 \times (6-2)}{6 \times 6}x^3 + \frac{10 \times \{x-2\}^3}{6} + \frac{10 \times 2}{6 \times 6}(2 \times 6^2 - 3 \times 2 \times 6 + 2^2)x\right]$$

$$= [-1.11x^3 + 1.67\{x-2\}^3 + 22.22x]/EI$$

At one metre from the left-hand support $x = 1$ metre:

Hence
$$v = [-1.11 \times 1^3 + 1.67\{1-2\}^3{}^0 + 22.22 \times 1]/EI$$
$$= 21.11/EI$$
$$= 21.11/20\,000$$
$$= 0.00106 \text{ m} = 1.06 \text{ mm}$$

At mid span $x = 3$ metres:

Hence
$$v = [-1.11 \times 3^3 + 1.67\{3-2\}^3 + 22.22 \times 3]/EI$$
$$= 38.36/EI$$
$$= 38.36/20\,000$$
$$= 0.00192 \text{ m} = 1.92 \text{ mm}$$

The example given above illustrates the technique of using Macaulay brackets to develop a single expression to describe the displacements at every point along the span of a beam.

What are the two important features of the use of Macaulay brackets that you must always remember?

> (a) Terms within the curled brackets must be integrated without expanding the brackets; and
> (b) On substituting values of the variable x, the bracketed terms are ignored or set equal to zero if negative.

Now go on to the next frame.

39

Once the bending moments along the span of a beam are defined in terms of a Macaulay bracket expression, the mathematical procedures to be followed are practically the same in all cases, although the appropriate boundary conditions used to evaluate the integration constants may vary.

To give you more practice at setting up the moment equations, let's look at a more complicated problem where the end reactions have been calculated by the usual methods involving taking moments and resolving forces.

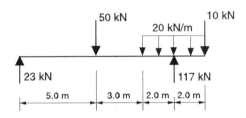

To set up the moment equation you should start at the left-hand side and write down the general expression for a moment at any distance x from the origin at the left. To begin, cover up the sketch of the beam with a piece of card (or your hand) and move the card to the right until you expose the first force, which in this case is the end reaction. Write down the moment at a distance x from the origin:

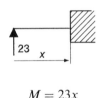

$$M = 23x$$

Now move the card to the right and expose the next load. Write down the moment at a distance x from the origin, which must include the term written above and a further term within curled brackets.

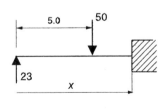

$$M = 23x - 50\{x - 5\}$$

Now repeat the operation until you reach the end of the beam at the right-hand side:

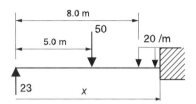

$$M = 23x - 50\{x - 5\} - \frac{20\{x - 8\}^2}{2}$$

Note the third term for the UDL, and finally:

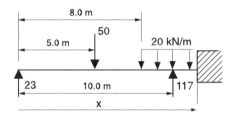

$$M = 23x - 50\{x - 5\} - \frac{20\{x - 8\}^2}{2} + 117\{x - 10\}$$

This final expression fully describes the bending moments at all positions along the span provided that the rules for the use of the terms contained within the curled brackets are remembered.

Carry out the integration of this expression and hence calculate the deflection under the 50 kN load. Take EI = 20 × 10³ kN m².

40

$$v = -\frac{1}{EI}\left[\frac{23x^3}{6} - \frac{50\{x - 5\}^3}{6} - \frac{20\{x - 8\}^4}{24} + \frac{117\{x - 10\}^3}{6} - 277.83x\right]$$

deflection under load = 45.50 mm

If you didn't get this answer, check your integration, particularly the term relating to the uniformly distributed load. The solution is given in the next frame.

41

Check your solution.

The general equation is given by:

$$\frac{d^2v}{dx^2} = -\frac{1}{EI}\left[23x - 50\{x-5\} - \frac{20\{x-8\}^2}{2} + 117\{x-10\}\right]$$

Integrate once:

$$\frac{dv}{dx} = -\frac{1}{EI}\left[\frac{23x^2}{2} - \frac{50\{x-5\}^2}{2} - \frac{20\{x-8\}^3}{6} + \frac{117\{x-10\}^2}{2} + A\right]$$

Integrate again:

$$v = -\frac{1}{EI}\left[\frac{23x^3}{6} - \frac{50\{x-5\}^3}{6} - \frac{20\{x-8\}^4}{24} + \frac{117\{x-10\}^3}{6} + Ax + B\right]$$

Boundary condition: $x = 0$; $v = 0$ gives $B = 0$ (all bracketed terms are negative and are ignored)

Boundary condition: $x = 10$ metres; $v = 0$ gives

$$0 = -\frac{1}{EI}\left[\frac{23 \times 10^3}{6} - \frac{50\{10-5\}^3}{6} - \frac{20\{10-8\}^4}{24} + \frac{117\{10-10\}^3}{6} + A \times 10 + 0\right]$$

which solves to give $A = -277.83$.

Substituting for A and B gives:

$$v = -\frac{1}{EI}\left[\frac{23x^3}{6} - \frac{50\{x-5\}^3}{6} - \frac{20\{x-8\}^4}{24} + \frac{117\{x-10\}^3}{6} - 277.83x\right]$$

and under the 50 kN load, $x = 5$ metres giving:

$$v = -\frac{1}{EI}\left[\frac{23 \times 5^3}{6} - \frac{50\{5-5\}^3}{6} - \frac{20\{5-8\}^4}{24} + \frac{117\{5-10\}^3}{6} - 5 \times 277.83\right]$$

$$= 909.98/EI = 909.98/20\,000$$

$$= 0.0455 \text{ m} = \underline{45.50 \text{ mm}}$$

42

PROBLEMS

1. A cantilevered beam carries a point load and a uniformly distributed load as shown in figure Q1 on the next page. Calculate the deflection at the free end in terms of the flexural stiffness, EI.

Ans. 1278.67/EI.

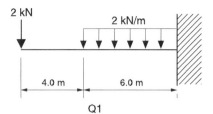

Q1

2. Calculate the deflection and slope of the free end of the cantilever shown in figure Q2. Express your answer in terms of the flexural stiffness, *EI*.

  Ans. 1566.67/EI; −208/EI.

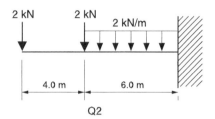

Q2

3. What is the deflection at the mid-span of the beam shown in figure Q3? (*Hint*: this problem is symmetrical – can you make use of the symmetry?)

  Ans. 23.05/EI.

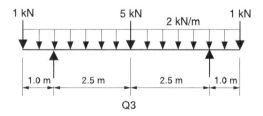

Q3

4. Calculate the deflection under each of the point loads which act on the beam shown in figure Q4. Take $EI = 15 \times 10^3$ kN m^2.

  Ans. 7.45 mm; 3.82 mm.

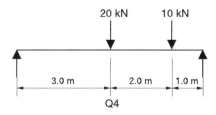

Q4

5. The cantilevered beam in figure Q5 carries a triangular load and a point load as shown. Determine an expression for the deflection at the free end of the cantilever.

Ans. $169WL^3/60EI$.

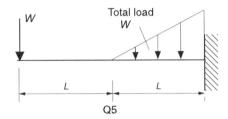

Q5

6. A simply supported beam supports two identical point loads as shown in figure Q6. Determine a formula for the mid-span deflection of this beam. Use your formula to determine the standard formula for a point load acting at the centre of a simply supported span.

Ans. $\dfrac{Wa(3L^2 - 4a^2)}{48EI}$, $\dfrac{WL^3}{48EI}$.

Q6

43

In all the problems that we have considered so far that involve uniformly distributed loads, these loads have all extended either across the whole span or, if partially covering the span, up to the extreme right-hand end of the span when our origin has been taken at the left.

If, however, this is not the case, as illustrated in figure (a) below, the expression that you would write down for the bending moment at, say, section Z–Z would not be correct.

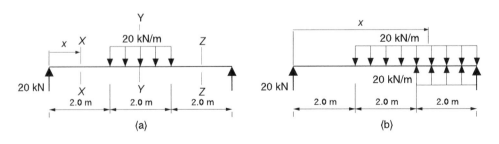

To show that this statement is valid we can write down the bending moment expressions at sections X–X, Y–Y and Z–Z:

$$M_{X-X} = 20x$$
$$M_{Y-Y} = 20x - 20\{x - 2\}^2/2$$
and
$$M_{Z-Z} = 20x - 40\{x - 3\}$$

from which it can be seen that the final equation cannot define the bending moments in the region of the UDL (say, section Y–Y) if the rules for the use of the Macaulay brackets are observed.

For example, substituting $x = 2.5$ metres (which lies within the UDL) into the equation for M_{Z-Z} gives:

$$M_{Z-Z} = 20x - 40\{2.5 - 3\}^0 = 20x$$

whereas from the equation for M_{Y-Y}, when $x = 2.5$ metres:

$$M_{Y-Y} = 20x - 20\{2.5 - 2\}^2/2 = 20x - 20 \times 0.5^2/2$$

which is obviously not the same answer.

Hence we cannot find a single expression to define the moments at all points along the span. To avoid this problem we can introduce a dummy load of 20 kN/m over the right-hand span and an equal and upward-acting load over the underside of the span in the same region, as shown in figure (b). Because the two dummy loads are equal and opposite, effectively they cancel each other out and don't alter the overall behaviour of the beam.

However, both loads now extend to the right-hand support and hence the use of Macaulay brackets to this 'new' loading system will be correct. Once the bending moment expression is written down correctly, the integration procedures and general solution methods are exactly the same as for any other problem.

Write down the bending moment expression for diagram (b) using Macaulay brackets.

44

$$\boxed{M = 20x - 20\{x - 2\}^2/2 + 20\{x - 4\}^2/2}$$

The third term in this expression accounts for the upward-acting load on the right-hand 2 metres of the span, and the introduction of this term means that this single expression describes the complete variation of bending moment over the whole span provided that the rules of the Macaulay brackets are observed.

Any problem where the load does not extend to the extremities of the beam would be treated in the same way.

Now move to the next frame where we shall discuss the final section of theory relating to beam deflections.

45

In Frame 36 you looked at a problem of a 6-metre span beam supporting a load of 10 kN at 2 metres from the left-hand support, and calculated that the mid-span deflection was 1.92 mm.

*Is this mid-span deflection the **maximum** deflection that will take place in this beam?*

46

No

If the load had been in the middle of the span, by symmetry the mid-span deflection would have been at the maximum. Generally, the maximum deflection will not occur at mid-span, although in practice the mid-span deflection will usually be close to the maximum.

How can you determine the exact position where the maximum deflection will occur?

47

It will occur where the slope of the beam is zero.

A little thought should tell you that this must be the case – if in doubt sketch a deflected beam and draw the tangents to the curve at different locations along the span. Mathematically, we would say that the slope is zero when $dv/dx = 0$. In other words, once we have constructed the equation for v we can equate dv/dx to zero to find the location where the deflection is at a maximum. Once this position is known, we can then substitute the value of x at that position into the deflection equation to calculate the maximum deflection.

Refer back to the calculations in Frame 37 and find the position and value of the maximum deflection.

48

1.94 mm at 2.73 metres from the left support

The deflection equation for this beam was found to be:

$$v = [-1.11x^3 + 1.67\{x - 2\}^3 + 22.22x]/EI$$

Differentiating to obtain the slope (remembering *not* to expand the term within the curled brackets):

$$dv/dx = [-3.33x^2 + 5.01\{x - 2\}^2 + 22.22]/EI = 0 \text{ for maximum deflection}$$

By inspection, the point of maximum deflection must be somewhere in the middle region of the span, to the right of the point load. The solution is likely to be for some value of x greater than 2 metres. On this assumption, the term within the Macaulay brackets will be positive, and hence *at this stage in the calculation* we can expand the brackets to solve for x. That is

$$-3.33x^2 + 5.01x^2 + 20.04 - 20.04x + 22.22 = 0$$

which solves to give $x = 2.73$ metres; hence the maximum deflection is given by:

$$
\begin{aligned}
v &= [-1.11x^3 + 1.67\{x - 2\}^3 + 22.22x]/EI \\
&= [-1.11 \times 2.73^3 + 1.67\{2.73 - 2\}^3 + 22.22 \times 2.73]/EI \\
&= 38.73/EI \\
&= 38.73/20\,000 = 0.00194 \text{ m} = \underline{1.94 \text{ mm}}
\end{aligned}
$$

In this case, the maximum deflection is very nearly the same as the mid-span deflection, but occurs 0.27 metres from the centre of the span.

Although this is a simple example, it illustrates the technique to be adopted in all problems where the position of maximum deflection cannot be identified readily by inspection. Note that the equation for the slope (dv/dx) will usually be obtained as one of the stages in the integration procedure used to develop the deflection equation. When this is the case, it is not necessary to differentiate the deflection equation to arrive at the equation for the slope. Some of the further problems in Frame 51 are based on this approach.

49

A final point to remember is that, in this programme, we have been considering the deflection of simply supported and cantilevered beams and have only taken into account deflections caused by bending moments. The shearing forces in the beams also cause deformations and contribute to the total deflection. The study of shear deflections is beyond the scope of this book, but in any case such deflections are usually only significant in deep beams, which are not usually encountered in everyday design.

50

$$\boxed{\text{TO REMEMBER}}$$

$$EI\frac{d^2v}{dx^2} = -M$$

where sagging moments are taken as positive and deflections are positive downwards.

Maximum deflection occurs when $dv/dx = 0$.

Terms within Macaulay brackets *must* be integrated without expansion, and on substitution if a bracketed term is negative it is neglected in subsequent calculations.

For a simply supported beam supporting a UDL over the whole span:

$$v_{max} = \frac{5wL^4}{384EI}, \text{ where } w = \text{load/unit length.}$$

For a simply supported beam supporting a point load at mid span:

$$v_{max} = \frac{WL^3}{48EI}, \text{ where } W = \text{total load.}$$

51

| FURTHER PROBLEMS |

1. A beam is to be designed as simply supported over a span of 4 metres and to carry a uniformly distributed load (inclusive of self-weight) of 5 kN/m. The maximum permissible bending stress is 12.5 MN/m^2 and the maximum deflection is limited to 0.003 of the span length. Calculate the minimum required depth of a rectangular beam section which is 150 mm wide. Take $E = 10$ GN/m^2.

Ans. 223 mm.

2. Figure Q2 shows a beam which is to be designed to carry a maximum loading of 5 kN/m and a minimum loading of 1 kN/m. To calculate the maximum deflection of the cantilever section of the beam, the loading is located as shown. Calculate the end deflection of the cantilever in terms of the flexural stiffness (EI) of the beam section. (*Hint:* make use of the symmetry of the problem.)

Ans. 16.05/EI.

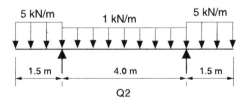

Q2

3. To determine the maximum mid-span deflection of the beam considered in question 2, the loading is repositioned as shown in figure Q3. Calculate the maximum mid-span deflection in terms of the flexural stiffness (*EI*) of the beam section. (*Hint*: make use of the symmetry of the problem.)

Ans. 14.42/EI.

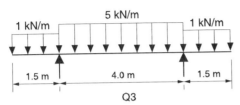

Q3

4. The beam in figure Q4 supports three point loads, as shown. Calculate the deflection under each load.

Ans. 30.14/EI; 5.15/EI; 46.30/EI.

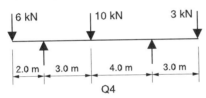

Q4

5. Calculate the location of the point of maximum deflection of the beam shown in figure Q5 and determine the value of the maximum deflection. Take $EI = 170 \times 10^3$ kN m².

Ans. 26.52 mm at 10.05 metres from left support.

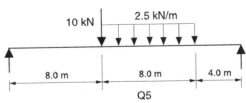

Q5

6. Calculate the maximum deflection of the steel beam shown in figure Q6. Take $E = 200$ GN/m² and $I = 7500$ cm⁴.

Ans. 6.77 mm.

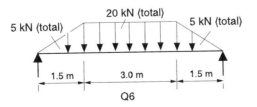

Q6

7. Show that the central deflection of the beam in figure Q7 is given by the expression:

$$\delta = \frac{W}{384EI}(8L^3 - 4Lb^2 + b^3)$$

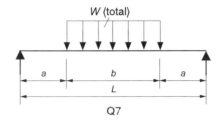

Q7

8. Determine an expression for the deflection at A and the slope at B for the beam shown in figure Q8.

Ans. $121wL^4/43\,740EI;\ -101wL^3/9720EI$.

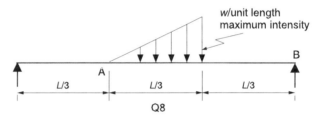

Q8

Programme 11

STRAIN ENERGY

On completion of this programme you will be able to:

- Explain the concept of Strain Energy
- State the units of energy
- Define 'Modulus of Resilience'
- Apply energy principles to calculate the deflection of pin-jointed frames at the point of application of a single load
- Apply energy principles to calculate the deflection of statically determinate beams at the point of application of a single load
- State and apply Castigliano's Theorem for the deflection of straight and curved beams subject to complex load systems
- State and apply the Unit Load method for the deflection of straight beams and curved beams subject to complex load systems
- Calculate the stress and deformation conditions within components subject to dynamic loading

1

Drop a hammer on the floor and the initial potential energy is converted to kinetic energy. As soon as the hammer hits the floor it is brought to an abrupt halt. The kinetic energy is dissipated, some in the form of noise (acoustic energy), but most is absorbed within the floor resulting in short-term and, normally, recoverable deformation of the floor. The energy stored within the floor is termed *strain energy*.

Strain energy is created whenever a component or system deforms under the action of a load system. You can illustrate this by stretching and then suddenly releasing an elastic band – the release of the strain energy will be quite apparent. Since the strain energy is associated with an elongation resulting from a direct load this is a *direct* form of strain energy. An alternative form is *bending* strain energy. An example of this type of strain energy can be seen if you consider a bow used in archery. As the archer pulls back the arrow the bow bends so that the stored strain energy can be released to impart kinetic energy to the arrow.

As these two examples illustrate, strain energy is normally recoverable when the component or system returns to its original undeformed state provided that the material from which the component is manufactured has only been stressed within its elastic range.

There are several methods of stress analysis based on the study of the strain energy within loaded components and the fundamental concepts of these methods are introduced in this programme.

A spring is an elastic component which when compressed absorbs energy stored as recoverable strain energy within the compressed spring. Can you think of any common situations where use is made of this property?

2

There are many possible answers to this question: did you think of the springs used in railway buffers to absorb the kinetic energy of moving rail carriages, or those used in cars to deaden vertical rolling movement caused by the vertical movement of the wheels? A more everyday situation is the release of strain energy in the spring of a mechanical watch which, as it slowly uncoils, provides the energy to operate the watch mechanism.

DIRECT STRAIN ENERGY

To begin our study of direct strain energy let's consider a bar of uniform cross-section, as shown below, which is made from a linearly elastic material.

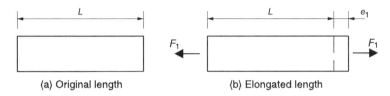

(a) Original length   (b) Elongated length

If the bar is subject to an axial force, F_1, it will elongate by an amount e_1 as shown in figure (b).

Remembering that the bar is linearly elastic and will obey Hooke's Law, can you plot a graph to show the variation of axial load with increasing values of axial extension?

3

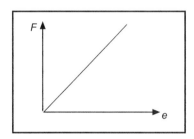

The form of this diagram should be quite familiar to you. For any linearly elastic material there will be a linear relationship between load and extension. Provided that the limit of proportionality is not exceeded, this relationship will always apply.

Now let's suppose that the bar is extended by an amount e_1 by the application of a force F_1 as shown in figure (a) and that the bar is stretched by a small additional displacement δe_1. This is shown on the load-extension graph in figure (b) below.

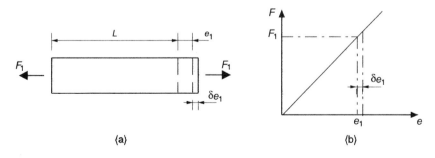

(a)   (b)

What amount of work is done by this force F_1 in extending the bar by the small displacement δe_1?

301

4

$$\boxed{\text{Work done} = F_1 \times \delta e_1}$$

This follows from the normal definition of work done as force multiplied by the distance through which the force moves, and is represented graphically by the shaded area under the load-extension graph shown below.

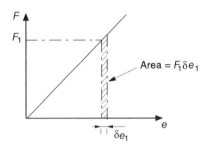

If the bar is extended from zero extension to a total extension, e, the work done by the load F_1 as it increases from zero to a maximum value F is therefore given by:

$$\text{work} = \int_0^e F_1 \delta e_1$$

which must be represented by the total area under the load-extension graph between zero extension and the extension e. This work done by the externally applied load must be stored as *strain energy* within the bar, which will act like an elastic spring and release the energy when the external load is removed and the bar is allowed to return to its original length. The strain energy stored (which is commonly given the symbol U) is therefore also given by the expression:

$$U = \int_0^e F_1 \delta e_1 \tag{11.1}$$

By inspection of the load-extension graph above, can you evaluate Equation (11.1) and express the strain energy in terms of the maximum load F and the overall extension e ?

5

$$\boxed{U = \frac{F \times e}{2}}$$

We have already stated that the work done, and hence the strain energy stored, is represented by the area under the load-extension graph between zero extension and the extension e. This area is triangular and the area of the triangle is one-half the base times the height: hence the above formula.

This formula can be derived alternatively by integration as follows:

$$U = \int_0^e F_1 \delta e_1$$

But we know (from Hooke's Law) that, for an elastic bar:

$$E = \frac{\text{stress}}{\text{strain}} = \frac{F/A}{e_1/L}$$

Hence:

$$F_1 = \frac{EAe_1}{L}$$

where: E = the elastic modulus; and
A = the cross-sectional area of the bar.

Hence U can be expressed as:

$$U = \int_0^e \frac{EA}{L} e_1 \delta e_1$$
$$= \frac{EA}{L} \left(\frac{e_1^2}{2}\right)_0^e$$
$$= \frac{EA}{L}\frac{e^2}{2}$$

But as $F = EAe/L$, then:

$$U = \frac{Fe}{2} \text{ as before} \qquad (11.2)$$

If, alternatively, we substitute for e in Equation (11.2) where $e = FL/AE$, then the equation for strain energy can be written as:

$$U = \frac{F^2 L}{2AE} \qquad (11.3)$$

which is often a more usable expression for the strain energy stored in an elastic bar.

As the strain energy stored in the bar is equal to the work done to extend the bar, what is the unit of strain energy?

6

Joule (Nm)

You should recall this from the work we did in Programme 7.

A 50 mm diameter steel bar is 2 metres long and carries a tensile load of 100 kN. Determine the strain energy stored in the bar. Take $E = 200$ GN/m^2.

7

$$\boxed{25.46 \text{ J}}$$

You should have used Equation (11.3) to get this answer:

$$U = \frac{F^2 L}{2AE}$$

$$= \frac{\left(100 \times 10^3\right)^2 \times 2}{2 \times \left(\pi \times 0.05^2/4\right) \times \left(200 \times 10^9\right)}$$

$$= 25.46 \text{ J}$$

Note that all dimensions have been converted to Newtons and metres to express the final answer in Joules (J).

Equation (11.3) can be further rearranged to give another formula for the strain energy stored, as follows:

From Equation (11.3) $\qquad\qquad\qquad\qquad\qquad\qquad U = \dfrac{F^2 L}{2AE}$

But F/A is the axial stress in the bar:

Hence: $\qquad\qquad\qquad U = \dfrac{F^2 L}{2AE} = \dfrac{F^2}{A^2} \dfrac{(A \times L)}{2E} = \dfrac{\sigma^2 (A \times L)}{2E}$

But as $A \times L$ is the volume of the bar, then the *strain energy per unit volume of material* is given by:

$$\text{Strain energy/unit volume} = \frac{U}{A \times L} = \frac{\sigma^2}{2E} \qquad (11.4)$$

As σ/E is the strain ε in the bar, Equation (11.4) can also be written as:

$$\text{Strain energy/unit volume} = \frac{U}{A \times L} = \frac{\sigma^2}{2E} = \frac{\sigma}{2} \times \frac{\sigma}{E} = \frac{\sigma \times \varepsilon}{2} \qquad (11.5)$$

which shows that the strain energy per unit volume is represented by the area under the material stress–strain curve as shown in figure (a) on the next page. If the material is stressed to the proportional limit as shown in figure (b), then the area under the stress–strain curve up to the proportional limit $\bar{\sigma}$ is given, from Equation (11.4) as:

$$\text{Strain energy/unit volume} = \frac{\bar{\sigma}^2}{2E} = \text{the modulus of resilience} \qquad (11.6)$$

The modulus of resilience of a material is a measure of its ability to absorb energy while still remaining elastic and permitting full elastic recovery. The higher the modulus of resilience, the greater the ability of the material to absorb energy while still remaining elastic.

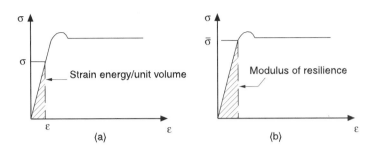

Which is the most resilient material – mild steel or high yield steel? The elastic modulus of steel is 200 GN/m². The proportional limit of mild steel is 250 MN/m² and for high yield steel is 460 MN/m².

8

High yield steel.

Equation (11.6) shows that the modulus of resilience is proportional to the square of the proportional limit of the material. The elastic modulus is the same for both steels, and as high yield steel has a higher proportional limit it therefore has a greater ability to absorb energy while still remaining elastic.

In answering the question, you might have calculated the value of the modulus of resilience for both steels. The values that you should have obtained are as follows.

Mild steel:

$$\text{Modulus of resilience} = \frac{\bar{\sigma}^2}{2E} = \frac{(250 \times 10^6)^2}{2 \times 200 \times 10^9}$$

$$= 156.25 \times 10^3 \text{ N/m}^2$$

High yield steel:

$$\text{Modulus of resilience} = \frac{\bar{\sigma}^2}{2E} = \frac{(460 \times 10^6)^2}{2 \times 200 \times 10^9}$$

$$= 529.00 \times 10^3 \text{ N/m}^2$$

Note that the modulus of resilience has been defined as the strain energy per unit volume. Its units must therefore be Joules per cubic metre (J/m³ = Nm/m³ = N/m²). Hence the units for the modulus of resilience are the same as the units of stress, which we can take as being N/m².

Now try some problems.

9

$$\boxed{\text{PROBLEMS}}$$

1. A steel bar is 500 mm long and is compressed by an axial force of 50 kN. The cross-sectional area of the bar is 1500 mm^2 and the elastic modulus of steel is 200 GN/m^2. Calculate the strain energy stored in the bar.

Ans. 2.08 J.

2. A steel tie of circular cross-section is 2 metres long. For half of its length the diameter of the bar is 50 mm and the remainder has a diameter of 40 mm. If the elastic modulus of steel is 200 GN/m^2 calculate the strain energy stored in the bar when an axial force of 80 kN is applied.

Ans. 20.87J.

3. To what value would the axial force in question 2 have to be increased to double the strain energy in the bar?

Ans. 113.14 kN.

4. Calculate the modulus of resilience of aluminium alloy which has an elastic modulus of 70 GN/m^2 and a stress at the proportional limit of 270 MN/m^2.

Ans. 520.71 × 10^3 N/m^2.

5. Calculate the total strain energy stored in the two members of the pin-jointed frame shown in figure Q5. Each member has a cross-sectional area of 1500 mm^2 and an elastic modulus of 200 GN/m^2

Ans. 23.57 J

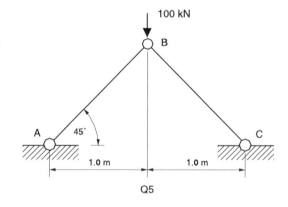

10

SINGLE LOAD DEFLECTIONS OF PIN JOINTED FRAMES

Since the members of a pin jointed frame are subject to axial loads, direct strain energy principles can be used to calculate the deflection under the point of application of a single load. For example, consider problem 5 in Frame 9. Did you calculate the total strain energy stored in the frame as follows?

The force in each member of the frame is determined by resolving at joint B to give a compressive force in each member of $50\sqrt{2}$ kN. Equation (11.3) should then have been used to calculate the strain energy in one member and, as the members are identical, the total strain energy is twice that in one member.

Hence, the total strain energy is given by:

$$U = 2 \times \frac{F^2 L}{2AE} = 2 \times \frac{\left(50\sqrt{2} \times 10^3\right)^2 \times \sqrt{2}}{2 \times (1500 \times 10^{-6}) \times (200 \times 10^9)}$$

$$= 23.57 \text{J}$$

The vertical displacement of joint B is also the displacement of the 100 kN vertical load in the direction of the load. If this displacement is δ, then this external load will do the work as the frame deforms under load.

Can you write down an expression for the work done by the external load?

11

$$\boxed{\text{Work done} = \frac{1}{2} W \times \delta = \frac{1}{2} \times 100 \times 10^3 \times \delta = 50 \times 10^3 \times \delta \text{ J}}$$

Did you remember to include the multiplying factor of one-half? As we are dealing with the application of a gradually applied force to a linear elastic system, the external loads and internal forces will vary from zero to the maximum values. The load-displacement relationship will be as shown in the graph at the top of Frame 3 and the work expression will therefore be given by Equation (11.2) in Frame 5. We have therefore established that the internal energy stored in the frame is 23.57 J and the work done by the external load is $50 \times 10^3 \delta$?

Can you calculate the vertical deflection at joint B?

12

$$\boxed{0.47\text{mm}}$$

From the principle of conservation of energy you can equate the external work done to the internal strain energy:

$$50 \times 10^3 \times \delta = 23.57$$

$$\therefore \quad \delta = 0.47 \times 10^{-3} \text{ m} = 0.47 \text{ mm}$$

Now go on to the next frame.

13

The method we employed in the previous problem can be extended to any statically determinate pin-jointed plane frame *subject to a single load*. The steps in the method can be summarised as:

(i)   Calculate the forces in each member using the method of resolution at joints;
(ii) Calculate the strain energy in each member $\left(F^2L/(2AE)\right)$;
(iii) Calculate the total strain energy stored in the structure by summing the strain energy components for all members:

$$U = \sum \frac{F^2 L}{2AE};$$

(iv) Calculate the external work done by the single load, W:

$$\text{External work done} = \frac{W \times \delta}{2}$$

(v)   Equate external work done and internal strain energy:

$$U = \frac{W \times \delta}{2} = \sum \frac{F^2 L}{2AE}$$

or $\quad \delta = \frac{1}{W} \sum \frac{F^2 L}{2AE}$ \hfill (11.7)

In practice, Equation (11.7) can be used directly to calculate the deflection of a load. When using this equation it is best to set out the solution in tabular form, as this is another situation where a systematic approach to presentation is less prone to error. Try the following problem, the solution to which is given in the next frame.

Calculate the vertical deflection of joint E in the frame shown below. take the elastic modulus as 200 GN/m² and the cross-sectional area as 1500 mm² for all members.

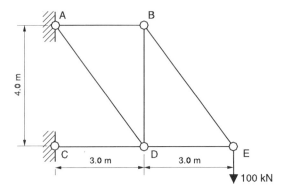

$$\boxed{9.92 \text{ mm}}$$

The forces in the members have already been determined in Frames 46 to 48 of Programme 2 and are shown below:

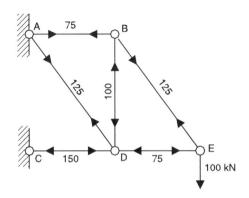

Member	F (kN)	Length (metres)	$F^2 \times L$
AB	75	3	16 875
BE	125	5	78 125
CD	−150	3	67 500
DE	−75	3	16 875
AD	125	5	78 125
BD	−100	4	40 000
			$\sum = 297\,500$

From Equation (11.7):

$$\delta = \frac{1}{W}\sum\frac{F^2 L}{2AE} = \frac{1}{W \times AE}\sum F^2 L$$

$$= \frac{297\,500 \times 10^6}{(100 \times 10^3) \times (1500 \times 10^{-6}) \times (200 \times 10^9)} = 9.92 \times 10^{-3} \text{ m} = 9.92 \text{ mm}$$

Note that, in tabulating the axial forces in each member, tensile forces have been taken as positive. However, as in this instance, the force term in Equation (11.7) is squared, the signs of the forces do not really matter. This is not always the case and it is good practice to adopt and show the sign convention being used. Note also that in this problem the AE terms are identical for all members. If this is not the case, then include additional columns in the table when evaluating Equation (11.7)

This method permits the calculation of the deflections at the point of application of the load when a frame is subject to a single load. Now move on to the next frame and we shall look at problems involving *bending strain energy*.

15

BENDING STRAIN ENERGY

Consider a *short* section of a beam with a length δx. If it is acted on by a constant bending moment M it will bend into an arc of radius R, as shown in figure (a) below.

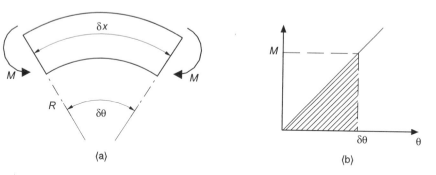

(a)   (b)

If the moment is gradually applied then, as shown in figure (b), the strain energy is equal to $\frac{1}{2} M \times \delta\theta$. But, for small angular deformations, we can see from figure (a) that $\delta x = R\delta\theta$ or $\delta\theta = \delta x / R$ such that, for this short section, the strain energy can be expressed as:

$$U = \frac{M}{2R}\delta x$$

Hence, if the beam is of length L, the total strain energy is given by:

$$U = \int_0^L \frac{M}{2R}\delta x \tag{11.8}$$

But from Equation (5.8) of Programme 5 we know that:

$$\frac{M}{I} = \frac{E}{R} \quad \text{or} \quad R = \frac{EI}{M}$$

Therefore, substituting in Equation (11.8):

$$U = \int_0^L \frac{M}{2R}\,\mathrm{d}x = \int_0^L \frac{M^2}{2EI}\,\mathrm{d}x \tag{11.9}$$

This equation gives the strain energy in a beam or component caused by pure bending. For most practical situations, it is realistic to assume that additional strain energy caused by shear forces and shear deformations will be negligible. Let's now consider the application of Equation (11.9) to a typical beam problem.

Consider the cantilever beam shown on the next page which is of a length L and has a load W applied at the free end of the cantilever.

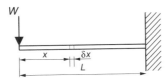

If we consider a small element of length δx at a distance x from the free end of the cantilever, then the bending moment at this location is given by $M = -Wx$. The negative sign indicates that the element is subject to a hogging moment to be consistent with the sign convention we have used previously for bending moments. Hence, substituting into Equation (11.9) the strain energy in the beam can be expressed as:

$$U = \int_0^L \frac{M^2}{2EI}\,dx = \int_0^L \frac{(-Wx)^2}{2EI}\,dx = \left(\frac{W^2 x^3}{6EI}\right)_0^L = \frac{W^2 L^3}{6EI}$$

Using this result, derive an expression for the deflection at the free end of the cantilever.

16

$$\boxed{\dfrac{WL^3}{3EI}}$$

You will remember from Frame 13 that the work done by a single, gradually applied load is given as $U = \dfrac{W \times \delta}{2}$. Hence, equating the work done by the load to the strain energy within the beam we can write:

$$\frac{1}{2}W\delta = \frac{W^2 L^3}{6EI} \qquad \therefore\ \delta = \frac{WL^3}{3EI}$$

This solution can be compared with that given in Frame 22 of Programme 10, where an identical problem has been solved using a different analytical approach but obtaining the same answer. Now let's see if we can apply the same technique to beams with other forms of loading.

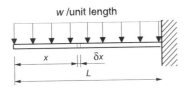

The figure shows a cantilever beam which supports a uniformly distributed load w.
Use Equation (11.9) to determine an expression for the total strain energy in the beam.

17

$$U = \frac{w^2 L^5}{40EI}$$

The strain energy can be determined as shown below. The moment at a distance x from the left-hand end is given by:

$$M = -\frac{wx^2}{2}$$

Hence, substituting into Equation (11.9) the strain energy in the beam can be expressed as:

$$U = \int_0^L \frac{M^2}{2EI}\,dx = \int_0^L \frac{\left(-wx^2/2\right)^2}{2EI}\,dx = \left(\frac{w^2 x^5}{40EI}\right)_0^L = \frac{w^2 L^5}{40EI}$$

Is it possible now to calculate the deflection at the free end of the cantilever?

18

No

We cannot use the strain energy equation to calculate the end deflection as there is no single load at the free end to which to relate the strain energy. In order to solve this type of problem we need to extend our approach to beams subject to any type of load system. Consider a simply supported beam supporting two concentrated loads W_1 and W_2 as shown below.

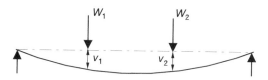

The deflections under each load are v_1 and v_2, respectively. The total strain energy in the beam, which must equal the external work done by the loads, can therefore be expressed as:

$$U = \frac{1}{2}W_1 v_1 + \frac{1}{2}W_2 v_2 \qquad (11.10)$$

If we were now to increase just one of the loads by a small increment – say W_1 increases to $(W_1 + \delta W_1)$ – then the deflections will increase to $(v_1 + \delta v_1)$ and $(v_2 + \delta v_2)$, respectively.

The load-deformation graph for W_1, as a result of this additional loading, is shown on the next page. It can be seen that the *additional* strain energy, δU, which must equal the *additional* work done by W_1, is given by the shaded area as shown in the graph.

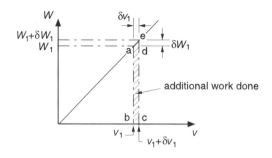

$$\delta U = \text{area of rectangle abcd} + \text{area of triangle ade}$$

$$= W_1 \times \delta v_1 + \left(\frac{1}{2}\delta W_1 \times \delta v_1\right) = \left(W_1 + \frac{1}{2}\delta W_1\right)\delta v_1$$

Since we have assumed that only W_1 increases in value, W_2 remains constant and the *additional* work done by this load is simply $W_2 \times \delta v_2$. Hence, the *additional* strain energy in the beam caused by the increase in W_1 can be expressed as:

$$\delta U = \left(W_1 + \frac{1}{2}\delta W_1\right)\delta v_1 + W_2\delta v_2 \approx W_1\delta v_1 + W_2\delta v_2 \qquad (11.11)$$

The *total* strain energy for the beam when the additional load is applied is given by:

$$U + \delta U = \sum \frac{W \times \delta}{2} = \frac{1}{2}(W_1 + \delta W_1)(v_1 + \delta v_1) + \frac{1}{2}W_2(v_2 + \delta v_2)$$

$$= \frac{1}{2}[W_1 v_1 + W_1\delta v_1 + \delta W_1 v_1 + \delta W_1\delta v_1 + W_2 v_2 + W_2\delta v_2]$$

If the second order term $\delta W_1\delta v_1$ is ignored, this equation becomes:

$$U + \delta U = \frac{1}{2}[W_1 v_1 + W_1\delta v_1 + \delta W_1 v_1 + W_2 v_2 + W_2\delta v_2] \qquad (11.12)$$

Subtracting Equation (11.10) from (11.12), we obtain:

$$\delta U = \frac{1}{2}[W_1\delta v_1 + \delta W_1 v_1 + W_2\delta v_2]$$

or $\qquad\qquad 2\delta U = W_1\delta v_1 + \delta W_1 v_1 + W_2\delta v_2 \qquad\qquad (11.13)$

and subtracting Equation (11.11) from (11.13) we obtain:

$$\delta U = \delta W_1 v_1 \quad \text{or} \quad v_1 = \frac{\delta U}{\delta W_1}$$

In the limit, this expression becomes:

$$v_1 = \frac{\partial U}{\partial W_1} \qquad (11.14)$$

This is rather a long-winded proof and you may have to work through it again in order to understand each step.

What do you think Equation (11.14) tells us?

19

> That the deflection under load W_1 can be obtained by partially differentiating the strain energy expression with respect to W_1.

This is true for any general beam situation subject to any number of loads. Equation (11.14) forms the basis of *Castigliano's Theorem for deflection*, which can be stated as:

> *If the total strain energy of a body is expressed in terms of the external loads and is partially differentiated with respect to one of these loads, the result gives the deflection at the point of application of that load and in the direction of the load.*

We can apply this theorem directly to bending situations in order to evaluate the deflection at the point of application of a particular load, but first we must adapt the deflection equation we have developed, as follows.

For a beam the deflection, δ, under a load W is given from Equation (11.14) as

$$\delta = \frac{\partial U}{\partial W}$$

Alternatively, we can write this expression as $\delta = \frac{\partial U}{\partial M} \times \frac{\partial M}{\partial W}$

and from Equation (11.9) we can write:

$$\frac{\partial U}{\partial M} = \frac{\partial}{\partial M} \int_0^L \frac{M^2}{2EI}\,\mathrm{d}x = \int_0^L \frac{2M}{2EI}\,\mathrm{d}x = \int_0^L \frac{M}{EI}\,\mathrm{d}x$$

it follows therefore that Equation (11.14) can be expressed as:

$$\delta = \frac{\partial U}{\partial W} = \frac{\partial U}{\partial M} \times \frac{\partial M}{\partial W} = \int_0^L \frac{M}{EI}\frac{\partial M}{\partial W}\,\mathrm{d}x \tag{11.15}$$

which is the more usual way of expressing Castigliano's Theorem.

Let's look at the application of this theorem to the solution of the simple cantilever beam we analysed in Frame 15.

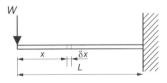

The bending moment M at a distance x along the span is given by $-Wx$. Use Equation (11.15) to calculate the deflection at the free end of the cantilever (that is, under the point load W).

$$\boxed{\delta = \frac{WL^3}{3EI}}$$

Check your calculations:

$$M = -Wx$$

$$\therefore \quad \frac{\partial M}{\partial W} = -x$$

Hence:

$$\delta = \int_0^L \frac{M}{EI} \frac{\partial M}{\partial W}\, \mathrm{d}x = \int_0^L \frac{(-Wx)}{EI}(-x)\, \mathrm{d}x = \int_0^L \frac{Wx^2}{EI}\, \mathrm{d}x = \left(\frac{Wx^3}{3EI}\right)_0^L = \frac{WL^3}{3EI}$$

which is the same answer as obtained previously.

This simple example illustrates the application of the theorem to determine the deflection under the point of application of a point load. When we need to determine the deflection at a position where there is no point load we can still make use of Equation (11.15) by applying an imaginary load at the position where the deflection is required and then simply equate the value of this imaginary load to zero.

Let's look at the example of the cantilever beam subject to a UDL that we considered in Frame 16. We can determine the deflection at the end of the cantilever if we apply an imaginary load at that position, as shown.

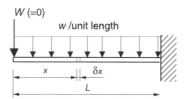

The moment at a distance x from the left-hand end is given by:

$$M = -Wx - \frac{wx^2}{2}$$

and differentiating with respect to W:

$$\frac{\partial M}{\partial W} = -x$$

Did you remember that, when you differentiate partially with respect to one variable, all other variables are treated as constants?

Use these equations, together with Equation (11.15) to determine an expression for the deflection at the free end of the cantilever.

21

$$\boxed{\dfrac{wL^4}{8EI}}$$

Check your calculations:

Since $W = 0$ then $M = -Wx - \dfrac{wx^2}{2} = -0x - \dfrac{wx^2}{2} = -\dfrac{wx^2}{2}$

Hence:
$$\delta = \int_0^L \frac{M}{EI}\frac{\partial M}{\partial W}\,\mathrm{d}x = \int_0^L \frac{\left(-Wx^2/2\right)}{EI}(-x)\,\mathrm{d}x = \left(\frac{Wx^4}{8EI}\right)_0^L = \frac{WL^4}{8EI}$$

If we look carefully at the above solution we can see that M is the bending moment resulting from the *external load system* acting on the beam because our imaginary load has zero value. Also, we see that the value of $\partial M/\partial W = -x$ is equivalent to the bending moment that would result from a *unit load* $\{-(1) \times x\}$ located at the position where we are calculating the deflection. For this reason, it is easier to consider a *unit load* applied at the point where deflection is to be calculated, and *acting in the same direction* as the required deflection. This alternative approach is often referred to as the *unit load method*.

UNIT LOAD METHOD

Following on from the above argument, it follows that Equation (11.15) can be expressed in an alternative way as:

$$\delta = \int_0^L \frac{M}{EI}\frac{\partial M}{\partial W}\,\mathrm{d}x = \int_0^L \frac{M \times M_1}{EI}\,\mathrm{d}x \qquad (11.16)$$

where: M = bending moment caused by the external load system; and
M_1 = bending moment caused by a unit load applied at the point at which deflection is required.

This alternative method can be used irrespective of whether or not there is a load at the point where we are calculating the deflection. Its advantage is that it avoids any confusion arising from the creation of imaginary loads of zero value. Let's look at its application to the cantilevered beam we have just considered, but this time we shall evaluate the mid-span deflection.

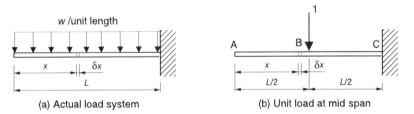

(a) Actual load system   (b) Unit load at mid span

Make use of Equation (11.16) to determine the mid-span deflection of the cantilevered beam shown above.

$$\boxed{\dfrac{17wL^4}{384EI}}$$

Did you appreciate that the beam has to be considered as two separate halves – AB and BC? The moment caused by the unit load has zero value at all points between A and B. (If you are not sure about this, then sketch the bending moment diagram for figure (b).) Hence, when using Equation (11.16) it is only necessary to carry out the integration over the right-hand half-span from B to C with integration limits from $L/2$ to L; that is:

For $L/2 < x < L$: $\qquad M = -wx^2/2$ and $M_1 = -(1)(x - L/2)$

$$\therefore \quad \delta = \int_{L/2}^{L} \frac{M \times M_1}{EI}\, dx = \int_{L/2}^{L} \frac{(-wx^2/2) \times (-(x - L/2))}{EI}$$

$$= \frac{w}{2EI} \int_{L/2}^{L} x^2 \left(x - \frac{L}{2} \right) dx = \frac{w}{2EI} \left(\frac{x^4}{4} - \frac{Lx^3}{6} \right)_{L/2}^{L}$$

$$= \frac{17wL^4}{384EI}$$

To use Equation (11.16) you had to evaluate the product integral $\int MM_1 dx$ where both M and M_1 are functions of the variable distance x. The equation can be modified in order to apply it to problems of curved beams, where the bending moments and distances can be expressed in terms of a variable angular measurement as in the figure of the curved cantilever beam shown below.

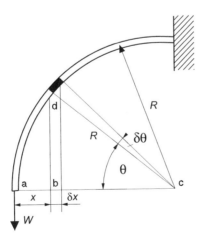

The moment, M, at distance, x, from the free-end of the cantilever is given by $-Wx$. Can you express this moment in terms of the radius, R, and the angle θ?

23

$$\boxed{M = -W(R - R\cos\theta)}$$

This follows directly from the geometry of the figure $(x = ac - bc)$. To calculate the vertical deflection at the end of the cantilever, the moment caused by the required *unit load* applied in the vertical direction at the cantilever end can similarly be expressed as:

$$M_1 = -1(R - R\cos\theta) = -(R - R\cos\theta)$$

and for a small increment of distance δx: $\delta x = R\delta\theta$

Hence Equation (11.16) can be expressed as:

$$\delta = \int_0^R \frac{M \times M_1}{EI}\,\mathrm{d}x = \int_0^{\frac{\pi}{2}} \frac{-W(R - R\cos\theta) \times (-(R - R\cos\theta))}{EI} R\,\mathrm{d}\theta$$

$$= \int_0^{\frac{\pi}{2}} \frac{WR^3(1 - \cos\theta)^2}{EI}\,\mathrm{d}\theta$$

Integrate this equation and calculate the vertical deflection at the end of the cantilever.

24

$$\boxed{\dfrac{0.356WR^3}{EI}}$$

The integration of this equation can be carried out as follows:

$$\delta = \int_0^{\frac{\pi}{2}} \frac{WR^3(1 - \cos\theta)^2}{EI}\,\mathrm{d}\theta = \frac{WR^3}{EI}\int_0^{\frac{\pi}{2}}(1 - 2\cos\theta + \cos^2\theta)\,\mathrm{d}\theta$$

but, as $\qquad \cos^2\theta = \dfrac{1 + \cos 2\theta}{2}$

then $\qquad \delta = \dfrac{WR^3}{EI}\int_0^{\frac{\pi}{2}}\left(1 - 2\cos\theta + \dfrac{(1 + \cos 2\theta)}{2}\right)\mathrm{d}\theta$

$$= \frac{WR^3}{EI}\left(\theta - 2\sin\theta + \frac{\theta}{2} + \frac{1}{2}\sin 2\theta\right)_0^{\frac{\pi}{2}}$$

$$= \frac{WR^3}{EI}\left(\frac{3\pi}{4} - 2\right)$$

$$= 0.356\frac{WR^3}{EI}$$

*How would you calculate the **horizontal** deflection at the end of the cantilever?*

> Apply a unit horizontal load at the cantilever end.

In calculating M_1, you should apply a unit load in the horizontal direction at the end of the cantilever. This load should be applied in the positive x direction (that is, to the right). If the answer turns out to have a negative value this simply implies that the deflection is in the negative x direction (that is, to the left).

Let's now look at a more complex beam problem. Consider the beam shown below. The units shown are kN and metres, but we shall not show units in the calculations so as to concentrate on the principles involved. Figure (a) shows the actual bending moments in the beam caused by the external load system. The requirement is to calculate the mid-span deflection of the beam, and hence figure (b) shows the bending moment diagram caused by unit load applied at the mid-span position.

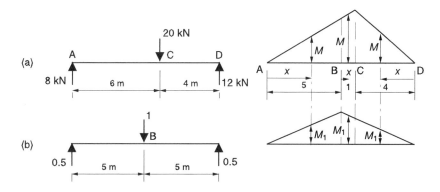

From the above diagrams you will note that there are three separate lengths over which the integration of Equation (11.16) must be performed (A to B, B to C, and C to D). This is because there is a change in one or other of the two bending moment diagrams in each of these regions, and it is not possible to find a general equation for the bending moments over the full length of the beam.

Hence the problem will be split into three parts and three separate integrations performed. The results of the three integrations will be summed to give the final answer. Because Equation (11.16) is independent of the chosen origin of integration, we can choose separate (and the most convenient) origins to evaluate the three integrals. Hence in region A–B, A will be taken as the origin; in B–C, B will be taken; and in C–D, D will be taken with the integration performed from D to C.

Write down the expressions for M and M_1 in each of the three regions.

26

	M	M_1	
A–B	$8x$	$0.5x$	Moments taken to left of point
B–C	$8(5+x)$	$0.5(5-x)$	M: moments taken to left of point
			M_1: moments taken to right of point
D–C	$12x$	$0.5x$	Moments taken to right of point

Use these expressions and Equation (11.16) to evaluate the mid-span deflection of the beam in terms of its stiffness properties (EI). The complete solution is in the next frame.

27

$$\delta = \frac{393.33}{EI}$$

Check your solution.

Section	Origin	M	M_1	$M.M_1$	Limits	$\int MM_1\,dx$	$\delta\ (\times 1/EI)$
A–B	A	$8x$	$0.5x$	$4x^2$	0–5	$4x^3/3$	166.67
B–C	B	$8(5+x)$	$0.5(5-x)$	$(100-4x^2)$	0–1	$100x - 4x^3/3$	98.66
C–D	D	$12x$	$0.5x$	$6x^2$	0–4	$6x^3/3$	128.00

$$\text{Deflection} = \frac{393.33}{EI}$$

This approach to calculating deflections can be applied to any problem where the variation of bending moment from both loading systems can be established over discrete lengths of the beam. As in all similar problems, it will always help if you sketch the shape of the bending moment diagrams before doing any calculations.

28

PROBLEMS

1. Determine the deflection at the free end of the cantilever shown in figure Q1.

Ans. $ML^2/2EI$.

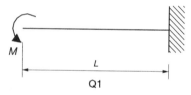

Q1

320

2. Determine the vertical deflection at the free end of the aircraft wing shown in figure Q2. Take $EI = 2$ MN/m^2

Ans. 1.02m.

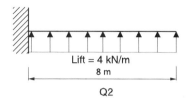

Lift = 4 kN/m

8 m

Q2

29

DYNAMIC LOADING

So far we have looked at strain energy problems where the component, or system, is subjected to loads applied gradually. There are many situations where the applied loading is dynamic in nature: that is, the load varies over time . If the time interval is very short, we can assume the load is applied suddenly. For example, a car suddenly hitting a hole in the road would cause shock loading on the suspension system. A nail being driven into a block of wood is subjected to a sudden impact load from the hammer-head. On a larger scale, a drop forge uses a heavy weight to form a component. To analyse these and many other problems of a similar nature, the principles of strain energy we have developed must be extended further.

To illustrate the principles involved, let's consider a short vertical bar made from a linear elastic material. The bar is fixed rigidly at one end, and a heavy weight W is dropped on to it from a height h. Assuming that the load was initially at rest, and on impact remains in contact with the bar and does not rebound, the energy of the falling load will be converted into strain energy within the bar as the bar shortens by an amount e.

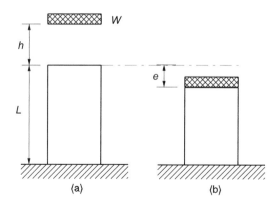

(a)   (b)

What form of energy does the load possess just before it comes in contact with the bar?

30

Potential and kinetic energy.

You should be familiar with these two concepts of energy. Potential energy is the energy possessed by a body by virtue of its height above some datum point, and kinetic energy is the energy possessed by a body by virtue of its motion.

Initially, the load will be at rest and its kinetic energy will be zero, but it will possess potential energy. However, as it falls, some of its potential energy will be converted to kinetic energy as its velocity increases, and after impact this kinetic energy will be converted to strain energy within the column. This assumes that none of the energy of the falling load is converted to any other form of energy such as heat.

As the load causes shortening of the bar it will eventually come to rest at the point of maximum shortening. After this, the bar will recover elastically and will attempt to return to its original length, resulting in longitudinal oscillations until a state of equilibrium is reached eventually.

Consult figure (b) in Frame 29 and assume that the shortening e represents the maximum shortening of the bar. Can you write down expressions for (i) the loss of potential energy of the load; (ii) the kinetic energy of the load; and (iii) the strain energy in the bar in terms of the axial force F within the bar at the instant of maximum shortening?

31

(i) $W(h + e)$; (ii) Zero; (iii) $\dfrac{F^2 L}{2AE}$

The potential energy expression follows from the definition of potential energy. The kinetic energy is zero as the load is just at rest at the instant of maximum shortening, and the equation for the strain energy follows from Equation (11.3) in Frame 5.

The principle of conservation of energy allows us to equate the energy lost by the falling load to the strain energy gained by the bar, that is:

$$W(h + e) = \frac{F^2 L}{2AE}$$

However, in most practical situations the drop, h, is considerably larger than the shortening, e, so e can be neglected and the above equation can be written as:

$$Wh = \frac{F^2 L}{2AE} \qquad (11.17)$$

Equation (11.17) is an equation that can be solved to give the *instantaneous* axial force, F, in a bar which is subjected to the impact of a falling load. This axial force occurs at the instant that the falling load first comes to rest. The corresponding *instantaneous axial stress* can be calculated once the axial force is known (stress = force/area). Try the following example.

A load of 1 kN falls from a height of 0.25 metres on a short bar which has a length of 0.4 metres and a circular section of 100 mm diameter. Calculate the maximum instantaneous stress set up in the bar if the elastic modulus is 70 GN/m².

32

$$\boxed{105.58 \text{ MN/m}^2}$$

The cross-sectional area: $\qquad A = \pi \frac{d^2}{4} = \pi \frac{\left(100 \times 10^{-3}\right)^2}{4} = 7.85 \times 10^{-3} \text{ m}^2$

From Equation (11.17): $\qquad Wh = \dfrac{F^2 L}{2AE}$

Substituting known values: $\qquad 1000 \times 0.25 = \dfrac{F^2 \times 0.4}{2 \times 7.85 \times 10^{-3} \times 70 \times 10^9}$

which solves to give: $\qquad F = 828.78$ kN

From which the axial stress in the bar $= \dfrac{F}{A} = \dfrac{828.78 \times 10^3}{7.85 \times 10^{-3}} = 105.58$ MN/m²

Assuming that, instead of dropping the load from a height, it is applied gradually to the top of the column. What would be the stress in the column?

33

$$\boxed{0.127 \text{ MN/m}^2}$$

This answer follows from the fact that, for a static loading, the stress is simply given by:

$$\sigma = \frac{W}{A} = \frac{1000}{7.85 \times 10^{-3}} = 0.127 \text{ MN/m}^2$$

What do you deduce from these last two stress calculations about the effect of dynamic loading?

34

> Dynamic loading causes much greater stress than does static loading.

By comparing the answers from the stress caused by static (0.13 MN/m^2) and dynamic (105.58 MN/m^2) loading, it is obvious that dynamic loading acting on any component will produce instantaneous stresses many times higher than the stresses arising from a static load of comparable magnitude. The instantaneous deformation of the component under the application of dynamic loading will also be correspondingly higher.

The theory we have been developing assumes that the material remains elastic and that full elastic recovery is possible. It should be obvious that, if dynamic loading is applied to a component, the high instantaneous stresses arising make it possible for the proportional limit, to be, exceeded. This occurs in drop forging, where the material flows plastically to take up the internal shape of the die.

The dynamic stress can be related to the static stress as follows. The static stress is given by:

$$\sigma_{\text{stat}} = \frac{W}{A}$$

and the stress caused by the dynamic loading if the load is dropped through a height h is given by:

$$\sigma_{\text{dyn}} = \frac{F}{A}$$

hence, if the energy equation (11.17):

$$Wh = \frac{F^2 L}{2AE}$$

is written as:

$$\frac{W}{A} = \left(\frac{F}{A}\right)^2 \frac{L}{2Eh}$$

then:

$$\sigma_{\text{stat}} = \sigma_{\text{dyn}}^2 \frac{L}{2Eh}$$

which rearranges to give:

$$\sigma_{\text{dyn}} = \left[\sigma_{\text{stat}} \frac{2Eh}{L}\right]^{\frac{1}{2}} \tag{11.18}$$

Use Equation (11.18) to solve the problem given in Frame 31.

$$\boxed{105.42 \text{ MN/m}^2}$$

From Frame 32, the static stress is 0.127 MN/m². Hence the dynamic stress is given by:

$$\sigma_{\text{dyn}} = \left[\sigma_{\text{stat}} \frac{2Eh}{L}\right]^{\frac{1}{2}}$$

$$= \left[0.127 \times 10^6 \times \frac{2 \times 70 \times 10^9 \times 0.25}{0.4}\right]^{\frac{1}{2}}$$

$$= 105.42 \text{ MN/m}^2$$

Further examination of Equation (11.18) will lead to some interesting conclusions about the nature of stress induced by dynamic loading. The equation can be expressed in the following form:

$$\sigma_{\text{dyn}} = \left[\sigma_{\text{stat}} \frac{2Eh}{L}\right]^{\frac{1}{2}}$$

$$= \left[\frac{W}{A} \times \frac{2Eh}{L}\right]^{\frac{1}{2}}$$

$$= \left[Wh \times \frac{2E}{AL}\right]^{\frac{1}{2}}$$

$$= \left[\text{the available potential energy of the load} \times \frac{2 \times \text{elastic modulus}}{\text{volume of the bar}}\right]^{\frac{1}{2}}$$

Study the above equation and write down your conclusions about the factors that affect dynamic stresses and how these differ from the factors that affect static stresses.

36

Dynamic stresses are increased by (i) increased energy in the impacting load; and
     (ii) higher values of elastic modulus.
Dynamic stresses are reduced by increasing the volume of material in a structure.

Did you come to these conclusions? Move on to the next frame and we shall give further consideration to the significance of these conclusions.

37

The conclusions in the preceding frame show that, for an axially loaded member of constant cross-section, dynamic stresses are influenced by different factors from those that affect static stresses. Static stresses in such members are independent of both the elastic modulus and the volume of material.

When constructing bridges, the bridge substructure, when built on soft ground, may be supported on piles that are driven down to solid foundation material. Two typical piles, manufactured from steel, have identical cross-sections. Pile A is twice as long as pile B, and both piles are driven into the ground until they reach solid rock at their bases. If they are driven by dropping a heavy drop-hammer from a constant height above the top of each pile, which one do you think is most likely to be damaged if it is subjected to continuous driving after it has hit solid rock?

38

> Pile B

Pile A is longer and has greater volume. It therefore has a greater capacity to absorb the energy of the drop-hammer, with resulting smaller dynamic stresses. The stresses in pile B will be higher and, if excessive, could exceed the proportional limit of steel and result in plastic deformation or even fracture of the steel section.

Let's assume that the stresses induced in pile B are so large that they do exceed the proportional limit. The figure shows two possible stress–strain graphs for two differing grades of steel (X and Y), out of which the pile section could be made.

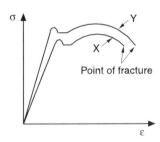

Which of the two steels would be the better steel for manufacture of the pile? Give your reasons.

Steel Y

The figure shows that both steels have the same fracture stress but the area contained under the curve for steel Y is much greater than that for steel X. Remembering that the area under the stress–strain curve represents the energy absorbed by the material, this means that steel Y has a greater capacity for absorbing energy than has steel X, and can therefore sustain higher impact loading before material failure takes place.

The stress–strain diagrams above are typical of ductile materials that undergo large strains before failure. Generally, materials that are ductile are more able to resist impact loading than brittle materials, because the area contained under the stress–strain graph for a ductile material is usually large, indicating a high-energy absorption capacity.

SPRINGS

At the beginning of this programme we made reference to a spring as an elastic structure which has a capacity for absorbing and releasing energy. Structurally, a spring behaves in a similar manner to an elastic bar.

From Hooke's Law we know that for an elastic bar:

$$F = \frac{EAe}{L}$$

where the symbols have the usual meaning. This can be written as:

$$F = Ke$$

where:

$$K = \frac{EA}{L}$$

$$= \text{the elastic stiffness of the bar} = \frac{F}{e}$$

The *elastic stiffness* is defined as the force required for a unit extension (or compression) of the bar $(K = F/e = F/1 = F)$. This concept of stiffness is one that you will come across in your further studies of solid mechanics. In the case of a spring, the elastic properties of the spring are also described in terms of a *spring stiffness*, which is the force required to produce a unit extension or compression of the spring. The spring stiffness will have units of N/m or other appropriate force/length units.

Two springs are subjected to equal compressive forces. Spring A has a stiffness of 10 kN/m and spring B has a stiffness of 20 kN/m. Which spring will compress the least?

40

Spring B

As $F = Ke$, then $e = F/K$. Hence, the spring with the largest stiffness will compress the least. It is important to remember that the *stiffer* the spring, the *smaller* will be the deformation under load.

Most problems involving energy stored within springs can be analysed by applying fundamental energy principles and simply recalling that the spring stiffness is given by the expression $F = K \times e$. Try the following problem; the complete solution is in the next frame.

A railway truck with a mass of 1000 kg is travelling at a constant speed of 10 km/h when it collides with a buffer which brings it to rest. The buffer consists of a spring with a stiffness of 200 kN/m. Calculate the maximum shortening and the maximum force developed in the spring. (Hint: this is not a problem involving a falling body: you will have to decide what form of energy the truck possesses.)

41

196 mm; 39.20 kN

Speed of truck = 10 km/h $\quad = \dfrac{10 \times 1000}{60 \times 60} = 2.78$ m/s

Kinetic energy of truck $\quad = \dfrac{1}{2}mv^2 = \dfrac{1}{2} \times 1000 \times 2.78^2 = 3864.20$ J

Strain energy stored in spring $\quad = \dfrac{1}{2}F \times e = \dfrac{1}{2}(K \times e) \times e = \dfrac{1}{2}Ke^2$

$\qquad\qquad = \dfrac{1}{2} \times 200\,000 \times e^2$

$\qquad\qquad = 100\,000e^2$

Hence equating energy:

$\qquad$ energy gained by spring $\quad$ = energy lost by truck

$\qquad\qquad \therefore \quad 100\,000e^2 = 3864.20$

Hence $\qquad\qquad\qquad\quad e \; = 0.196$ m

$\qquad\qquad\qquad\qquad = 196$ mm

The maximum force developed = spring stiffness $(K) \times$ compression (e)

$\qquad\qquad\qquad\qquad = 200 \times 0.196$

$\qquad\qquad\qquad\qquad = 39.20$ kN

42

TO REMEMBER

The strain energy stored in an elastic bar, $U = \dfrac{F \times e}{2} = \dfrac{F^2 L}{2AE}$

Strain energy/unit volume $= \dfrac{\sigma^2}{2E} = \dfrac{\sigma \times \varepsilon}{2}$

Modulus of resilience $= \dfrac{\bar{\sigma}^2}{2E}$

Deflection at the point of application of a single load, W, applied to a pin jointed frame (in the direction of the load):

$$\delta = \frac{1}{W} \sum \frac{F^2 L}{2AE}$$

The strain energy stored in a beam, $U = \displaystyle\int_0^L \frac{M^2}{2EI}\, \mathrm{d}x$

The deflection of a beam at a particular point can be found by using:

$$\delta = \int_0^L \frac{M}{EI} \frac{\partial M}{\partial W}\, \mathrm{d}x$$

or the unit load method: $\qquad \delta = \displaystyle\int_0^L \frac{M \times M_1}{EI}\, \mathrm{d}x$

To calculate forces and stresses caused by a falling load use: $Wh = \dfrac{F^2 L}{2AE}$

or $\sigma_{\mathrm{dyn}} = \left[\sigma_{\mathrm{stat}} \dfrac{2Eh}{L} \right]^{\frac{1}{2}}$

For a spring: force in spring = spring stiffness × compression (or extension)

$$F = K \times e$$

43

FURTHER PROBLEMS

1. A cast iron bar has a rectangular section of 250 mm by 500 mm and is 3 metres long. It is stressed by the application of a compressive force of 2000 kN which acts along the longitudinal central axis of the section. If the elastic modulus (E) of the cast iron is 100 GN/m^2, calculate the strain energy stored in the beam.

Ans. 480 J.

2. A steel bar loaded under tension is to be replaced by an aluminium bar of the same length. If they are both subjected to the same load and are to store the same amount of strain energy, what will be the ratio of the stresses? Take $E_{steel} = 200$ GN/m^2, $E_{aluminium} = 70$ GN/m^2

Ans. 2.86.

4. Determine the strain energy stored in a solid bar of 40 mm diameter and 1 metre length when subjected to (i) a tensile load of 10 kN; and (ii) a bending moment of 10 kN m. Take $E = 200$ GN/m^2

Ans. 0.199 J; 1989 J.

4. The cantilevered beam in figure Q4 carries a point load W at the end of the cantilever. Determine an expression for the deflection under W. (*Hint*: you will have to integrate over two lengths of the beam.)

Ans. $WL^3/8EI$.

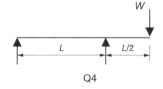

Q4

5. Calculate the horizontal deflection at the free end of the curved bracket shown in figure Q5 when it has a load of 50 N applied as shown. Take $EI = 10^3$ Nm^2.

Ans. 0.133 mm.

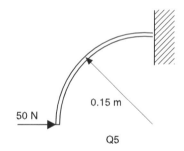

Q5

6. Figure Q6 shows a jib designed to suspend a robot over a workstation. The jib mast is a tube 3 m long, of 400 mm outside diameter and 20 mm wall thickness. The jib arm is a box section 200 mm square with a wall thickness of 20 mm. Determine the vertical deflection at the end of the arm if the robot has a weight of 3 kN. Take $E = 200$ GN/m^2 (*Hint*: you will have to integrate over the length of the mast then over the length of the arm.)

Ans. 0.925 mm.

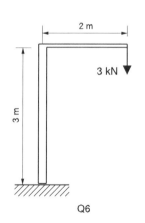

Q6

7. A vertical steel bar is 1 metre long and has a circular section of 25 mm diameter. It is fitted with a collar at the bottom end (see figure Q7) and is held firmly at the top. A load of 0.4 kN falls through a height of h metres and is arrested by the collar. If the maximum instantaneous stress in the bar is not to exceed 75 MN/m^2, what is the maximum allowable value of h? Take $E = 200$ GN/m^2.

Ans. 17.27 mm.

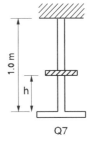

Q7

8. A railway truck with a mass of 500 kg starts from rest at the top of an incline and rolls down freely, as shown in figure Q8. At the bottom of the slope it is brought to rest when it collides with a buffer which consists of a spring with stiffness of 400 kN/m and a reaction frame. Calculate the maximum shortening of the spring and the maximum force transmitted to the reaction frame.

Ans. 145.92 mm; 58.37 kN.

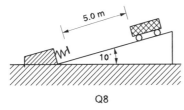

Q8

9. A metal stamping machine consists of a load of 5 kN which falls through a vertical height of 1.5 metres. The machine sits on a rigid foundation which is rectangular in plan and supported in each corner on bearings which can be idealised as spring supports as shown in figure Q9. If the vertical movement of the foundation must not exceed 3 mm, what value of spring stiffness is required and what is the maximum reactive force transmitted to the ground below each bearing?

Ans. 417.5 MN/m, 1.25 MN.

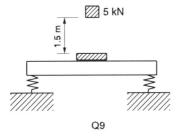

Q9

Programme 12

ELASTIC BUCKLING
OF AXIALLY LOADED
COMPONENTS

On completion of this programme you will be able to:

- Describe the different modes of failure of components loaded in axial compression
- Derive and quote the *Euler* buckling formula for a pin-ended component
- Define and calculate *radius of gyration*
- Define and calculate *slenderness ratio*
- State what is meant by a *short* component
- State what is meant by a *slender* component
- Describe the differences between the theoretical and actual behaviour of axially loaded components
- Define *effective length* (height)
- Describe the effect of different end conditions on the strength of components in axial compression
- Carry out simple theoretical calculations to determine the load carrying capacity of components

1

In Programme 4 we examined the behaviour of axially loaded components including those subjected to compressive loads; such as a connecting rod within a reciprocating engine. We saw how any externally applied axial load would result in the development of an internal elastic stress system. Such components would continue to resist any increase in load by developing proportionately higher internal stresses provided that the material is not strained beyond the elastic range. If the loading is increased beyond this limit, then some form of material failure will eventually occur.

However, such considerations neglect the possibility of other forms of failure. In this programme we shall examine another type of failure that can occur in axially loaded members, and is of particular concern when designing long slender components in mechanical systems. We shall explain the principles within the context of steel fabrication, since this is the most widely used engineering material, although these principles are equally applicable to other materials.

A hollow cylindrical steel tube is used as a column to support a piece of equipment. It has an outer diameter of 200 mm and a wall thickness of 20 mm. Calculate the stress in the section if it is subject to an axial compressive load of 2500 kN.

2

$$\boxed{221.04 \text{ MN/m}^2}$$

You should have obtained the answer as follows:

$$\text{Area of section} = \frac{\pi}{4}\left(D_{\text{out}}^2 - D_{\text{in}}^2\right) = \frac{\pi}{4}\left(200^2 - 160^2\right) = 11.31 \times 10^3 \text{ mm}^2$$

$$= 11.31 \times 10^{-3} \text{ m}^2$$

$$\text{Stress, } \sigma \quad = \frac{\text{Force}}{\text{Area}} = \frac{2500 \times 10^3}{11.31 \times 10^{-3}} = 221.04 \text{ MN/m}^2$$

This is a relatively straightforward calculation and should not have caused you any problems. If we assume that the steel will yield at a typical value of yield strength of, say, 265 MN/m^2 the calculation implies that the column has a reserve of strength and will sustain a load somewhat greater than 2500 kN before failure by yielding of the steel occurs. The question did not give any information about the height of the column and, indeed, we did not have any need to know the height when calculating the axial compressive stress. This would imply that the column's response to loading is independent of its height. However, let's consider two columns, (a) 1 m high; and (b) 10 m high, both fabricated from the same hollow steel tubular section and both subject to an increasing axial load.

Would you expect the two columns to fail in the same way?

3

| It's unlikely! |

The first column is a *short* column and will probably fail by *yielding* of the steel when the load is of sufficient magnitude to develop a yield stress of 265 MN/m^2 within the section (figure (a)). The second column is *slender* and will fail by *buckling* as indicated in figure (b). If you want to demonstrate the effect of buckling for yourself, take a long plastic ruler, stand it on a table and press downwards on the top as shown in figure (c) – it will be immediately apparent what we are talking about. Don't push too hard unless you want to break your ruler!

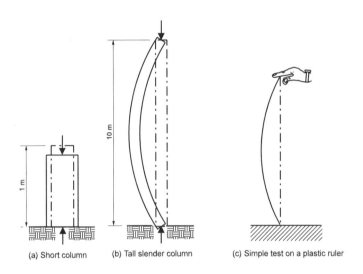

(a) Short column   (b) Tall slender column   (c) Simple test on a plastic ruler

Assuming that you haven't broken your ruler, what happened to the ruler when you removed your hand?

4

| The ruler straightened itself. |

In fact, if you repeat this simple experiment several times, each time the ruler will return to its original, undeformed position. The ruler, and the slender column of figure (b), has become *unstable*, and can carry much less of a load than if it were of a much shorter length.

What does the fact that the ruler fully recovers on unloading tell you about the stress–strain behaviour of the material of which the ruler is made?

5

The material has remained elastic.

The fact that the ruler fully recovers its shape means that the material of which it is made has not been strained beyond the elastic range, and hence we can say that the ruler has become *elastically unstable*. In other words, it has buckled and failed while still strained within the elastic range of material behaviour. This is an important observation because it implies that axially loaded components that are slender, rather than short and stocky, may fail by buckling at stress levels well below those that would cause those components to fail by yielding. Hence, in the design of such components, account must be taken of both likely modes of failure, which will depend on whether or not the component is short or slender.

Now let's look at the classical theory of buckling which we can develop by considering the axially loaded, pin-ended, slender strut A–B shown in figure (a). The strut is shown just on the point of buckling.

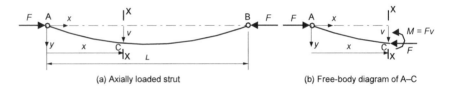

(a) Axially loaded strut   (b) Free-body diagram of A–C

If you look back at Programme 10, for a laterally loaded beam of flexural stiffness *EI*, we developed the equation that describes the moment–curvature relationship at a section X–X, distance *x* from the left-hand origin as:

$$EI\frac{d^2v}{dx^2} = -M$$

This equation can now be applied to the above strut if the moment, *M*, at the section is defined. If we look at the free-body diagram of A–C, by taking moments about C, we can see that the moment at C is given by $F \times v$. Hence we can write:

$$EI\frac{d^2v}{dx^2} = -Fv$$

which can readily be rearranged and simplified to give:

$$\frac{d^2v}{dx^2} + k^2v = 0 \qquad \text{where } k = \sqrt{\frac{F}{EI}} \tag{12.1}$$

As in Programme 10, in order to determine the deflection, *v*, at the section we can carry out a double integration of Equation (12.1) to determine an expression for *v* which can be applied at any point along the strut.

Can you carry out the double integration of this expression?

$$v = A\cos kx + B\sin kx \qquad (12.2)$$

The double integration of Equation (12.1) is not as straightforward as some of the integral calculations we carried out in Programme 10. If you are good at mathematics you may have obtained this solution. If you didn't, differentiate the solution given in Equation (12.2) twice and substitute back into Equation (12.1) to show that the solution is valid.

A and B in Equation (12.2) are constants of integration and can be determined by applying the equation at two known locations (two values of x), where the deformations (v) are known, and hence A and B can be solved in terms of these known deformations. As in Programme 10, these are known as the *boundary conditions*.

Can you identify appropriate boundary conditions here?

$$\begin{aligned} x = 0: \ v = 0 \\ x = L: \ v = 0 \end{aligned}$$

The boundary conditions come from the fact that the deflection at both ends of the strut must be zero. If we substitute these values into Equation (12.2) we get:

when $x = 0$: $\quad v = A\cos(k \times 0) + B\sin(k \times 0) \qquad \therefore \ A = 0$

when $x = L$: $\quad v = A\cos(k \times L) + B\sin(k \times L) = 0 \qquad \therefore \ B\sin kL = 0 \qquad (12.3)$

There are two possible solutions that can be derived from Equation (12.3). The equation is satisfied if $B = 0$ but, if this were the case, then substitution of $A = 0$ and $B = 0$ into Equation (12.2) implies that the deformation, v, is zero at all points along the strut. Thus the strut remains undeformed, which is not the case when it has buckled, and, hence, $B = 0$ is not a valid solution. The only other possible solution of Equation (12.3) is that $\sin kL = 0$, in which case the constant B will have a real but not definable value. Thus Equation (12.2) becomes simply:

$$v = B\sin kx \qquad (12.4)$$

where B is a constant of unknown value but, from Equation (12.3), we know has non-zero values when $\sin kL = 0$. Hence, when $\sin kL = 0$, Equation (12.4) indicates that when the strut buckles it assumes a sinusoidal shape of unknown magnitude.

What values of k would ensure that $\sin kL = 0$?

8

$$\boxed{k = 0 \quad k = \frac{\pi}{L} \quad k = \frac{2\pi}{L} \quad k = \frac{3\pi}{L} \quad \cdots \quad k = \frac{n\pi}{L}}$$

As we are considering a sinusoidal equation, there is an infinite number of solutions for k that will ensure that the equation equates to zero. In Equation (12.1) k was defined as $k = \sqrt{F/EI}$ and, hence, $F = k^2 EI$. The above solutions for k therefore give the values of F shown in the table below together with the corresponding equation for the deformed shape of the strut as given by substitution into equation (12.4).

k	0	π/L	$2\pi/L$	$3\pi/L$	$\cdots$	$n\pi/L$
$F\,(= k^2 EI)$	0	$\dfrac{\pi^2 EI}{L^2}$	$\dfrac{4\pi^2 EI}{L^2}$	$\dfrac{9\pi^2 EI}{L^2}$	$\cdots$	$\dfrac{n^2\pi^2 EI}{L^2}$
$v\,(= B\sin kx)$	0	$B\sin \pi x$	$B\sin 2\pi x$	$B\sin 3\pi x$	$\cdots$	$B\sin n\pi x$

Each of the above values of F will result in instability in the strut and a different mode of buckling, each mode being defined by a sinusoidal curve. If we ignore the trivial solution of $F = 0$, then the critical (least) value of load at which buckling will occur is given by:

$$F_{\text{crit}} = \frac{\pi^2 EI}{L^2} \tag{12.5}$$

This critical value is often referred to as the *Euler buckling load* and is given the symbol F_e. The other values of F are mathematical solutions to the equations but have little practical relevance, as the strut will buckle once it reaches the Euler buckling load. If we apply the Euler formula to the problem of the steel tube we first considered in Frames 1 and 2, we can calculate the buckling load of both the 1 m column and the 10 m column. The section had an outer diameter of 200 mm and a wall thickness of 20 mm and we can take E for steel as 200 GN/m^2.

I for the section $= \dfrac{\pi}{4}\left(R_{\text{out}}^4 - R_{\text{in}}^4\right) = \dfrac{\pi}{4}\left(100^4 - 80^4\right) = 46.37 \times 10^6 \text{ mm}^4$

$$= 46.37 \times 10^{-6} \text{ m}^4$$

For the 1m high column: $F_{\text{crit}} = F_e = \dfrac{\pi^2 EI}{L^2} = \dfrac{\pi^2 \times 200 \times 10^9 \times 46.37 \times 10^{-6}}{(1)^2}$

$$= 91\,531 \text{ kN}$$

For the 10m high column: $F_{\text{crit}} = F_e = \dfrac{\pi^2 EI}{L^2} = \dfrac{\pi^2 \times 200 \times 10^9 \times 46.37 \times 10^{-6}}{(10)^2}$

$$= 915 \text{ kN}$$

The original problem in Frame 1 indicated that, based on considerations of yield, this hollow section could safely carry a load of 2500 kN. What the above calculation shows is that, as the height of the column increases, buckling becomes a more important consideration, and, when 10 m high, the column can only support a fraction of the original 2500 kN load.

9

> PROBLEMS

1. A length of steel of rectangular section, 100×100 mm is used to support an axial compressive load. If the stress in the section should not exceed 265 MN/m^2 what is the maximum load that this section can sustain based on considerations of yield in the steel?

Ans. 2650 kN

2. If the section in question 1 is to be used as a pin-ended strut, 5 m long, what is the maximum load it can carry, based on considerations of buckling? Take $E = 200$ GN/m^2

Ans. 658 kN.

3. What would be the maximum length of strut such that yielding of the steel and buckling of the strut occur simultaneously?

Ans. 2.49 m.

What we have seen so far is that components loaded in axial compression can fail by yielding or crushing, but if they are very long and become *slender*, then they may fail by buckling. Question 3, above, indicates that there is a transition point when both modes of failure may occur simultaneously. Now let's look in a little more detail at what we mean by a *slender* member. The Euler buckling formula tells us that the *load* at which buckling occurs is given by:

$$F_e = \frac{\pi^2 EI}{L^2}$$

If we divide the buckling load by the area of the section we shall get the *stress* at which buckling occurs:

$$\sigma_e = \frac{F_e}{A} = \frac{\pi^2 EI}{AL^2} = \frac{\pi^2 E(I/A)}{L^2} \tag{12.6}$$

We can define the second moment of area, I, to be equal to $A \times r^2$, where A is the cross-sectional area of the section and r is the *radius of gyration* of the section; r is therefore equal to $\sqrt{I/A}$. Hence Equation (12.6) becomes:

$$\sigma_e = \frac{F_e}{A} = \frac{\pi^2 EI}{AL^2} = \frac{\pi^2 E(I/A)}{L^2} = \frac{\pi^2 Er^2}{L^2} = \frac{\pi^2 E}{(L/r)^2} \tag{12.7}$$

where L/r is a non-dimensional factor known as the *slenderness ratio*, and is a simple way of expressing the length and geometrical shape of any axially loaded member.

Assuming that we are dealing with a steel strut, and taking $E = 200$ GN/m^2, use Equation (12.7) to calculate and plot a graph of σ_e for values of slenderness ratio varying from 100 to 350 in increments of 50.

11

L/r	100	150	200	250	300	350
σ_e (MN/m^2)	197	88	49	32	22	16

The above values are obtained by simple substitution into equation 12.7. Plotted as a graph, these will give:

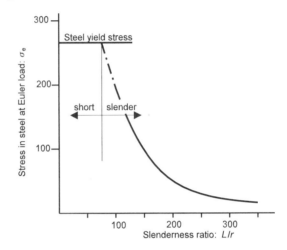

From the graph we can see that as the *slenderness ratio* increases the stress at buckling reduces significantly, indicating a rapid decline in the load-carrying capacity of the strut because of buckling effects. Although stress values could be plotted for low values of slenderness ratio, in practice the stress values calculated from Equation (12.7) are limited as the strut would fail by yielding in direct compression once it reaches the yield strength of steel. This transition from buckling to direct yielding is shown by the upper curtailment of the plotted diagram which you can draw on your graph at a typical value of 265 MN/m^2. Save your graph: you will need it to solve problems later.

The diagram clearly indicates that at a slenderness ratio of somewhere between 50 and 100, depending on the yield strength of the steel, there is a transition in the mode of failure of the strut. For low slenderness ratios, the strut can be considered to be *short*, and failure will be by yielding in direct compression. For higher slenderness ratios the strut can be considered to be *slender* ,and failure will be by buckling at much reduced loads. The important fact is that this change of behaviour depends on the *slenderness ratio* which is a function of both the length and the geometry of the cross-section as expressed by its *radius of gyration*.

A steel bar, considered pinned at both ends, has a length of 6 m and, from standard steel tables, has a radius of gyration about the axis of buckling of 53 mm and a cross-sectional area of 11 000 mm^2. Use the graph you have just plotted to determine the failure load of the bar. Is the bar short or slender?

> 1705 kN; Slender.

Check your calculations:

$\dfrac{L}{r} = \dfrac{6000}{53} = 113$ which is in the *slender* zone of the graph

$\therefore$ from the graph $\sigma_e \approx 155$ MN/m^2

$\therefore$ $F = \sigma_e \times A \approx 155 \times 11\,000 \times 10^{-3} \approx 1705$ kN

The graph we plotted and used to solve this last problem was based on the assumption of an idealised, perfectly straight component with an idealised perfect axial load. In practice, columns and struts are rarely perfectly straight, and loads are rarely perfectly axial, and often are applied at an eccentricity to the longitudinal axis of the component. Hence, the real behaviour of a steel component in compression is more complex than indicated so far and is more likely to follow the typical design curve indicated below with, for a given slenderness ratio, lower stresses developing at failure than indicated by the Euler formula.

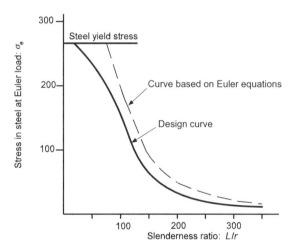

Such curves, which depend on the type of section (for example, hollow circular or I-shaped) are based on the *Perry–Robertson* equation which takes into account imperfections in geometry and loading. The derivation of the *Perry–Robertson* equation is beyond the scope of this book, but you should recognise that design practice is based on the principles we have covered so far, with, usually, tables of data rather than graphs given to determine maximum stress levels. These stress levels are, as indicated above, a function of *slenderness ratio* and depend on the type of component section.

What is the factor that governs whether or not a steel compression component will fail by yielding of the steel or by buckling?

13

Its slenderness ratio.

When we introduced the idea of slenderness in Frame 3 we looked at a short steel column and a slender steel column made from the same section. Conceptually, we could see that the slender column was likely to buckle, whereas the short one was more likely to fail by yielding. What is important to remember is that it is not the height that is important but rather the *slenderness ratio*. Hence a very high column can still be classified as *short* if its section has a sufficiently high radius of gyration.

So far we have discussed the *radius of gyration* as if any shape of section has just one radius. In fact sections, such as I-shaped sections, will have two radii of gyration, each one corresponding to one of the two axes of bending. Consider the standard column section shown. $I_{XX} = 9000$ cm^4, $I_{YY} = 3000$ cm^4 and its cross-sectional area is 100 cm^2.

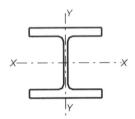

What are the radii of gyration for the X–X axis and the Y–Y axis, respectively?

14

$r_{XX} = 94.9$ mm; $r_{YY} = 54.8$ mm

Check your calculations:

$$r_{XX} = \sqrt{\frac{I_{XX}}{A}} = \sqrt{\frac{9000}{100}} \times 10 = 94.9 \text{ mm}; \quad r_{YY} = \sqrt{\frac{I_{YY}}{A}} = \sqrt{\frac{3000}{100}} \times 10 = 54.8 \text{ mm}$$

Hence, we can see that whereas square or circular sections have the same second moment of area about both axes of bending, and hence just one radius of gyration, sections such as I-shapes or T-shapes will have two radii of gyration corresponding to the different I values of the two axes of bending.

The I-shaped section shown above is used as a pin-ended column of 4 m height. Calculate the slenderness ratio for each axis and state which is the most critical axis as far as buckling is concerned.

$$\frac{L}{r_{XX}} = \frac{4000}{94.9} = 42.2 \qquad \frac{L}{r_{YY}} = \frac{4000}{54.8} = 73.0.$$

The Y–Y axis is critical.

The calculation shows that the column is most slender in relation to the Y–Y axis, and hence this axis will be the most critical in the design of the column, which should be based on the slenderness ratio of 73.0.

EFFECTIVE LENGTH OR EFFECTIVE HEIGHT

The theory we have looked at so far has been based on components that are considered to be pinned at both ends. In practice, one or both ends of a component may be welded or bolted at the end connections and the ends may, more realistically, be considered as being fixed rigidly rather than pinned. Such fixity implies that the ends of the component cannot rotate freely. If full fixity is not certain, then the actual fixity may be considered to be somewhere between pinned and fully fixed. Similarly, a component or a machine may be bolted or welded to a base plate that prevents end rotation, and a certain degree of fixity may be assumed.

Such types of connection will have the effect of stiffening the component and increasing its buckling load. If you take your plastic ruler, grasp both ends firmly in your fists and push hard to compress the ruler, you will see that it will buckle at a greater load than when you simply pressed down on it as indicated in Frame 3. The effect of providing rigid or partially rigid end joints is to increase the buckling load and hence the load-carrying capacity of the member. Rather than develop different buckling theories for each different type of end condition, most design relies on the concept of *effective lengths* or *effective heights*, where the theory and data developed for pin-ended members is used but calculations are based on *effective* rather than actual lengths. The *effective length* is taken as being the actual length multiplied by a coefficient that is dependent on the type of connection at each end of the component. In such cases the *slenderness ratio* is defined as:

$$\text{Slenderness ratio} = \frac{\text{Effective length (height)}}{\text{Radius of gyration}}$$

This modified slenderness ratio is then used in the calculation of the buckling stress, and hence the buckling load. For example, a strut that is fixed rigidly at both ends has a theoretical effective length of one-half of its actual length. We are not going to derive the theoretical values of effective length for different end conditions, but we shall examine briefly the practical implications of this concept.

A slender pin-ended steel component will fail, theoretically, at its Euler buckling load. If its ends are restrained rigidly such that its effective length can be considered to be one-half of the actual length, what is the increase in its load-carrying capacity? Assume that the steel does not yield.

16

It will increase by a factor of 4.

We know from the Euler equation that $F_{crit} = \pi^2 EI / L_e^2$, where L is now taken as the *effective length*. If the effective length (L_e) is taken as one-half of the actual length (L), then:

$$F_{crit} = \frac{\pi^2 EI}{L_e^2} = \frac{\pi^2 EI}{(0.5L)^2} = \frac{4\pi^2 EI}{L^2} = 4F_e$$

Hence we can see that restraining the ends of the strut leads to a dramatic increase in its theoretical load carrying capacity. This concept of effective length is shown diagrammatically below. The effective length is, in effect, that length of the component that buckles between contraflexure points and can be determined theoretically by using similar integration techniques to those used in Frame 5, when we first examined the case of a pin-ended component.

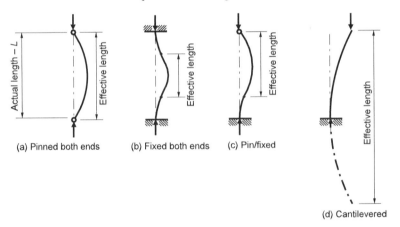

(a) Pinned both ends   (b) Fixed both ends   (c) Pin/fixed   (d) Cantilevered

The table below gives the theoretical values of effective length and, for comparison and interest, typical, more conservative values used in design for the four cases shown above:

Case	(a)	(b)	(c)	(d)
Theoretical effective length	L	0.5L	0.7L	2.0L
Design values of effective length	L	0.7L	0.85L	2.0L

A steel bar has a length of 6 m, a radius of gyration about the axis of buckling of 53 mm, and a cross-sectional area of 11000 mm². Use the graph you plotted in Frame 10 to determine the theoretical failure load of the bar for each of the cases (a) to (d) above. In each case, state whether or not the bar is short or slender.

> (a) 1705 kN, slender; (b) 2915 kN, short; (c) 2915 kN, short; (d) 440 kN, slender.

Check your calculations:

Case (a)

$\dfrac{L}{r} = \dfrac{6000}{53} = 113$ which is in the *slender* zone of the graph

$\therefore$ from the graph $\sigma_e \approx 155$ MN/m^2

$\therefore$ $F = \sigma_e \times A \approx 155 \times 10^6 \times 11\,000 \times 10^{-6} \times 10^{-3} \approx 1705$ kN

Case (b)

$\dfrac{L}{r} = \dfrac{0.5 \times 6000}{53} = 57$, which is in the *short* zone of the graph

$\therefore$ from the graph $\sigma_e \approx 265$ MN/m^2

$\therefore$ $F = \sigma_e \times A \approx 265 \times 10^6 \times 11000 \times 10^{-6} \times 10^{-3} \approx 2915$ kN

Case (c)

$\dfrac{L}{r} = \dfrac{0.7 \times 6000}{53} = 79$ which is in the *short* zone of the graph

$\therefore$ from the graph $\sigma_e \approx 265$ MN/m^2

$\therefore$ $F = \sigma_e \times A \approx 265 \times 10^6 \times 11\,000 \times 10^{-6} \times 10^{-3} \approx 2915$ kN

Case (d)

$\dfrac{L}{r} = \dfrac{2.0 \times 6000}{53} = 226$ which is in the *slender* zone of the graph

$\therefore$ from the graph $\sigma_e \approx 40$ MN/m^2

$\therefore$ $F = \sigma_e \times A \approx 40 \times 10^6 \times 11\,000 \times 10^{-6} \times 10^{-3} \approx 440$ kN

These calculations show clearly the effect, and importance, of different end conditions on the load-carrying capacity of bars and other axially loaded components and are important considerations in the design of such members.

18

TO REMEMBER

The Euler formula: $F_e = \dfrac{\pi^2 EI}{L^2}$

Radius of gyration: $r = \sqrt{\dfrac{\text{second moment of area}}{\text{cross-sectional area}}} = \sqrt{\dfrac{I}{A}}$

Slenderness ratio: $SR = \dfrac{\text{effective length (height)}}{\text{radius of gyration}} = \dfrac{L_e}{r}$

Effective length $L_e = \text{coefficient} \times \text{actual length}$

19

1. If a pin-ended bar of solid circular section is 2 m long and 80 mm in diameter, what is its slenderness ratio?

Ans. 100.

2. If the material in the bar in question 1 is reshaped into a bar of square section and of the same length, what would be the new slenderness ratio?

Ans. 97.72.

3. A hollow steel tube of outside diameter 50 mm and wall thickness 5 mm is to be used as a compression component. Determine the critical length of the tube such that it will reach its full strength before it buckles for (a) both ends pinned; and (b) both ends fully fixed. Take $\sigma_y = 265$ MN/m^2; $E = 200$ GN/m^2.

Ans. 1.38 m; 2.76 m.

4. The arm of an excavator is a box section 150 mm square with a wall thickness of 8 mm. Assuming that it is pin-ended, what axial load can be applied if the arm has a length of 2.5 m? Assume $E = 200$ GN/m^2.

Ans. 4.84 MN.

5. An aluminium wing strut on a light aircraft is 2 m long between pinned ends. The strut has a streamlined, oval-shaped section with outside dimensions of 110×38 mm and a wall thickness of 2 mm. What is the axial load under which it will buckle? Assume that 'I' for the oval-shaped section is given by the expression $\{(b \times d^3)/24\}$, and that $E = 70$ GN/m^2.

Ans. 13.46 kN.

6. A piece of mechanical equipment has a mass of 8000 kg and is supported by four vertical steel tubes of 80 mm outside diameter and with a wall thickness of 5 mm. Each tube is fixed firmly at its base but unrestrained at the top end where it supports the equipment (case (d) in the table in Frame 16). Determine the maximum height of the tubes before buckling occurs. Take $E = 200$ GN/m^2.

Ans. 4.57 m.

7. A steel component of solid circular section is 3 m long. It is fully fixed at one end but is completely unrestrained at the other end, such that it is effectively a cantilever. It carries an axial load of 500 kN. Determine the minimum required diameter of the component. Take $E = 200$ GN/m^2.

Ans. 117 mm.

Programme 13

STRESSES IN CYLINDERS

On completion of this programme you will be able to:

- Calculate the state of stress in thin cylinders
- Calculate the state of stress in thin spheres
- State the difference in behaviour between thin and thick cylinders
- Sketch the variation of hoop and radial stress across the walls of thick cylinders
- Quote the Lamé equations for thick cylinder stress analysis
- Calculate the variation of longitudinal, hoop and radial stress in thick cylinders subject to both internal and external pressure
- Solve thick cylinder problems using a graphical, Lamé line, approach
- Calculate the state of stress within compound thick cylinders caused by interference effects
- Solve compound thick cylinder problems using a graphical, Lamé line, approach

1

In this programme we shall study the stresses formed within the walls of cylinders that are subjected to fluid pressure. In this context, the term 'cylinder' covers a range of different components with a wide variety of functions. In Programme 2 we saw that in a reciprocating engine the piston moved within a cylinder. Such a cylinder not only constrains the movement of the piston but also contains gas under pressure, the internal pressure causing stresses within the cylinder wall.

Cylinders can take the form of sealed pressure vessels. For example, scuba divers carry air tanks on their backs. Each tank contains air under high pressure and takes the form of a circular cylinder. Under water, the tank will be subjected to external hydrostatic pressure and so will have both internal and external pressure applied to the wall.

Tubes and pipes are basically long cylinders and can carry fluids at high pressure. Alternatively, the pressure can be applied externally. Imagine a boiler for a steam locomotive. It comprises an outer shell within which there are a large number of parallel tubes. These are termed 'fire-tubes', as the hot gases from the fire flow within them, while the high pressure steam is generated outside the tubes. The outer shell is also a cylinder and is subjected to internal steam pressure.

Pressure is a distributed form of loading which is applied over each unit area of the component.

What are the units of pressure?

2

$$\boxed{N/m^2}$$

Pressures are also quoted in Pa (Pascal). In reality, pressure has values several orders of magnitude greater than 1 N/m^2 (1 Pa), so it is useful to work with pressures quoted in bars, where 1 bar = 10^5 N/m^2. This also avoids confusion between pressure and stress, which also have units of N/m^2.

Express a pressure of 1.5 MN/m^2 in bar.

3

$$\boxed{\text{15 bar.}}$$

This comes from the basic definition of a bar:

$$P = 1.5 \times 10^6 = 15 \times 10^5 = 15 \text{ bar}$$

If you are happy with the use of bars to define values of pressure, we can now proceed to consider stresses in cylinders.

THIN CYLINDERS

Cylinders are categorised according to the thickness of the wall in relation to the radius. As the name implies, thin cylinders have thin walls relative to the radius of the cylinder. The figure below shows such a cylinder, having closed ends with internal radius R of length L, and containing a fluid at a pressure P.

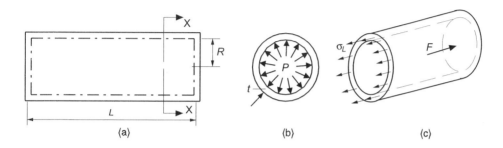

(a)   (b)   (c)

The pressure P will be uniform over the entire internal surface and will act normal; that is, at right angles to the surface. The net longitudinal force F acting on one end will thus be:

$$F = \text{pressure} \times \text{area} = P \times \pi R^2$$

A force of equal magnitude acts on the other end to ensure equilibrium. You can see in the free-body diagram in figure (c) that the two equal and opposite forces create a stress in the cylinder wall.

The two equal and opposite forces on the ends put the material in the wall into tension and hence the stress will be a direct tensile stress. Such a stress is uniform over the cross-sectional area it is acting upon, so if we define this area we can evaluate the stress.

Since the thickness t of the wall is small compared to the radius R, the area at cross-section X–X is given by:

$$\text{circumference} \times \text{thickness} = 2\pi R t$$

This gives the longitudinal tensile stress σ_L as:

$$\sigma_L = \frac{\text{force}}{\text{area}} = \frac{P\pi R^2}{2\pi R t} = \frac{PR}{2t} \tag{13.1}$$

A pressure vessel has a radius of 100 mm and a wall thickness of 2 mm. If the internal pressure is 10 bar determine the longitudinal stress in the wall.

4

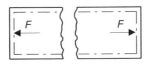

$$25 \text{ MN/m}^2$$

The longitudinal stress is given by:

$$\sigma_L = \frac{PR}{2t} = \frac{\left(10 \times 10^5\right) \times \left(100 \times 10^{-3}\right)}{2 \times (2 \times 10^{-3})} = 25 \text{ MN/m}^2$$

If the longitudinal stress is greater than the failure stress of the material, the cylinder could fail by tearing apart, as shown in the following figure.

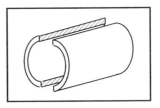

Try to visualise another form of failure.

5

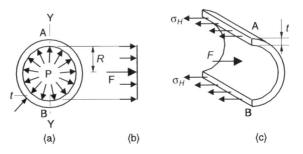

The figure shows how the two sides of the cylinder might tear apart by splitting along two failure lines which are diametrically opposite each other.

Now consider the vertical plane Y–Y in figure (a) below. The uniform internal pressure P acting normally on the curved surface of the cylinder will create a net resultant force F on the semi-circular section of the cylinder to the right of Y–Y. This horizontal resultant force can be calculated by multiplying the pressure by the area of the cylinder *projected on to a vertical plane*, as shown in figure (b).

If the cylinder is of length L, write down a relationship for the net resultant force F.

6

$$F = P \times 2RL$$

There will be an equal but opposite force acting to the left of section Y–Y and the two forces will together tend to tear the wall of the cylinder along its length at A and B. *The material in the wall of the cylinder at A and B is thus in tension* and a direct tensile stress σ_H exists (see the free-body diagram, figure (c)). The direction of this stress is tangential to the cylinder. You should realise that similar tensile stresses of the same value σ_H will exist in the material at all points around the circumference. The stress situation is similar to that in a steel hoop put round a wooden barrel to hold the staves together, hence the use of the term 'hoop stress' to describe this type of stress.

The hoop stress σ_H is given by:

$$\sigma_H = \frac{\text{force}}{\text{area}} = \frac{2PRL}{2tL} = \frac{PR}{t} \tag{13.2}$$

If we consider the same pressure vessel as defined in Frame 4, having a radius of 100 mm, a wall thickness of 2mm and an internal pressure of 10 bar, the hoop stress in the cylinder wall is:

$$\sigma_H = \frac{PR}{t} = \frac{\left(10 \times 10^5\right) \times \left(100 \times 10^{-3}\right)}{\left(2 \times 10^{-3}\right)} = 50 \text{ MN/m}^2$$

This can be compared with the longitudinal stress σ_L of 25 MN/m^2 for the same pressure vessel.

What is the direction of the longitudinal stress in relation to the hoop stress?

7

At right angles.

In fact, a thin cylinder provides a classic example of a two-dimensional stress situation as discussed in Programme 8. If we take a small element of the pressure vessel considered above, the stresses expressed in MN/m^2 acting on the element are as shown below.

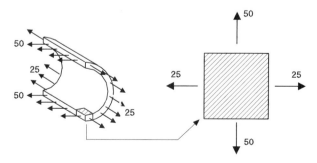

What is the maximum principal stress acting on this element?

8

$$\boxed{50 \text{ MN/m}^2}$$

Since there are no shear stresses acting on the element, the maximum principal stress equals the maximum direct stress which, in this case, is the hoop stress σ_H. The calculation of the hoop stress provides a basis for the design of thin cylinders and this is illustrated in the following example:

In a hydroelectric system water flows from a reservoir through a 500 mm diameter pipe. If the inlet to the turbine is situated 200 m below the free surface of the water in the reservoir, determine the thickness of the pipe wall. Assume a limiting stress in the wall of 100 MN/m^2 and the density of water as 1000 kg/m^2.

From Programme 2, the maximum hydrostatic pressure is:

$$P = \rho g z = 1000 \times 9.81 \times 200$$
$$= 19.62 \times 10^5 \text{ N/m}^2 = 19.62 \text{ bar}$$

The maximum stress in the pipe wall is the hoop stress, as given by Equation (13.2), which can be rearranged to give:

$$t = \frac{PR}{\sigma_H} = \frac{19.62 \times 10^5 \times \left(250 \times 10^{-3}\right)}{100 \times 10^6}$$
$$= 0.0049 \text{ m} = 4.9 \text{ mm}$$

so that a safe thickness would be 5 mm.

So far, we have considered cylinders subjected to internal pressure. Can you think of any situation in which a cylinder would be subjected to a hoop stress as a result of external pressure?

9

$$\boxed{\text{Undersea pipelines.}}$$

With offshore oil rigs, oil is carried in pipelines under the sea. When the flow of oil stops the pipe will be empty and subjected to the external hydrostatic pressure of the sea above it.

Another example has already been discussed in Frame 1, where the tubes of a fire tube boiler are subject to external steam pressure.

The same equations for longitudinal stress and hoop stress that have been developed for internal pressure can also be applied to external pressure situations, except that the stresses will now be compressive.

THIN SPHERES

In cylinders we can distinguish clearly between the longitudinal stress and the hoop stress. In the case of a spherical pressure vessel, the symmetry of the situation means that there is only one type of stress acting within the wall.

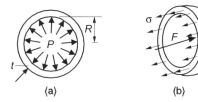

(a)   (b)

The pressure P will be uniform over the entire inner surface of the sphere. If we consider one half of the sphere as shown in figure (b) the resultant force F caused by pressure is:

$$F = \text{pressure} \times \text{projected area} = P \times \pi R^2$$

This will cause a stress in the wall acting over the cross-sectional area $(2\pi R) \times t$. Hence, the stress in the wall is given by:

$$\sigma = \frac{\text{force}}{\text{area}} = \frac{P\pi R^2}{2\pi Rt} = \frac{PR}{2t} \tag{13.3}$$

This stress is uniform over the whole wall of the sphere and, for the same radius, will be half the value of the hoop stress in a cylinder. Similarly, the wall thickness will only be half that of a cylinder, which is why many gas containers are spherical in shape.

10

$$\boxed{\text{PROBLEMS}}$$

1. A cylindrical tank is used with an air compressor. If the tank has a radius of 300 mm and a wall thickness of 3 mm, determine the maximum working pressure in the tank. Assume the stress in the wall is not to exceed 100 MN/m^2.

Ans. 10 bar.

2. A cylindrical water tank is filled with water to a height of 6 m. If the internal radius of the tank is 5 m and the stress in the wall is limited to 50 MN/m^2, determine the required thickness of the wall. Take the density of water as 1000 kg/m^3.

Ans. 5.9 mm.

3. A spherical gas container has a diameter of 600 mm. If the gas pressure is 20 bar and the allowable stress in the wall is 120 MN/m^2, find the wall thickness.

Ans. 2.5 mm.

11

THICK CYLINDERS

So far, we have considered situations where the wall thickness has been very small compared to the internal radius. In other words, what we have considered are typical thin cylinders, and they are thin because the pressures have been low compared to the allowable stresses in the cylinder wall.

We shall now consider situations in which the working pressures are considerably greater. In power stations, for example, steam pressures can be as high as 200 bar. If steam at this pressure flows through a pipe of 100 mm internal radius having a maximum allowable stress of 100 MN/m^2 the wall thickness, as given by the theory considered so far, is given by:

$$t = \frac{PR}{\sigma_H} = \frac{200 \times 10^5 \times \left(100 \times 10^{-3}\right)}{100 \times 10^6}$$
$$= 0.020 \text{ m}$$
$$= 20 \text{ mm}$$

With a wall thickness of 20 mm for a radius of 100 mm, the wall can no longer be considered thin.

This example has a thickness/radius ratio of 1:5 whereas thin cylinders generally have ratios of 1:10 or less. With a ratio of above 1:10 the wall is considered to be thick. Such situations come into the category of *thick cylinders*, and the equations derived for thin cylinders no longer apply. This is because the assumptions made previously are no longer valid – for example, we can no longer assume that the hoop stress has a constant value across the wall thickness.

In a thick cylinder, as well as the longitudinal stress and hoop stress, there will be a third stress set up within the wall as a direct result of the pressure acting on the wall.

Can you visualise the direction that this third stress will act within the cylinder wall?

12

In a radial direction.

Since the pressure acts normally to the wall in a radial direction, there will be a stress caused by the pressure, which acts, in the same radial direction. This stress is termed the radial stress σ_r. Figures (a) and (b) on the next page show a small element of a thick cylinder and the direction of the three stresses acting upon it.

It will be seen that the three stresses are perpendicular to each other and represent a practical example of a three-dimensional stress situation.

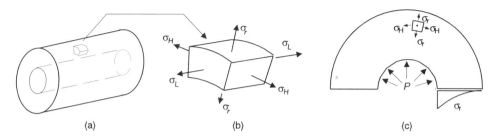

(a) (b) (c)

If we consider a thick cylinder having an internal pressure P and an external pressure of zero, as shown in section in figure (c), the numerical value of the radial stress will vary across the cylinder wall from P at the inner radius to 0 at the outer radius.
Will the radial stress be tensile or compressive?

13

Compressive.

Since the radial stress, and hence the radial strain, will be zero at the outer surface of the cylinder, the effect of the pressure will be to compress the cylinder wall. We take compressive stresses as negative, so that at the inner radius:

$$\sigma_r = -P$$

For a working internal pressure of 200 bar, the radial stress at the inner radius will therefore be -20 MN/m^2. This is a value of significant magnitude compared to the longitudinal and hoop stresses.

Since the radial stress varies across the cylinder wall, we need to consider if either the longitudinal and/or the hoop stresses also vary. Look at the figure below, which shows a section through a thick cylinder. The equilibrium relationship between the net longitudinal force caused by the internal pressure and the resulting longitudinal stress is valid irrespective of whether the wall is thin or thick. Since the cross-sectional area of a cylinder is constant throughout its length, it follows that the longitudinal stress is a direct tensile stress which must be uniform. However, as the wall is thick, a new equation must be derived for the longitudinal stress.

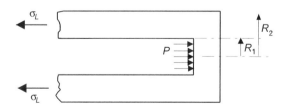

Write down an expression for the net longitudinal force acting on the closed end.

14

$$\boxed{F = P\pi R_1^2}$$

This follows directly from multiplying the pressure, P, by the area of the inside circular end-face of the cylinder (πR_1^2). As the cylinder has an internal radius of R_1 and an external radius of R_2, the cross sectional area through the wall is $\pi(R_2^2 - R_1^2)$, hence the longitudinal stress is given by:

$$\sigma_L = \frac{\text{force}}{\text{area}} = \frac{P\pi R_1^2}{\pi(R_2^2 - R_1^2)}$$

$$= \frac{PR_1^2}{(R_2^2 - R_1^2)} \tag{13.4}$$

A thick cylinder has an internal radius of 100 mm and external radius of 150 mm. If it is subjected to an internal test pressure of 400 bar, determine the longitudinal stress in the wall.

15

$$\boxed{32 \text{ MN/m}^2}$$

The longitudinal stress is given by:

$$\sigma_L = \frac{PR^2}{(R_2^2 - R_1^2)} = \frac{(400 \times 10^5) \times (100 \times 10^{-3})^2}{\left[(150 \times 10^{-3})^2 - (100 \times 10^{-3})^2\right]}$$

$$= 32 \text{MN/m}^2$$

If we had used the equation for thin cylinders to calculate the longitudinal stress incorrectly the answer would have been 40 MN/m², an error of 25 per cent. This indicates the importance of distinguishing correctly between thin and thick cylinders.

Since the longitudinal stress is uniform it means that the longitudinal strain ε_L is also uniform. The longitudinal strain is a function of not only the longitudinal stress but also of the radial and hoop stresses, which together form a three-dimensional set of principal stresses.

The *longitudinal strain, ε_L,* caused by the longitudinal stress equals σ_L/E, where E is Young's Modulus of Elasticity. Similarly, the radial strain caused by the radial stress equals σ_r/E and, allowing for Poisson's Ratio effects (see Programme 4), the longitudinal strain as a result of the radial strain can be expressed as $\varepsilon_L = -v\dfrac{\sigma_r}{E}$.

Likewise the longitudinal strain, as a result of the hoop strain, can be expressed as $\varepsilon_L = -v\dfrac{\sigma_H}{E}$.

Hence the net longitudinal strain, taking account of the effect of all three stress components, can be expressed as:

$$\varepsilon_L = \frac{1}{E}(\sigma_L - v\sigma_r - v\sigma_H)$$

We have seen that, for a given internal pressure, the longitudinal stress and longitudinal strain are of constant, uniform value and that the radial stress varies across the cylinder wall.

What does the above expression tell you about the variation of the hoop stress σ_H within the cylinder wall?

16

> That it also varies across the wall.

We can see this if we rearrange the above equation for the longitudinal strain into the form

$$\varepsilon_L = \frac{1}{E}(\sigma_L - v[\sigma_r + \sigma_H])$$

As, for a given internal pressure, ε_L, σ_L, E and v are all constants it follows that:

$$\sigma_r + \sigma_H = \text{constant}$$

As in Frame 12, we concluded that the radial stress varied across the cylinder wall. It therefore follows from the above expression that the hoop stress must also vary across the wall. As σ_r increases the value of σ_H will decrease as the sum of the two stresses must remain constant.

If we now consider a thick cylinder having an internal pressure P and an external pressure of zero, the radial stress will be compressive. Since, according to our sign convention, compressive stresses have negative values (tensile stresses are considered positive) the radial stress σ_r will vary from $-P$ at the inner surface to zero at the outer surface. It follows that, for an internal pressure, the hoop stress σ_H must be tensile throughout the wall. Both stress distributions are shown in the figure below.

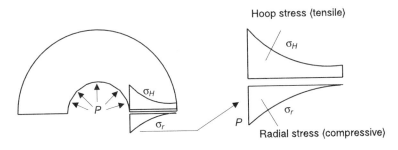

A thick cylinder has an internal pressure of 200 bar and a value of hoop stress of 25 MN/m^2 at the outer wall. What is the value of hoop stress at the inner wall?

17

$$\boxed{45 \text{ MN/m}^2}$$

From Frame 16: $\sigma_r + \sigma_H = \text{constant } (C)$

at the outer surface: $\sigma_r = 0,$

              so that: $0 + \sigma_{H(\text{outer})} = C = 25 \text{ MN/m}^2$

at the inner surface: $\sigma_r = -P = -20 \text{ MN/m}^2$

              so that: $-20 + \sigma_{H(\text{inner})} = C = 25 \text{ MN/m}^2$

and $\sigma_{H(\text{inner})} = 25 + 20 = 45 \text{ MN/m}^2$

Having established that both σ_r and σ_H vary across the wall of a thick cylinder, we can now proceed to derive equations for both stresses.

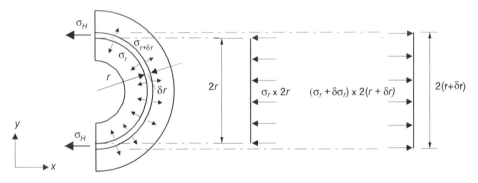

Stresses acting on thin ring   Force acting on projected area for ring of radius r Force acting on projected area for ring of radius $r + \delta r$

Consider a thick cylinder split in half as shown above. If we take a thin ring at radius r, having a thickness of δr, all the forces acting on this ring must be in equilibrium. The forces result from the stresses acting on the semi-circular ring. Since the radial stress varies with radius, it will vary from a stress of σ_r at the inner surface to $(\sigma_r + \delta\sigma_r)$ at the outer surface of the ring. To be consistent with the sign convention we have used in this programme all stresses are shown as *positive tensile* stresses. Also, in subsequent calculations, all forces acting to the right are taken as being positive.

The tendency of the radial stresses will be to try and displace the ring in the radial direction. However, the ring will be constrained by the tangential hoop stress σ_H. As the hoop stress acts on the thin ring it is assumed to be uniform across the thickness of the ring.

Resolving forces horizontally for a unit (1 metre) length of the thin ring:

(i) force caused by the hoop stress

$$= \text{stress} \times \text{area} = -2 \times [\sigma_H \times (\delta r \times 1)] = -2\sigma_H \delta r \qquad \text{(a)}$$

(ii) force caused by the radial stress acting on the inner surface of the ring

$$= \text{stress} \times \text{area} = -[\sigma_r \times (2r \times 1)] = -2\sigma_r r \qquad \text{(b)}$$

Write down an expression for the force caused by the radial stress acting on the outer surface of the ring

18

$$\boxed{2(\sigma_r + \delta\sigma_r)(r + \delta r)}$$

The derivation of this force is identical to the derivation of Equation (b) with a small increase in the stress ($\delta\sigma_r$) and a small increase in the projected area (δA) for the outer ring, that is:

(iii) force caused by the radial stress acting on the outer surface of the ring

$$= [(\sigma_r + \delta\sigma_r) \times (2\{r + \delta r\} \times 1)] = 2(\sigma_r + \delta\sigma_r)(r + \delta r) \qquad \text{(c)}$$

Hence if we consider the horizontal equilibrium of the thin ring we can combine Equations (a), (b) and (c) to write:

$$\sum H = 0: \qquad -2\sigma_H \delta r - 2\sigma_r r + 2(\sigma_r + \delta\sigma_r)(r + \delta r) = 0$$

$$\therefore \qquad -\sigma_H \delta r - \sigma_r r + \sigma_r r + \delta\sigma_r \delta r + \delta\sigma_r r + \sigma_r \delta r = 0$$

where forces acting to the right are taken as positive. The term ($\delta\sigma_r \delta r$) can be assumed to be negligible. Ignoring this term, cancelling terms and dividing throughout by δr, in the limit the above expression becomes:

$$r\frac{d\sigma_r}{dr} + \sigma_r - \sigma_H = 0 \qquad \text{(d)}$$

But, we know, from Frame 16, that $\sigma_r + \sigma_H = \text{constant} = 2A$ (say), so that Equation (d) becomes:

$$r\frac{d\sigma_r}{dr} + 2\sigma_r - 2A = 0 \qquad \text{(e)}$$

for which the solution is:

$$\sigma_r = A - \frac{B}{r^2} \qquad \text{(13.5)}$$

where both A and B are constants.

A thick cylinder has an internal radius of 100 mm and external radius of 150 mm. If it is subjected to an internal test pressure of 400 bar determine the radial stress at a radius of 120 mm. (Hint: use the given information to first calculate the constants A and B in equation (13.5).)

19

$$\boxed{-18 \ \mathrm{MN/m^2}}$$

Check your solution.

At $r = 0.1\mathrm{m}$: $\sigma_r = -P = -400 \ \mathrm{bar} = -40 \ \mathrm{MN/m^2}$. (Note the negative value of stress indicating compression as a result of the internal pressure.) Substituting into Equation (13.5) and working in $\mathrm{MN/m^2}$ gives:

$$-40 = A - \frac{B}{0.1^2} = A - 100B$$

Similarly, at $r = 0.15$ m: $\sigma_r = 0$ which gives:

$$0 = A - \frac{B}{0.15^2} = A - 44.44B$$

This pair of simultaneous equations can be solved directly to give $A = 32$ and $B = 0.72$ from which the equation of radial stress is given by:

$$\sigma_r = 32 - \frac{0.72}{r^2}$$

Hence, when $r = 0.12$ m then

$$\sigma_r = 32 - \frac{0.72}{0.12^2} = -18 \ \mathrm{MN/m^2}$$

The following figure shows the variation of radial stress with radius.

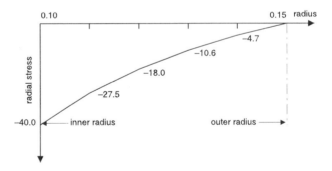

If you look back at Frame 15 you will see that the value of constant A equals the value of σ_L calculated in that frame for the identical problem. In fact, it can be shown that A is *always equal to the value of* σ_L. Therefore, Equation (13.5) for radial stress is particularly useful, as it not only enables the evaluation of the values of radial stress but also the value of longitudinal stress at the same time. In addition, it can be used as a basis for deriving the equation for hoop stress.

In Frame 18 we used the fact that, in a thick cylinder at any radius, the sum of the hoop and radial stresses is a constant in order to derive Equation (13.5). Can you now derive an equation for the variation of hoop stress across the wall of a thick cylinder?

$$\sigma_H = A + \frac{B}{r^2}$$

In Frame 18 we assumed that: $\sigma_H + \sigma_r = 2A$. Hence, combining this expression with Equation (13.5) we obtain:

$$\sigma_H = 2A - \sigma_r = 2A - \left(A - \frac{B}{r^2}\right) = A + \frac{B}{r^2}$$

The two equations:

$$\text{Radial stress:} \quad \sigma_r = A - \frac{B}{r^2} \tag{13.5}$$

$$\text{Hoop stress:} \quad \sigma_H = A + \frac{B}{r^2} \tag{13.6}$$

are generally referred to as the *Lamé equations*.

The Lamé equations define the variation of both the radial and hoop stresses across the wall of a thick cylinder. A knowledge of the pressures acting on the internal and external faces will allow the two constants, A and B to be evaluated: these constants can then be substituted in the hoop stress equation.

A thick cylinder has an internal radius of 100mm and an external radius of 150mm. If it is subjected to an internal test pressure of 400bar determine the maximum and minimum values of hoop stress.

21

$$\boxed{104 \text{ MN/m}^2; \ 64 \text{ MN/m}^2}$$

The problem is the same as that analysed in Frame 19, for which $A = 32$ and $B = 0.72$. The maximum hoop stress will occur on the inside face and the minimum on the outside face of the cylinder respectively. (See the diagram in Frame 16 if in doubt.)

Substituting in the hoop stress equation:

At $r = 0.1$ m $\qquad \sigma_H = A + \dfrac{B}{r^2} = 32 + \dfrac{0.72}{0.1^2} = 104 \text{ MN/m}^2$

At $r = 0.15$ m $\qquad \sigma_H = A + \dfrac{B}{r^2} = 32 + \dfrac{0.72}{0.15^2} = 64 \text{ MN/m}^2$

Can you calculate the hoop stress at other radii and plot a graph to show the variation of hoop stress across the cylinder wall?

22

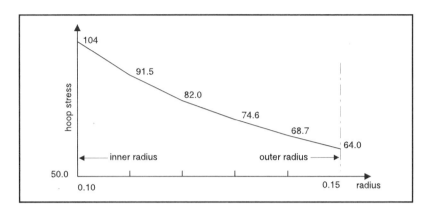

Comparing this curve with the one for radial stress in Frame 19, it will be seen that at each radius $\sigma_H + \sigma_r = 2A = 64$ MN/m^2.

Having analysed a thick cylinder with an internal pressure we can now apply the Lamé equations to a thick cylinder with an external pressure.

*A thick cylinder has an internal radius of 120 mm and an external radius of 200 mm. If it is subjected to an **external** pressure of 200 bar determine the equation for hoop stress across the cylinder wall. (Assume the internal pressure to be zero.)*

23

$$\sigma_H = -31.25 - \frac{0.45}{r^2}$$

Check your solution.

At $r = 0.20$ m: $\sigma_r = -P = -200$ bar $= -20$ MN/m^2. (Note the negative value of stress, indicating compression as a result of the external pressure) Substituting into Equation (13.5) and working in MN/m^2 gives:

$$-20 = A - \frac{B}{0.20^2} = A - 25B$$

Similarly, at $r = 0.12$ m: $\sigma_r = 0$ which gives:

$$0 = A - \frac{B}{0.12^2} = A - 69.44B$$

This pair of simultaneous equations can be solved directly to give $A = -31.25$ and $B = -0.45$ from which the equation of hoop stress is given by:

$$\sigma_H = -31.25 + \frac{(-0.45)}{r^2} = -31.25 - \frac{0.45}{r^2}$$

Calculate the maximum and minimum values of hoop stress

24

$$-62.50 \text{ MN/m}^2; \quad -42.50 \text{ MN/m}^2$$

At $r = 0.12$ m: $\qquad \sigma_H = -31.25 - \dfrac{0.45}{0.12^2} = -62.50 \text{ MN/m}^2$

At $r = 0.20$ m: $\qquad \sigma_H = -31.25 - \dfrac{0.45}{0.20^2} = -42.50 \text{ MN/m}^2$

In the case of a thick cylinder subjected to an external pressure both the radial and the hoop stresses are compressive, as indicated by the negative signs. However, in all cases, the maximum value of hoop stress (tensile or compressive) occurs at the inner radius.

Determine the longitudinal stress for the same thick cylinder with the external pressure as given above.

25

$$-31.25 \text{ MN/m}^2$$

Consider the thick cylinder with external pressure of 200 bar as shown:

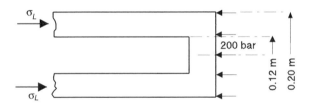

The resultant force acting on the end of the thick cylinder is:

$$F = \text{stress} \times \text{area} = -200 \times 10^5 \times \pi \times 0.20^2 = -2513 \times 10^3 \text{ N} = -2513 \text{ kN}$$

The cross-sectional area of the wall is:

$$A = \pi(0.20^2 - 0.12^2) = 0.0804 \text{ m}^2$$

Hence, the longitudinal stress is:

$$\sigma_L = \frac{\text{force}}{\text{area}} = \frac{-2513 \times 10^3}{0.0804} = -31.25 \text{ MN/m}^2$$

This is the same value as the constant A in Frame 23. In practice, *the constant A always equals the longitudinal stress σ_L for a thick cylinder, irrespective of pressures being applied internally, externally or on both surfaces. Now try some problems.*

26

$$\boxed{\text{PROBLEMS}}$$

1. A thick cylinder has an internal radius of 200 mm and an external radius of 300 mm. If it is subjected to an internal pressure of 200 bar find the maximum hoop stress in the wall.

   Ans. 52 MN/m².

2. An external pressure of 100 bar is applied to a cylinder of external radius 200 mm and internal radius 150 mm. Assuming no internal pressure, determine the maximum stress in the cylinder wall.

   Ans. -45.7 MN/m².

3. If the cylinder described in question 2 is also subjected to an internal pressure of 250 bar, determine the new maximum stress.

   Ans. 43.55 MN/m².

27

GRAPHICAL SOLUTION

Frames 18 and 21 considered the radial and hoop stresses in a thick cylinder having an internal radius of 100 mm and an external radius of 150 mm, subject to an internal pressure of 400 bar. We found that the appropriate Lamé equations for this problem were:

$$\text{Radial stress: } \sigma_r = A - \frac{B}{r^2} = 32 - \frac{0.72}{r^2}; \quad \text{hoop stress: } \sigma_H = A + \frac{B}{r^2} = 32 + \frac{0.72}{r^2}$$

If we were to plot the variation of both σ_r and σ_H against $1/r^2$ instead of against radius we would obtain the following *straight-line* graphs

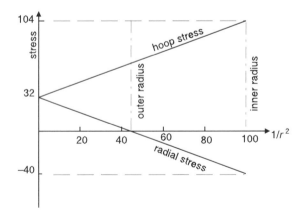

where, for both lines, the intercept with the vertical axis is equal to the constant A ($= 32$). Both lines have slopes of the same value, equal to the constant B ($= 0.72$), except that one slope is negative and the other positive. Therefore, the two graphs of σ_r and σ_H can be combined into *one* straight line graph by plotting hoop stress to the left of the vertical axis, as shown in the figure below for an internal pressure situation:

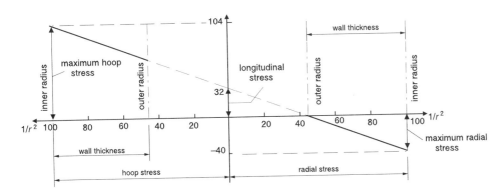

The single-line graph for both radial and hoop stress is termed the *Lamé line* and can be used to solve thick cylinder problems with both internal and external pressures. Note that to draw the straight line we need to plot only two points. Provided there are two known stress values at known radii, the line can be established and other stress values determined, either by geometric calculation or simply by scaling from an accurately produced drawing.

Sketch the Lamé line for a thick cylinder subject to a known external pressure, P, if the internal pressure is zero.

28

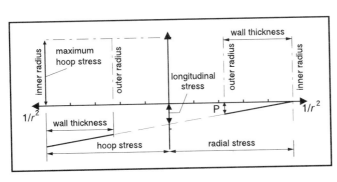

What does the Lamé line tell you about the state of stress in the cylinder when subjected to an external pressure?

29

For the case of external pressure only we can see that the radial stress, hoop stress and longitudinal stress are all compressive. This agrees with the findings in Frame 23. The Lamé line not only allows the calculation of stress values but also gives a visual indication of the stress types. We can also use the line to evaluate the required wall thickness.

A thick cylinder has an internal radius of 200 mm. If it is subjected to an internal pressure of 300 bar, the external pressure is zero and the maximum allowable stress is 100 MN/m², determine the minimum required outer radius. (Hint: draw the Lamé line from the given information and use the line to determine the point that represents zero external pressure.)

30

273 mm

It is important to recognise that the maximum hoop stress occurs at the inner radius. (see previously drawn Lamé lines) The hoop stress, σ_H, must therefore not exceed the given maximum allowable stress of 100 MN/m².

At the inner radius $r_{inner} = 0.2$m, $\dfrac{1}{r_{inner}^2} = 25$

and the radial stress, $\sigma_r(\text{inner}) = -300$ bar $= -30$ MN/m².

Hence the Lamé line can be constructed as shown below. The line is drawn by first plotting point A, which represents the hoop stress at a radius of 0.2 m; and second, point B, which represents the radial stress at the inner radius of 0.2 m. These two points are connected together, and where they cross the horizontal axis, the point E defines the outer radius where the radial stress is zero.

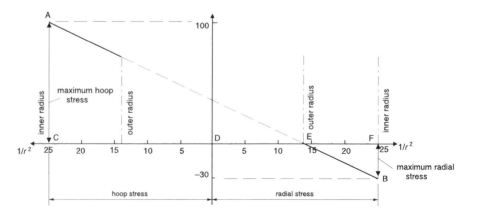

The exact location of E can be determined from an accurately produced scale drawing or from calculation using the geometry of similar triangles:

Using similar triangles: $\dfrac{100}{CE} = \dfrac{30}{EF}$ $\therefore$ $\dfrac{100}{(25 + DE)} = \dfrac{30}{(25 - DE)}$

so that $2500 - 100DE = 750 + 30DE$ or $DE = 13.46$. This value of DE represents $1/r^2_{outer} = 13.46$, so that $r_{outer} = 0.273$ m.

It would also have been possible to obtain this value directly using the Lamé equations having used the known, given stress conditions to find the values of constants A and B.

Determine the constants A and B in the Lamé equations for the above problem.

31

$$\boxed{A = 35; \quad B = 2.6}$$

At $r = 0.2$ m: $\sigma_r = A - \dfrac{B}{r^2} = A - \dfrac{B}{0.2^2} = -30$ MN/m^2 and

$$\sigma_H = A + \dfrac{B}{r^2} = A + \dfrac{B}{0.2^2} = 100 \text{ MN/m}^2$$

These two simultaneous equations can be solved to give $A = 35$ and $B = 2.6$. We know that the radial stress is zero at the outer radius. Hence:

$$\sigma_{r(outer)} = 35 - \dfrac{2.6}{r^2_{outer}} = 0 \text{ MN/m}^2, \text{ which solves to give } r_{outer} = 0.273 \text{ m,}$$

thus confirming the earlier solution determined using the Lamé line

32

$$\boxed{\text{PROBLEMS}}$$

Use the Lamé line to solve the following problems.

1. A thick cylinder has an internal and external radius of 200 mm and 300 mm. If it is subjected to an internal pressure of 250 bar find the maximum hoop stress in the wall.

Ans. 65 MN/m².

2. A thick cylinder of 100 mm internal radius is subjected to an internal pressure of 200bar. The maximum allowable stress in the wall is 120 MN/m²; determine the required wall thickness.

Ans. 18 mm.

33

The Lamé equations and the Lamé line offer alternative ways of analysing the stresses within the walls of thick cylinders, and you can choose whichever approach seems the most straightforward.

Comparing the analysis of thin cylinders with that for thick cylinders, it might be concluded that:

(i)   thin cylinders are not subject to radial stress; and
(ii) the hoop stress is constant across the wall of a thin cylinder.

However, neither of these statements is quite true. Since a thin cylinder is subject to pressure, the pressure must cause a radial stress within the wall.

In practice, the operating pressures for thin cylinders are very small, and consequently the resulting radial stress will be very small. It can therefore be assumed to be negligible, and similarly the variation of hoop stress across a thin cylinder wall can be ignored. There is a clear distinction regarding the use of thin and thick cylinders as the applied pressures are either relatively low, resulting in thin cylinders, or relatively high, resulting in thick cylinders.

As well as thin and thick cylinders, there is another type of cylinder we shall consider: a *compound cylinder*, in which one cylinder is strengthened by being enclosed within another. Alternatively, a compound cylinder can comprise two cylinders, each fulfilling a different purpose. For example, the cylinder of a reciprocating engine can be manufactured from an aluminium alloy to help cooling, but it would need an internal steel liner to minimise wear. The two would form a compound cylinder.

COMPOUND CYLINDERS

A compound cylinder is formed from two separate concentric cylinders, as shown in figure (a) below.

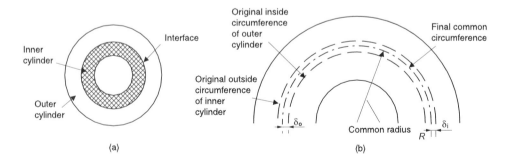

(a)

(b)

The stresses within a compound cylinder depend on what happens at the interface between the two parts. When the two parts are *just* touching, the two behave as one complete cylinder and the stresses can be determined using the techniques already described.

However, it is more usual to have an *interference* fit between the two, as shown in figure (b). This is when the inner radius of the outer part is slightly smaller than the outer radius of the inner part. The two cylinders can be assembled either by forcing together or by heating the outer cylinder so that it expands over the inner cylinder and then shrinks into place on cooling. Either way, there will be a resulting radial displacement of the two cylinders represented by δ_o for the outer part and δ_i for the inner part. These two radial displacements can be expressed as radial strains, δ_o/R and δ_i/R, respectively.

What do you think is the relationship between the radial strain and the circumferential (or hoop) strain at the interface between the two cylinders?

34

$$\boxed{\text{hoop strain} = \text{radial strain}}$$

We can see this if we consider that the circumference at the interface is $2\pi R$. If the interface displaces by a small amount, δR, then the new length of the interface circumference will be $2\pi(R + \delta R)$. Hence the circumferential or hoop strain will be given by:

$$\text{Hoop strain} = \frac{\text{change in length}}{\text{original length}}$$

$$= \frac{2\pi(R + \delta R) - 2\pi R}{2\pi R} = \frac{\delta R}{R}$$

which is the expression for the radial strain. If, as stated in the previous frame, there is a radial displacement represented by δ_o for the outer part and δ_i for the inner part it follows that:

$$\varepsilon_{H(\text{outer})} = \frac{\delta_o}{R} \quad \text{and} \quad \varepsilon_{H(\text{inner})} = -\frac{\delta_i}{R} \tag{13.7}$$

with the hoop strain of the inner part being negative because of a reduction in the radius of the inner cylinder. The sign convention used indicates that the outer part is subject to a tensile strain and the inner part to a compressive strain. At the interface, the two parts exert a mechanical pressure on each other, referred to as the shrinkage pressure, S, because generally it is created by shrinking the outer part on to the inner.

Effectively, the inner cylinder is subject to an external pressure, S, and the outer cylinder is subject to an internal pressure, S.

Will the radial stresses in the inner and outer cylinders be tensile or compressive at the interface?

35

They will both be compressive.

If you are not sure about this, look back at the Lamé line diagrams in Frames 26 and 27. The radial stress at both sides of the interface can therefore be expressed as:

$$\sigma_{r(\text{inner})} = \sigma_{r(\text{outer})} = -S$$

Taking into account the Poisson's Ratio effects (see Programme 4), the hoop strains can be expressed in terms of the hoop stresses and radial stresses at the interface as follows:

$$\varepsilon_{H(\text{outer})} = \frac{1}{E}\left(\sigma_{H(\text{outer})} - v\sigma_{r(\text{outer})}\right) = \frac{1}{E}\left(\sigma_{H(\text{outer})} - v[-S]\right) \tag{13.8}$$

and

$$\varepsilon_{H(\text{inner})} = \frac{1}{E}\left(\sigma_{H(\text{inner})} - v\sigma_{r(\text{inner})}\right) = \frac{1}{E}\left(\sigma_{H(\text{inner})} - v[-S]\right)$$

We do not need to take into account any longitudinal stress, since there will be no fluid pressure inside the compound cylinder during manufacture.

If you look back at the diagram in Frame 32 you can see that the total interference allowance for the compound cylinder is given by the sum of the radial displacements, δ_o and δ_i. Hence:

$$\text{Interference allowance} = \delta_o + \delta_i$$

and combining with Equation (13.7):

$$\text{Interference allowance} = \delta_o + \delta_i = \left(\varepsilon_{H(\text{outer})} - \varepsilon_{H(\text{inner})}\right) \times R$$

replacing the hoop strain expressions by the stress equations given in Equation (13.8):

$$\begin{aligned} \text{Interference allowance} = \delta_o + \delta_i &= \left(\varepsilon_{H(\text{outer})} - \varepsilon_{H(\text{inner})}\right) \times R \\ &= \frac{R}{E}\left(\sigma_{H(\text{outer})} - v[-S]\right) - \left(\sigma_{H(\text{inner})} - v[-S]\right) \\ &= \frac{R}{E}\left(\sigma_{H(\text{outer})} - \sigma_{H(\text{inner})}\right) \end{aligned} \tag{13.9}$$

Equation (13.9) is based on the assumption that the two parts making up the compound cylinder are made of the same material, so that both E and v are identical. It can be applied to any compound cylinder irrespective of whether the two constituent parts are thin- or thick-walled, although in the case of two thin cylinders, the shrinkage pressure would need to be relatively low. To illustrate how to apply the above equation attempt the following problem.

A compound cylinder has an outer radius of 100 mm, an inner radius of 50 mm and a common radius of 75 mm. The two parts of the cylinder are made of the same material. If the shrinkage pressure is 10 MN/m², determine the maximum and minimum values of hoop stress in the two parts of the cylinder.

$$35.83 \text{ MN/m}^2; \quad 25.80 \text{ MN/m}^2; \quad -26.0 \text{ MN/m}^2; \quad -36.0 \text{ MN/m}^2$$

Check your solution.

The shrinkage pressure will create a radial stress of -10 MN/m^2 on the bore of the outer part and also on the outside surface of the inner part.

For the outer part:
At $r = 0.075$ m: $\sigma_r = -10$ MN/m^2. Therefore, substituting into Equation (13.5) and working in MN/m^2 gives:

$$-10 = A - \frac{B}{0.075^2} = A - 177.78B$$

Similarly, at $r = 0.10$ m: $\sigma_r = 0$, which gives:

$$0 = A - \frac{B}{0.10^2} = A - 100B$$

This pair of simultaneous equations can be solved directly to give $A = 12.90$ and $B = 0.129$. These values of A and B can now be substituted in the Lamé equation for hoop stress:

At $r = 0.075$ m: $\qquad \sigma_H = A + \frac{B}{r^2} = 12.90 + \frac{0.129}{0.075^2} = 35.83$ MN/m^2

At $r = 0.10$ m $\qquad \sigma_H = A + \frac{B}{r^2} = 12.90 + \frac{0.129}{0.10^2} = 25.80$ MN/m^2

For the inner part:
The procedure is the same as for the outer part, and can be summarised as follows:

At $r = 0.075$ m, $\sigma_r = -10$ MN/m^2 and at $r = 0.05$ m, $\sigma_r = 0$ MN/m^2, giving values of $A = -18.0$ and $B = -0.045$.

The hoop stresses are given by:

At $r = 0.075$ m: $\qquad \sigma_H = A + \frac{B}{r^2} = -18.0 - \frac{0.045}{0.075^2} = -26.0$ MN/m^2

At $r = 0.05$ m $\qquad \sigma_H = A + \frac{B}{r^2} = -18.0 - \frac{0.045}{0.05^2} = -36.0$ MN/m^2

Determine the interference fit for the above problem if the material of which the cylinder is manufactured has a Young's Modulus of 200 GN/m^2.

37

0.02 mm

From Equation (13.9) the interference fit is given by:

$$\text{Interference fit} = \frac{R}{E}\left(\sigma_{H(\text{outer})} - \sigma_{H(\text{inner})}\right) = \frac{75 \times 10^{-3}}{200 \times 10^9}(35.83 - (-26)) \times 10^6$$
$$= 23.19 \times 10^{-6} \text{ m} = 0.023 \text{ mm}$$

Determine the maximum and minimum values of hoop stress in the two parts if the compound cylinder was subject to an internal pressure of 400 bar. (Hint: consider the stresses caused by (a) the interference fit as previously determined; and (b) the internal pressure and then use the principle of superposition to determine the combined stress condition.)

38

72.80 MN/m²; 52.43 MN/m²; 30.53 MN/m²; 10.97 MN/m²

When considering the effect of the internal pressure, the compound cylinder can now be treated as one cylinder.

At $r = 0.05$ m: $\sigma_r = 400$ bar $= -40$ MN/m². Substituting into Equation (13.5) and working in MN/m² gives:

$$-40 = A - \frac{B}{0.05^2} = A - 400B$$

Similarly, at $r = 0.10$ m: $\sigma_r = 0$ which gives:

$$0 = A - \frac{B}{0.10^2} = A - 100B$$

This pair of simultaneous equations can be solved directly to give $A = 13.33$ and $B = 0.133$ from which the equation of hoop stress is given by:

$$\sigma_H = 13.33 + \frac{0.133}{r^2}$$

Hence:

At $r = 0.05$ m: $\quad \sigma_H = 13.33 + \dfrac{0.133}{r^2} = 13.33 + \dfrac{0.133}{0.05^2} = 66.53$ MN/m²

At $r = 0.075$ m: $\quad \sigma_H = 13.33 + \dfrac{0.133}{r^2} = 13.33 + \dfrac{0.133}{0.075^2} = 36.97$ MN/m²

At $r = 0.10$ m: $\quad \sigma_H = 13.33 + \dfrac{0.133}{r^2} = 13.33 + \dfrac{0.133}{0.10^2} = 26.63$ MN/m²

Combining the hoop stresses for both shrinkage and internal pressure:

For the outer part:

At $r = 0.1$ m: $\qquad$ $\sigma_H = 26.63 + 25.80 = 52.43$ MN/m^2

At $r = 0.075$ m: $\qquad$ $\sigma_H = 36.97 + 35.83 = 72.80$ MN/m^2

For the inner part:

At $r = 0.075$ m: $\qquad$ $\sigma_H = 36.97 + (-26.00) = 10.97$ MN/m^2

At $r = 0.05$ m: $\qquad$ $\sigma_H = 66.53 + (-36.00) = 30.53$ MN/m^2

LAMÉ LINE

Compound cylinder problems can be solved graphically using a *Lamé line* approach as an alternative to using the Lamé equations. We first need to consider the Lamé line for the shrinkage pressure and then superimpose a separate line for the fluid pressure acting on the complete cylinder (we have already seen how to draw this second line).

The construction of the Lamé line for shrinkage pressure is similar to the approach we have already used. We need to draw two lines: one each for the inner and outer cylinders. In both cases, we need plot only two points, of known stress at known radius, to draw each line.

For the outer cylinder we would plot point A, which represents the shrinkage stress, S, at the common radius, and point B, representing zero stress at the outer radius as shown below. Projecting the line for radial stress in the outer part gives the tensile hoop stress on the left hand side of the figure. For the inner cylinder, we would plot the common point A, and point C, which represents zero stress at the inner radius. Projecting the line for radial stress in the inner part of the compound cylinder gives the compressive hoop stress on the left hand side of the figure.

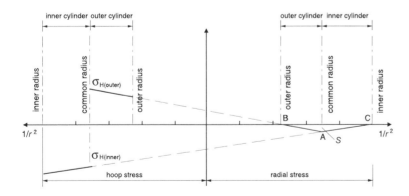

A compound cylinder has an inner radius of 100 mm, an outer radius of 200 mm and a common radius of 149 mm. If the interference allowance is 0.05 mm determine the shrinkage pressure. Take $E = 200$ GN/m^2. (Hint: draw the Lamé line for shrinkage pressure, S, and then make use of Equation (13.9).)

39

$$\boxed{10.93 \text{ MN/m}^2}$$

Check your calculations.

At the outer radius, $r_{\text{inner}} = 0.2$ m, $1/r_{\text{inner}}^2 = 25$
and the radial stress $\sigma_{r(\text{inner})} = 0$

At the common radius, $r_{\text{common}} = 0.149$ m, $1/r_{\text{common}}^2 = 45$
and the radial stress $\sigma_{r(\text{common})} = -S$

At the inner radius, $r_{\text{outer}} = 0.1$ m, $1/r_{\text{outer}}^2 = 100$
and the radial stress $\sigma_{r(\text{outer})} = 0$

Drawing the Lamé lines for this situation:

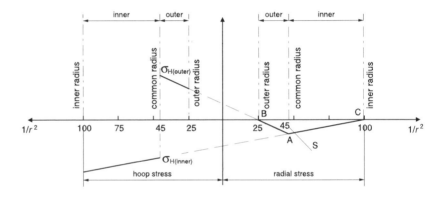

Using similar triangles:

$$\sigma_{H(\text{outer})} = \frac{45 + 25}{45 - 25} \times S = 3.50S \quad \text{and} \quad \sigma_{H(\text{inner})} = -\frac{100 + 45}{100 - 45} \times S = -2.64S$$

Substituting in Equation (13.9) for the interference allowance:

$$0.05 \times 10^{-3} = \frac{R}{E}\left(\sigma_{H(\text{outer})} - \sigma_{H(\text{inner})}\right) = \frac{0.149}{200 \times 10^9}\left(3.50S - (-2.64S)\right)$$

$$\therefore \quad S = \frac{0.05 \times 10^{-3} \times 200 \times 10^9}{0.149 \times 6.14} = 10.93 \times 10^6 \text{ N/m}^2 = 10.93 \text{ MN/m}^2$$

This value of shrinkage stress together with geometry of the Lamé line, as shown in the figure above, can be used to find the values of hoop stress for both the inner and outer cylinders. These stresses can be added to the hoop stress values arising from any fluid pressure for which another separate Lamé line would need to be drawn.

The Lamé equations and the Lamé lines give alternative ways of analysing stresses in the walls of compound cylinders. What is perhaps not so obvious is that the interference allowance, and shrinkage pressure, do not change when a fluid pressure is applied to the complete cylinders. The two parts of the compound cylinder are locked firmly together, and the two act as one cylinder. This is because we have assumed that the two parts are manufactured from the same material with the same elastic behaviour.

If we had considered a compound cylinder made of two different materials, the elastic constants for each would be different and the strains arising from fluid pressure would be different in the two materials, causing the interference allowance to change. The shrinkage pressure would, therefore, change with fluid pressure, which is a far more complex situation and beyond the scope of this programme.

TO REMEMBER

For thin cylinders:

$$\sigma_L = \frac{PR}{2t} \text{ and } \sigma_H = \frac{PR}{t}$$

For thin spheres:

$$\sigma = \frac{PR}{2t}$$

The Lamé equations for thick cylinders:

Radial stress: $\sigma_r = A - \dfrac{B}{r^2}$; Hoop stress: $\sigma_H = A + \dfrac{B}{r^2}$

where A = the longitudinal stress, σ_L.

For compound cylinders:

Interference allowance $= \dfrac{R}{E}\left(\sigma_{H(\text{outer})} - \sigma_{H(\text{inner})}\right)$

FURTHER PROBLEMS

1. In the cylinder of a foot pump, air is compressed to 10 bar. If the cylinder has a diameter of 60 mm and a wall thickness of 2 mm determine the stresses in the cylinder wall.

Ans. 15 MN/m²; 7.5 MN/m².

2. A submarine hull can be considered as a long, thin cylinder of 8 m diameter. If the submarine operates under the sea at a depth of 90 m, determine the wall thickness to ensure that the maximum stress does not exceed 100 MN/m². Take the density of sea water as being 1100 kg/m².

Ans. 39 mm.

3. A submersible spherical vessel is to operate under water. Determine the maximum depth to which it can operate if the radius/thickness ratio of the wall is 30 and the maximum stress 120 MN/m². Take the density of water as being 1000 kg/m².

Ans. 815.5 m.

4. A thick cylinder of 75 mm internal radius and 100 mm external radius is subjected to an internal pressure of 150 bar. Determine the maximum and minimum values of hoop stress in the wall.

Ans. 53.6 MN/m²; 38.6 MN/m².

5. A thick walled pipe carries a fluid at a pressure of 500 bar. The pipe has a bore radius of 250 mm and is not subjected to any external pressure. Determine the wall thickness if the stress is not to exceed 150 MN/m².

Ans. 104 mm.

6. A hydraulic cylinder has an internal diameter of 75 mm. When pressurised with hydraulic fluid it operates a ram exerting a force of 200 kN. If the maximum stress is not to exceed 100 MN/m², determine the required wall thickness.

Ans. 24 mm.

7. A compound cylinder has an outer radius of 150 mm, an inner radius of 50 mm and a common radius of 100 mm. On assembly, the maximum hoop stress in the outer part of the cylinder is 60 MN/m². Determine the values of hoop stress at the inner and outer radii of both parts.

Ans. 60 MN/m²; 36.9 MN/m²; −38.5 MN/m²; −61.5 MN/m².

8. If the compound cylinder defined in question 7 is subject to an internal pressure of 400 bar, determine the values of hoop stress in each part of the cylinder.

Ans. 76.2 MN/m²; 46.9 MN/m²; −22.3 MN/m²; −11.5 MN/m².

9. A compound cylinder has an outer diameter of 200 mm, an inner diameter of 100mm and a common diameter of 129 mm. If the interference allowance, based on diameter, is 0.1 mm determine the hoop stress at the inner diameter. Take the value of Young's Modulus as 200 GN/m².

Ans. −120.6 MN/m².

10. The compound cylinder described in question 9 is subject to an internal pressure of 250 bar, what will the maximum hoop stress be?

Ans. 86.9 MN/m².

Programme 14

FAILURE OF COMPONENTS

On completion of this programme you will be able to:

- Describe the failure characteristics of brittle materials
- Describe the failure characteristics of ductile materials
- Calculate minimum required yield stress values for simple axially loaded components
- Explain the various failure criterion for two dimensional stress problems including the Tresca and von Mise theories
- Determine the minimum required yield stress for two dimensional problems according to various failure theories
- Explain and apply the concept of a factor of safety against material failure.

1

The purpose of studying Solid Mechanics is to be able to analyse and subsequently design components to ensure that they do not fail in use. Failure may occur because of excessive distortion resulting from the applied loads. If the distortion is excessive, the component may no longer function as intended or it may be that the component actually breaks. It is possible to guard against either of these situations by analysing the stresses within the component and ensuring that they do not exceed a defined limit. This generally means operating well within the elastic region of the material behaviour.

However, not all components are subject to a simple, uni-axial stress situation which can readily be analysed. In Programme 13 we studied thin cylinders that had both hoop stresses and longitudinal stresses within the cylinder walls. This is a classic example, and is one of several possible illustrations of components subject to two-dimensional stress situations. To ensure the safe design of such components it is necessary to relate the complex, two-dimensional stress situation to a single limiting stress value to determine whether or not the loading on the component is excessive. This limiting value is normally determined from a simple tensile test carried out on samples of material in the laboratory. In this programme we shall look briefly at several theories that can be used to determine this relationship.

Before continuing, it is important that you remind yourself of the analysis of two-dimensional stress situations, particularly the interpretation of Mohr's Circle of Stress.

2

AXIAL DIRECT STRESS

In Programme 4 we looked at the stresses in components subject to axial loads. The resulting stresses are either *tensile* or *compressive*, depending on the direction of the loads. If a specimen of a material is tested in the laboratory under the action of an axial tensile load, the behaviour can be plotted in the form of a graph showing the relationship between stress, σ, and strain, ε.

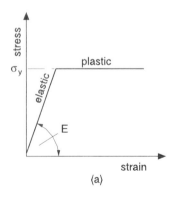
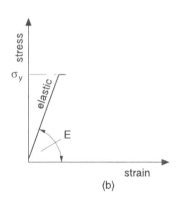

The figures on the previous page show the idealised stress–strain behaviour of two different engineering materials. We can see that, initially, both materials behave in a linear elastic manner in which stress is directly proportional to strain:

that is, $$E = \frac{\sigma}{\varepsilon} \quad \text{or} \quad \sigma = E \times \varepsilon$$

where E is Young's Modulus of Elasticity. However, once the strain exceeds the limit of proportionality the material *yields*. In the case of material (a) it continues to strain without any corresponding increase in stress, and we call this stage of material behaviour the *plastic* region. Such a material is termed *ductile*, because it will withstand large deformation before breaking. Figure (b), however, exhibits the typical characteristics of a *brittle* material.

Looking at figure (b) how could we describe a brittle material?

3

A material with little or negligible plastic deformation.

We could have also added that a brittle material breaks suddenly without warning. A typical example of a brittle material is glass, and we know from experience that glass shatters when subjected to a sudden load, such as when a bottle falls on the ground.

In engineering, cast iron is a brittle material, whereas steels and aluminium alloys represent ductile materials. When looking at engineering applications it is important to distinguish between the behaviour of ductile and brittle materials. Brittle materials perform better in compression than in tension, although some applications require cast iron components to resist tensile stress. A typical example is that of an engine cylinder block, in which the internal pressure causes a tensile hoop stress. In this case the wall thickness is chosen to give a relatively low tensile stress, well within the elastic region of the material behaviour.

Looking at the figures in Frame 2, what is the upper limit to the actual stress that can develop in a component?

4

The yield stress, σ_y.

This is the stress at which the material starts to yield and, according to our idealised graphs, the maximum achievable stress. The yield stress is defined by the symbol σ_y. In practice, most ductile materials exhibit some increase in stress in the plastic region, but by limiting the maximum allowable stress to σ_y this ensures that the component operates within the elastic region and that the material deformation is small.

Which has the highest yield stress – mild steel or cast iron?

5

> Mild steel.

Mild steel has a yield strength that is considerably higher than that of cast iron. Typical values of yield stress for some common engineering metals, including mild steel and cast iron, are listed below, although you should be aware that samples of material tested in the laboratory may have tensile strengths that vary on either side of these figures.

		σ_y (MN/m^2)
a	Aluminium alloy	250
b	Bronze	210
c	Cast iron	100
d	Mild steel	260

A cylinder head is attached to an engine by four 7 mm diameter bolts. If the bore of the cylinder is 60 mm and the maximum internal pressure is 50 bar, determine which of the materials listed above would be suitable for the manufacture of the bolts.

6

> a: Suitable; b: Suitable; c: Not suitable; d: Suitable.

Check your calculations.

The force acting on the cylinder head is given by:

$$F = P \times \pi R^2 = \left(50 \times 10^5\right) \times \left(\pi \times \left(\frac{30}{10^3}\right)^2 \right) = 14.14 \times 10^3 \text{ N} = 14.14 \text{ kN}$$

The force acting on each bolt is therefore $14.14/4 = 3.54$ kN and the axial stress in each bolt is given by:

$$\sigma = \frac{F}{A} = \frac{3.54 \times 10^3}{\pi \times (3.5 \times 10^{-3})^2} = 91.98 \text{ MN/m}^2$$

Because this stress is below the quoted yield stress for all four materials, you may have been tempted to assume that all were adequate for the purpose. However, the operating stress is very close to the quoted yield stress for cast iron. The quoted values are typical, but this does not mean that they are necessarily valid for all batches of a particular material type.

In practice, materials are not perfect or homogeneous, so that some batches of material could be weaker than quoted, and others stronger. It is therefore necessary to exercise caution and ensure a reasonable margin of safety between the operating stress and the yield stress. This would rule out cast iron as a suitable material for this application. In addition, being a brittle material, it is not ideal for the manufacture of a bolt subject to an axial tensile stress.

Apart from stress considerations are there any material properties we should consider in choosing a material for the bolts?

7

Young's Modulus of Elasticity.

Young's Modulus, E, relates the axial stress to the axial strain in the bolts. Hence the value of E will determine the amount of extension that will occur in the bolts. As the purpose of the bolts is to restrain the cylinder head and seal the top of the cylinder, excessive elongation of the bolts would cause the head to lift and the gases within the cylinder to escape. If this happened, the bolts would fail to perform their design function.

The amount of elongation depends on the strain in the material and, for a given stress, this is inversely proportional to Young's Modulus, E. Typical values of E for the four materials previously listed are:

	E (GN/m^2)
Aluminium alloy	70
Bronze	110
Cast iron	90
Mild steel	210

Clearly, mild steel is, of the materials listed, the most rigid, having the greatest value of E and hence would be the most suitable for the design of the cylinder bolt.

Before leaving this discussion of the influence of axial direct stresses it is necessary to consider the behaviour of a material when it fails during a simple tensile test. The figure below shows the fracture mechanisms for two different types of material when a specimen of each material is subjected to a tensile loading test.

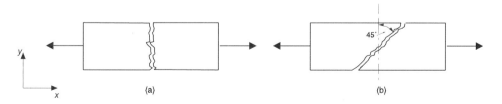

(a)   (b)

How do you think the two materials failed?

8

┌─────────────────────────────────────┐
│ (a) In tension; (b) In shear. │
└─────────────────────────────────────┘

The first failure is fairly obvious, as the specimen is in tension and the fracture occurred on a plane normal to the axial applied force. This is an example of a fracture in a *brittle material*; such a material is weak in tension, and little or no plastic deformation takes place before failure occurs.

The second failure is not so obvious, but if you remember the Mohr's Circle of Stress theory in Programme 8, an axial force will give rise to both direct and shear stress within the loaded specimen. If we assume that a tensile specimen fails at a yield stress, σ_y, the Mohr's Circle of Stress for the axially loaded specimen is shown in the figure below.

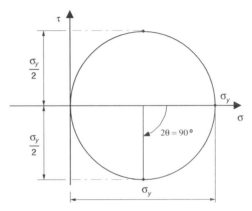

From the Mohr's Circle we can see that the maximum shear stress is equal to $\pm\sigma_y/2$ and the plane on which it acts is at an angle $\theta = 45°$ (or $\theta = 45° + 90°$) to the y-axis and hence to the longitudinal axis of the specimen. There are therefore shear stresses of significant magnitude acting on this plane and we can conclude that specimen (b) failed in shear along the $45°$ plane. This type of failure is exhibited by *ductile* materials where significant yielding and plastic deformation takes place before failure in shear occurs. Failure occurs when the *shear* stresses in the material reach a limiting value of $\sigma_y/2$. We shall refer to this finding in subsequent discussion on two-dimensional stress.

9

┌─────────────────┐
│ PROBLEMS │
└─────────────────┘

1. A stepped bar has a maximum diameter of 50 mm and a minimum diameter of 25 mm. If an axial tensile load of 60 kN is applied to the bar determine the minimum required yield stress of the material.

Ans. 122.23 MN/m².

2. A cast iron cylinder of 125 mm outside diameter and 75 mm inside diameter is subjected to an axial compressive load of 500 kN. Determine the minimum required compressive yield stress of the cast iron.

Ans. 63.66 MN/m².

3. In a petrol engine a piston of 60 mm diameter is joined to the connecting rod by means of a gudgeon pin of 12 mm diameter, as shown in figure Q3. The piston is subjected to a maximum uniform pressure of 40 bar. What is the minimum required yield stress of the connecting rod if it has a cross-sectional area of 100 mm²?
(*Hint*: assume that the compressive yield stress has the same magnitude as the tensile yield stress.)

Ans. 113.10 MN/m².

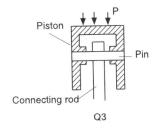

10

TWO-DIMENSIONAL STRESS

It is clear from the previous discussion and problems that, if a component is subject to a direct axial stress, the actual stress can be compared to yield stress values determined from a simple tensile test in order to choose the most suitable material.

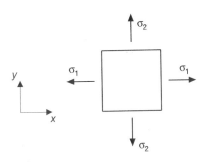

In Programme 13 we found that closed-ended thin cylinders were subject to two stresses – the hoop stress and the longitudinal stress, of which the hoop stress represented the maximum principal stress.

The figure above shows an element of a cylinder, or other similarly stressed component, subjected to two mutually perpendicular tensile stresses; that is, a two-dimensional stress situation. σ_1 represents the *maximum* principal stress and σ_2 the *minimum* principal stress. We need to be able to relate this complex stress situation to the data derived from a simple tensile test and the discussion that follows describes the various theories that will allow us to achieve this.

Why are there no shear stresses indicated on the element of material shown in the above figure?

11

> Because the principal planes on which the principal
> stresses act are not subjected to shear stress.

If you are not sure about this, look back at Mohr's Circle of Stress in Programme 8.
Now let's look at the various generally accepted theories that are available to analyse
two-dimensional stress situations.

Maximum principal stress (Rankine) theory

This theory assumes that when the maximum principal stress, σ_1, reaches the yield
stress, σ_y, determined from a simple tensile test, failure can occur. Therefore, the
minimum required yield stress within the material is governed by:

$$\sigma_1 = \sigma_y \ \text{ or } \ \sigma_{y(\min)} = \sigma_1 \tag{14.1}$$

*An element of a component is subjected to principal tensile stresses of 60 MN/m² and
100 MN/m², respectively. What minimum yield stress should the material have to
withstand these stresses?*

12

> $100 \ \text{MN/m}^2$

The maximum principal tensile stress has a value of 100 MN/m², and hence the
minimum required yield stress is 100 MN/m².

It is clear that the maximum principal stress theory is valid for the case where the
two axial stresses acting on an element are *both* tensile. However, is it equally valid
for the case where *both* axial stresses are *compressive*? The theory requires us to relate
these compressive stresses to the yield stress found from a simple tensile test. This is
not a problem, as for most engineering materials experimental evidence shows us that
material behaviour in both tension and compression is similar. Hence we can
reasonably assume that the compressive yield stress of a material has the same value
as the tensile yield stress.

Therefore in the above problem if the element had been subjected to principal
compressive stresses of −60 MN/m² and −100 MN/m² respectively the minimum
required yield stress would have simply been 100 MN/m². Let us now look at a case
where the axial stresses acting on an element are tensile in one direction and
compressive in the other.

*If the maximum principal stress, σ_1, is tensile and the minimum principal stress σ_2 is
compressive, is the criterion $\sigma_1 = \sigma_y$ valid?*

Not necessarily.

You may not have been able to answer this question intuitively, but to help you understand the answer look at the Mohr's Circles of Stress shown below.

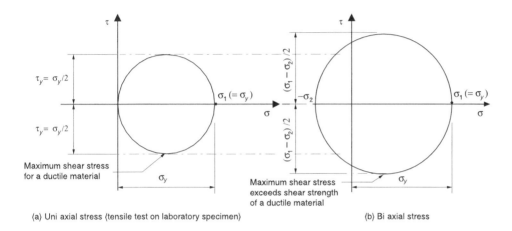

(a) Uni axial stress (tensile test on laboratory specimen)   (b) Bi axial stress

Figure (a) indicates the Mohr's Circle of Stress for a uni-axial stress condition for a material where the condition $\sigma_1 = \sigma_y$ applies. Figure (b) indicates the corresponding circle for the same material for a two-dimensional bi-axial stress situation. In this case, it is assumed that the maximum principal stress has the same value as in figure (a), but is accompanied by a minimum principal stress which is compressive.

It might appear that the condition $\sigma_1 = \sigma_y$ still applies. However you will recall from the discussion in Frame 8 that a ductile material will fail in shear when the maximum shear stress reaches a limiting value of $\sigma_y/2$. It can be seen from figure (b) that the effect of the compressive stress is to increase the diameter of the circle such that the maximum shear stress exceeds the shear strength of the material, that is,

$$(\sigma_1 - \sigma_2)/2 > \sigma_1/2$$

The maximum principal stress criterion would not predict this failure and is, therefore, unsatisfactory. For this reason the *maximum principal stress theory* is only strictly applicable to brittle materials and should not be applied to ductile materials where shear stresses are critical.

Move on to the next frame to study an alternative theory where the maximum shear stress is taken as the failure criterion.

14

Maximum shear stress (Tresca) theory

This theory assumes that when the maximum shear stress in a two-dimensional situation $(\sigma_1 - \sigma_2)/2$ reaches the maximum allowable shear stress in the material, $\sigma_y/2$, as determined from a simple tensile test, then failure will occur. Therefore, with reference to the Mohr's Circle diagram in Frame 13, the minimum required yield stress within the material is governed by:

$$(\sigma_1 - \sigma_2)/2 = \sigma_y/2$$

$$\text{or} \qquad (\sigma_1 - \sigma_2) = \sigma_y$$

$$\therefore \qquad \sigma_{y(min)} = (\sigma_1 - \sigma_2) \qquad (14.2)$$

This is generally referred to as the *Tresca yield criterion*, and this name will be used throughout the rest of this programme. Since it is based on the maximum shear stress it is particularly relevant for applications using ductile materials.

An element of a component is subject to tensile stresses both of magnitude 120 MN/m² *and at right angles to each other. What yield stress should the material have according* *to (a) the maximum principal stress theory; and (b) the Tresca yield criterion?*

15

> (a) 120 MN/m²; (b) 120 MN/m²

For this problem, both $\sigma_1 = \sigma_2 = 120$ MN/m².

(a) From the maximum principal stress theory:

$$\sigma_{y(min)} = \sigma_1 = 120 \text{ MN/m}^2$$

(b) For the Tresca yield criterion you may have been tempted to write:

$$\sigma_{y(min)} = (\sigma_1 - \sigma_2) = (120 - 120) = 0 \text{ MN/m}^2$$

To conclude that we need provide a yield stress value of zero is intuitively not realistic. So how do we apply the theory to get a valid, sensible answer? The Tresca yield criterion is based on the *maximum* shear stress within the component and this is given by:

(maximum principal stress − minimum principal stress)/2

What we have failed to do is to recognise that, if we take an element of material within the component, it is, in fact, a three-dimensional problem, as shown in the figure on the next page.

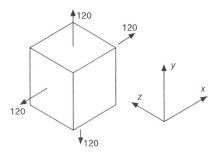

There is a stress of 120 MN/m^2 acting in both the x and y directions. Either of these can, in this case, be taken as the *maximum* principal stress. However, the stress in the z-direction is zero, and hence should be taken to be the *minimum* principal stress. There is still a shear stress created in the element between the maximum principal stress of 120 MN/m^2 and the minimum principal stress of 0 MN/m^2, giving:

$$\sigma_{y(min)} = 120 - 0 = 120 \text{ MN/m}^2$$

which is the answer given at the top of this frame. If the principal stresses are either both tensile or both compressive, then the minimum required yield stress determined from the Tresca yield criterion is equal to the maximum principal stress. Only when one principal stress is tensile and the other is compressive does the Tresca yield criterion give a minimum required yield stress value different from that determined by the maximum principal stress theory.

The Tresca yield criterion can be modified to cover all situations by re-expressing in the form:

$$\sigma_{y(min)} = \sigma_{max} - \sigma_{min}$$

and taking account of the signs of the stresses and that one of the principal stresses may have a zero value.

So far, we have only considered biaxial stress situations. The Tresca yield criterion can be extended to two-dimensional stress situations, including both direct and shear stresses. Consider the loading on the element shown below, where all the values of stress are in MN/m^2.

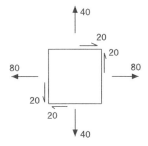

Draw a Mohr's Circle of Stress and determine the minimum required yield stress according to the Tresca theory.

16

$$\boxed{88.28 \text{ MN/m}^2}$$

Constructing a Mohr's Circle of Stress for the element gives:

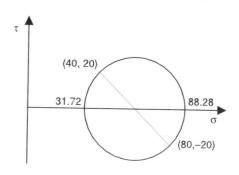

The values of principal stress acting on the element are:

$$\sigma_1 = 88.28 \text{ MN/m}^2 \quad \text{and} \quad \sigma_2 = 31.72 \text{ MN/m}^2$$

In this situation the minimum principal stress is zero and the required yield stress according to the Tresca criterion is given by:

$$\sigma_{y(\text{min})} = 88.28 - 0 = 88.28 \text{ MN/m}^2$$

17

$$\boxed{\text{PROBLEMS}}$$

1. An element of a component is subject to biaxial stresses of 120 MN/m^2 and 40 MN/m^2 respectively. What is the minimum required material yield stress?

Ans. 120 MN/m^2.

2. An element is subjected to a tensile stress of 80 MN/m^2 and a compressive stress of 40 MN/m^2 acting at right angles to each other. Determine the required minimum yield stress value.

Ans. 120 MN/m^2.

3. If the stresses acting on an element are 50 MN/m^2 tensile, 50 MN/m^2 compressive and 50 MN/m^2 in shear, what yield stress should the material have? (Assume that the shear stress associated with the tensile stress is positive in sign.)

Ans. 141.4 MN/m^2.

Maximum strain energy theory

We can apply the Tresca yield criterion to any two-dimensional stress situation, bearing in mind that one of the principal stresses we use may be zero. This means that, in reality, we are considering a three-dimensional stress situation. It is, however, useful to have failure criterion that could be applied directly to two-dimensional stress situations irrespective of the magnitude and sense of the two principal stresses. We can do this by developing a failure criterion based on the strain energy within the material.

This theory assumes that failure can occur in a two-dimensional stress situation when the *total strain energy per unit volume* of the component is equal to that at the yield point in a simple tensile test. In Programme 11, we saw that the expression for the strain energy per unit volume of material for an axially loaded component is given by:

$$U = \frac{1}{2}\sigma \times \varepsilon = \frac{1}{2}\frac{\sigma^2}{E}$$

where σ is the axial stress and ε is the longitudinal strain. Therefore, in the simple tensile test we can express the strain energy per unit volume at yield as:

$$U = \frac{1}{2}\sigma_y \times \varepsilon_y = \frac{1}{2E}\sigma_y^2 \qquad (14.3)$$

The strain energy per unit volume at yield, as we saw in Programme 11, is also referred to as the *modulus of resilience* of the material.

For the two-dimensional stress situation we have been considering, the total strain energy per unit volume is given by the sum of the strain energies attributable to the two principal stresses σ_1 and σ_2. In both cases, the strain energy per unit volume can be calculated using an analogous equation to that given above, provided that the strain expressions take into account the Poisson's Ratio effects.

The longitudinal strain, in the direction of the maximum principal stress, σ_1, is given by:

$$\varepsilon_1 = \frac{\sigma_1}{E} - v\frac{\sigma_2}{E}$$

So that the strain energy per unit volume attributable to σ_1 can be expressed as:

$$U_1 = \frac{1}{2}\sigma_1 \times \varepsilon_1 = \frac{1}{2}\sigma_1\left(\frac{\sigma_1}{E} - v\frac{\sigma_2}{E}\right) = \frac{1}{2E}\left(\sigma_1^2 - v\sigma_1\sigma_2\right)$$

where v is Poisson's Ratio.

Can you write down the expression for the strain energy per unit volume attributable to σ_2?

19

$$U_2 = \frac{1}{2}\sigma_2 \times \varepsilon_2 = \frac{1}{2}\sigma_2 \left(\frac{\sigma_2}{E} - v\frac{\sigma_1}{E} \right) = \frac{1}{2E}\left(\sigma_2^2 - v\sigma_1\sigma_2 \right)$$

This follows directly from the derivation of Equation (14.4). Hence, summing both these equations, the total strain energy per unit volume is given by:

$$U_{total} = \frac{1}{2E}\left(\sigma_1^2 + \sigma_2^2 - 2v\sigma_1\sigma_2 \right) \tag{14.5}$$

As failure is assumed to occur when the total strain energy per unit volume is equal to that at yield in a simple tensile test we can equate Equations (14.5) and (14.3) to give:

$$U_{total} = \frac{1}{2E}\left(\sigma_1^2 + \sigma_2^2 - 2v\sigma_1\sigma_2 \right) = \frac{1}{2E}\sigma_y^2$$

or $\quad\quad \left(\sigma_1^2 + \sigma_2^2 - 2v\sigma_1\sigma_2 \right) = \sigma_y^2$

$$\therefore \quad\quad \sigma_{y(min)}^2 = \sigma_1^2 + \sigma_2^2 - 2v\sigma_1\sigma_2 \tag{14.6}$$

An element of a component is subject to tensile stresses of 120 MN/m² and 60 MN/m² at right-angles to each other. What yield stress should the material have, according to the maximum strain energy criterion? Take Poisson's Ratio as 0.3.

20

$$116.96 \ \text{MN/m}^2$$

Substituting the stress values of 120 MN/m² and 60 MN/m² into equation (14.6):

$$\sigma_{y(min)}^2 = 120^2 + 60^2 - 2 \times 0.3 \times 120 \times 60 = 13\,680$$

$$\therefore \quad\quad \sigma_y = \sqrt{13\,680} = 116.96 \ \text{MN/m}^2$$

This value can be compared to those given in Frame 15 for the same problem. It can be seen that there is close agreement with the values obtained using both the maximum principal stress criterion (120 MN/m²) and the Tresca yield criterion (120 MN/m²). In order to use the maximum strain energy criterion it is necessary to know the Poisson's Ratio for the material, and this limits the usefulness of this criterion. However, this minor disadvantage is eliminated in the next failure criterion, which we shall now consider.

Maximum shear strain energy (von Mises) theory

A ductile material fails because of the development of excessive shear stress within the material. This theory takes account of the shear stress by assuming that failure can occur in a two-dimensional stress situation when *the shear strain energy per unit volume of the component is equal to that at the yield point* in a simple tensile test.

Unfortunately, the derivation of the equation is quite involved and requires consideration of a three-dimensional stress situation, which is beyond the scope of this book. However, the result for a two-dimensional stress situation has a similar form to that of the previous criterion:

$$\sigma^2_{y(min)} = \sigma^2_1 + \sigma^2_2 - \sigma_1\sigma_2 \tag{14.7}$$

This is generally referred to as the *von Mises yield criterion*, and this name will be used throughout the rest of this programme.

An element of a component is subject to two tensile stresses, of 120 MN/m² and 60 MN/m² at right-angles to each other. What yield stress should the material have according to the von Mises yield criterion?

21

$$\boxed{103.92 \text{ MN/m}^2}$$

Substituting the stress values of 120 MN/m² and 60 MN/m² in Equation (14.7):

$$\sigma^2_{y(min)} = 120^2 + 60^2 - 120 \times 60 = 10\,800$$
$$\therefore \qquad \sigma_y = \sqrt{10\,800} = 103.92 \text{ MN/m}^2$$

In spite of giving a slightly lower value of yield stress than the other failure criterion, the von Mises yield criterion is considered to be the most reliable, particularly for use with ductile materials. For most two-dimensional stress situations, the Tresca yield criterion results in the highest values of minimum required yield stress. Since it is more conservative than the von Mise criterion it is used more generally in design using both ductile and brittle materials. Both criteria can be used in practice if a suitable *factor of safety* is incorporated into the calculations.

FACTORS OF SAFETY

In the above example the minimum required yield stress, according to the von Mises yield criterion was 103.92 MN/m². If the quoted yield stress for the material is , say, 240 MN/m² this mean that there is a margin of safety between the quoted and minimum required value of the yield stress. The ratio:

$$n = \frac{\text{material yield stress}}{\text{minimum required yield stress}}$$

is termed the *factor of safety*.

What is the factor of safety for the example we have just quoted?

SOLID MECHANICS

22

$$\boxed{2.31}$$

Check your calculations:

$$n = \frac{\text{material yield stress}}{\text{minimum required yield stress}} = \frac{240}{103.92} = 2.31$$

The actual value of the factor of safety used depends on the design situation. Recommended values of n are $n = 1.5$ to 2.0 for ductile materials where there is confidence in the material properties; $n = 3$ for brittle materials where there is confidence in the material properties; and $n = 4$ for situations where there is uncertainty regarding the loading conditions and the material properties.

Factors of safety are discussed more fully in design text books. However, we can see their application in practice by considering a typical design problem as follows.

A solid circular shaft of 25 mm diameter is to transmit 10 kW at 720 rev/min. What is the factor of safety against failure according to the Tresca yield criterion if the shaft is manufactured from steel having a quoted yield stress of 280 MN/m²? (Hint: you should (i) calculate the torsional shear stress; (ii) draw the Mohr's Stress Circle for the case of pure shear; (iii) interpret the circle to determine the minimum required yield stress; and (iv) determine the factor of safety.)

23

$$\boxed{3.24}$$

(i) *Torsional shear stress*
From Programme 7, the torque, T, is given by:

$$T = \frac{30P}{\pi n} = \frac{30 \times 10 \times 10^3}{\pi \times 720} = 132.63 \text{ Nm}$$

The polar second moment of area, J, is given by:

$$J = \frac{\pi R^4}{2} = \frac{\pi \times \left(12.5 \times 10^{-3}\right)^4}{2} = 38.35 \times 10^{-9} \text{ m}^4$$

and the shear stress in the shaft, τ, is:

$$\tau = \frac{TR}{J} = \frac{132.63 \times \left(12.5 \times 10^{-3}\right)}{38.35 \times 10^{-9}} = 43.22 \text{ MN/m}^2$$

(ii) *Mohr's Circle of Stress*
If we look at an element on the outer surface of the shaft which is in a state of pure shear we can draw the corresponding Mohr's Circle of Stress as shown on the next page.

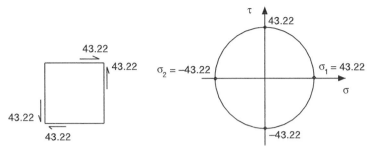

Element of material   Mohr's Stress Circle

which gives:

$$\sigma_1 = \tau = 43.2 \text{ MN/m}^2 \quad \text{and} \quad \sigma_2 = -\tau = -43.2 \text{ MN/m}^2$$

Using the Tresca yield criterion:

$$\sigma_{y(\text{min})} = \sigma_{\text{max}} - \sigma_{\text{min}} = 43.22 - (-43.22) = 86.44 \text{ MN/m}^2$$

This is minimum required yield stress in the shaft and hence the factor of safety against failure is given by:

$$n = \frac{\text{material yield stress}}{\text{minimum required yield stress}} = \frac{280}{86.44} = 3.24$$

24

TO REMEMBER

The Tresca yield criterion can be expressed as:

$$\sigma_{y(\text{min})} = \sigma_{\text{max}} - \sigma_{\text{min}}$$

where σ_{max} and σ_{min} are the maximum and minimum principal stresses acting on a component and where one of the values may be zero.

The von Mises yield criterion is given by:

$$\sigma_{y(\text{min})}^2 = \sigma_1^2 + \sigma_2^2 - \sigma_1\sigma_2$$

where σ_1 and σ_2 are the maximum and minimum principal stresses within a two-dimensional stress situation.

The factor of safety against material failure is defined as:

$$n = \frac{\text{material yield stress}}{\text{minimum required yield stress}}$$

25

FURTHER PROBLEMS

1. In a petrol engine a piston of 60 mm diameter is joined to the connecting rod by means of a gudgeon pin of 12 mm diameter, as shown in figure Q1. The piston is subjected to a maximum uniform pressure of 40 bar. What is the minimum required yield stress of the gudgeon pin?

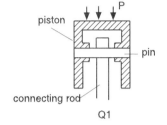

Ans. 50 MN/m².

2. In a biaxial stress situation both stresses are 80 MN/m² compressive. Determine the minimum required yield stress for (a) the Tresca yield criterion; and (b) the von Mises yield criterion.

Ans. (a) 80 MN/m²; (b) 80 MN/m².

3. A thin spherical container has an internal diameter of 600 mm and a wall thickness of 3 mm. It contains gas at 20 bar. What is the minimum required yield stress in the wall using the von Mises yield criterion?

Ans. 100MN/m².

4. A thin cylinder of 500 mm internal diameter holds air at a maximum pressure of 20 bar. The yield stress of the material is 200 MN/m² and a factor of safety against material failure of 2 is required. Determine the required wall thickness using (a) the Tresca yield criterion; and (b) the von Mises yield criterion.

Ans. (a) 5 mm; (b) 4.3 mm.

5. If the stresses acting on an element are 100 MN/m² tensile, 50 MN/m² tensile and 25 MN/m² shear, what minimum yield stress should the material have according to (a) the Tresca yield criterion; and (b) the von Mises yield criterion?

Ans. (a) 110.4 MN/m²; (b) 96.8 MN/m²

6. Find the power that can be transmitted by a 50 mm diameter shaft rotating at 1200 rev/min, using (a) the Tresca yield criterion; and (b) the von Mises yield criterion. Assume the yield stress to be 240 MN/m² and a factor of safety against material failure of 2 is required.

Ans. (a) 185 kW; (b) 213.6 kW.

Appendix

SOME USEFUL
MATHEMATICAL
REVISION NOTES

KEY MATHEMATICAL PRINCIPLES

You may find the following a useful summary of some of the key mathematical principles we have used in this book.

(i) Geometry

In a right-angled triangle:

$$\sin\theta = \frac{\text{opposite}}{\text{hypotenuse}} = \frac{b}{a} \quad \cos\theta = \frac{\text{adjacent}}{\text{hypotenuse}} = \frac{c}{a} \quad \tan\theta = \frac{\text{opposite}}{\text{adjacent}} = \frac{b}{c}$$

And from Pythagoras's theorem:

$$a^2 = b^2 + c^2 \quad \text{or} \quad a = \sqrt{b^2 + c^2}$$

Area of a triangle: $A = \dfrac{1}{2} \times \text{base} \times \text{height} = \dfrac{1}{2} \times c \times b$

For any triangle: Sine rule: $\dfrac{a}{\sin A} = \dfrac{b}{\sin B} = \dfrac{c}{\sin C}$

Cosine rule: $c^2 = a^2 + b^2 - 2ab\cos C$

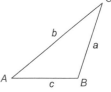

Area of a circle: $A = \pi r^2 = \pi\dfrac{D^2}{4}$ where r=radius; D=diameter of circle

(ii) Arithmetic

When operating on arithmetic expressions you should do so in the following sequence:

(a) terms in brackets   followed by
(b) powers and roots   followed by
(c) multiplication and division   and finally
(d) addition and subtraction

(iii) Algebraic identities

$$(a+b)^2 = a^2 + b^2 + 2ab$$

$$(a-b)^2 = a^2 + b^2 - 2ab$$

$$a^2 - b^2 = (a-b)(a+b)$$

(iv) Indices

Indices are a convenient mathematical shorthand used to express a repetitive multiplication in a simple way: e.g $y \times y \times y \times y \times y = y^5$, the index in this case being 5. When manipulating expressions written in index form the following rules apply:

$$y^a \times y^b = y^{(a+b)}$$

$$\frac{y^a}{y^b} = y^{(a-b)}$$

$$(y^a)^b = y^{(a \times b)}$$

$$y^0 = 1$$

(v) 10 in index form

When multiples of 10 are written in index form it is preferable to express them in *standard form* as multiples of 3:

$$\text{e.g.} \quad 10^3 \quad 10^6 \quad 10^9 \quad 10^{-3} \quad 10^{-6} \quad 10^{-9}$$

(vi) Simultaneous linear equations

Simultaneous linear equations, relating two or more variables, are of the form:

$$3x + 2y = 19 \qquad (1)$$

$$2x + 3y = 16 \qquad (2)$$

To solve such equations, the coefficient of one of the variables must be reduced to the same value in both equations. If we consider the variable x then equation (1) is multiplied by 2 (the coefficient of x in equation (2)) and the equation (2) is multiplied by 3 (the coefficient of x in equation (1)) to give:

$$6x + 4y = 38 \qquad (3)$$

$$6x + 9y = 48 \qquad (4)$$

Hence equation (3) may now be subtracted from equation (4) to give $5y = 10$; $\therefore$ $y = 2$ and substituting back into equation (1) $3x + (2 \times 2) = 19$; $\therefore$ $x = 5$. Other simultaneous equations will be solved in a similar way.

(vii) Solution of quadratic equations

The roots of quadratic equations of the form $ax^2 + bx + c = 0$ can be determined from the expression:

$$x = \frac{-b \pm \sqrt{b^2 - 4ac}}{2a}$$

or, if possible, by factorising the equation. For example, the equation $x^2 + 5x + 6 = 0$ can be factorised to give $(x + 3)(x + 2) = 0$ from which we can say that $x = -3$ or $x = -2$.

(viii) Trigonometric relationships

$$\sin^2 \theta + \cos^2 \theta = 1 \qquad \sin 2\theta = 2 \sin \theta \cos \theta$$

$$\cos 2\theta = \cos^2 \theta - \sin^2 \theta = 1 - 2 \sin^2 \theta = 2 \cos^2 \theta - 1$$

(ix) Standard differential equations

$y =$	1	x	x^2	x^3	x^4	x^n
$\dfrac{dy}{dx}$	0	1	$2x$	$3x^2$	$4x^3$	nx^{n-1}

$y =$	$\sin x$	$\cos x$	$\tan x$
$\dfrac{dy}{dx}$	$\cos x$	$-\sin x$	$\sec^2 x$

Differentiation of a quotient of two functions of the form $y = \dfrac{u}{v}$ is given by:

$$\frac{dy}{dx} = \frac{v\dfrac{du}{dx} - u\dfrac{dv}{dx}}{v^2}$$

(viii) Standard integral expressions

$y =$	1	x	x^2	x^3	x^4	x^n
$\int y\,dx$	$x + C$	$\dfrac{x^2}{2} + C$	$\dfrac{x^3}{3} + C$	$\dfrac{x^4}{4} + C$	$\dfrac{x^5}{5} + C$	$\dfrac{x^{n+1}}{n+1} + C$

$y =$	$\sin x$	$\cos x$
$\int y\,dx$	$-\cos x + C$	$\sin x + C$

UNITS

Units are important! You may find the following a useful summary of the units used in this book:

	Usual units	Alternative units	
Area (A)	m^2	mm^2	$1\ \text{m}^2 = 10^6\ \text{mm}^2$
Density (ρ)	kg/m^3		
Elastic modulus (E)	N/m^2	N/mm^2	$1\ \text{N/mm}^2 = 10^6\ \text{N/m}^2$
Energy (U)	joule		$1\ \text{joule} = 1\ \text{N m}$
Force (F)	N		
Length (L)	m	mm	$1\ \text{m} = 10^3\ \text{mm}$
Mass	kg		
Moment (M)	Nm		
Polar second moment of area (J)	m^4	mm^4	$1\ \text{m}^4 = 10^{12}\ \text{mm}^4$
Power	watts		$1\ \text{watt} = 1\ \text{J/s}$
Pressure	N/m^2	bar	$1\ \text{bar} = 10^5\ \text{N/m}^2$
Second moment of area (I)	m^4	mm^4	$1\ \text{m}^4 = 10^{12}\ \text{mm}^4$
Section modulus (Z)	m^3	mm^3	$1\ \text{m}^3 = 10^9\ \text{mm}^3$
Shear modulus (G)	N/m^2	N/mm^2	$1\ \text{N/mm}^2 = 10^6\ \text{N/m}^2$
Stiffness	N/m	N/mm	$10^3\ \text{N/m} = 1\ \text{N/mm}$
Stress (σ, τ)	N/m^2	N/mm^2	$1\ \text{N/mm}^2 = 10^6\ \text{N/m}^2$
Torsional moment or torque (T)	Nm		
Volume (V)	m^3	mm^3	$1\ \text{m}^3 = 10^9\ \text{mm}^3$

Note: The SI composite unit for stress or pressure is the pascal (Pa) where $1\ \text{Pa} = 1\ \text{N/m}^2$, and this will be found in some textbooks.

MULTIPLES

Multiple	Prefix	Symbol
10^9	giga-	G
10^6	mega-	M
10^3	kilo-	k
10^2	centi-	c
10^{-3}	milli-	m
10^{-6}	micro-	μ

INDEX